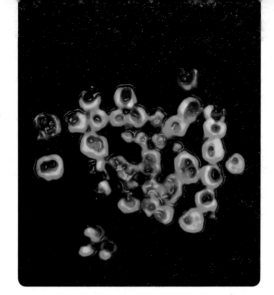

WJEC
A2 Biology

Gareth Rowlands

Published in 2012 by Illuminate Publishing Ltd, P.O. Box 1160, Cheltenham, Gloucestershire GL50 9RW

Orders: Please visit www.illuminatepublishing.com
or email sales@illuminatepublishing.com

British Library Cataloguing in Publication Data

A catalogue record for this book is available from the British Library

ISBN 978-1-908682-08-6

Printed by Barley Print, Cuffley, Hertfordshire

06.15

The publisher's policy is to use papers that are natural, renewable and recyclable products made from wood grown in sustainable forests. The logging and manufacturing processes are expected to conform to the environmental regulations of the country of origin.

Every effort has been made to contact copyright holders of material produced in this book. If notified, the publisher will be pleased to rectify any errors or omissions at the earliest opportunity.

Editor: Geoff Tuttle
Design and layout: Nigel Harriss

Cover image: © Dr Dan Kalman, Katie Vicari / Science Photo Library

Image Credits:

p34 © Y Tambe (Wikimedia Commons); p128 © Olaf Leillinger ×2 (Wikimedia Commons); p173 © Derwyn Rowlands

Science Photo Library: p33 © A. Dowsett, Health Protection Agency; p58 © Dr Keith Wheeler/; p68 © Science Pictures Limited; p69 © Wim Van Egmond, Visuals Unlimited; p89 © Science Pictures Ltd; p105 © Eye Of Science; p129 © Dr Morley Read; p153 © Martin Bond; p169 © Dr Linda Stannard, Uct

Shutterstock: p9 © Mopic; p22 © Leonid Ikan; p32 © Ron Kloberdanz; p33 © Alila Sao Mai; p36 © Alexander Raths; p37 © Myotis; p39 © catolla; p43 © yxowert; p47 © sakhorn; p47 © Action Sports Photography; p49 © Steve Bower; p56 © Creations; p66 © Alila Sao Mai; p76 © LiliGraphie; p81 © Andrea Danti; p82 © Iakov Filimonov; p94 © iDesign; p96 © vetpathologist; p96 © Sashkin; p97 © GRei; p99 © Convit; p99 © Alila Sao Mai; p100 © Monkey Business Images; p103 © Daniel Prudek; p105 © Daniel Prudek; p107 © Mauro Rodrigues; p108 © Richard Griffin; p108 © Bogdan Wankowicz; p112 © Jens Goepfert; p118 © mikeledray; p119 © Blamb; p123 © Sebastian Kaulitzki; p124 © Jens Goepfert; p130 © Imageman; p132 © Ryan M. Bolton; p132 © Natursports; p132 © Alan Lipkin, M.D.; p133 © Ryan M. Bolton; p134 © Kletr; p136 © Kimberley McClard; p139 © Alex Mit; p140 © Jason Bennee; p141 © SSSCCC; p144 © Image Wizard; p148 © Bork; p149 © Mjak; p152 © skyfish; p154 © Alila Sao Mai; p160 © vilainecrevette; p161 © udaix; p163 © Villiers Steyn; p168 © Christopher Kolaczan; p170 © IdeaStepConceptStock; p171 © Jolanta Wojcicka; p172 © Sam DCruz; p172 © Tan Wei Ming; p173 © Kletr; p174 © Christopher Kolaczan; p175 © Taina Sohlman; p175 © EMJAY SMITH; p176 © Barbara Tripp; p177 © Mikhail Olykainen; p177 © Jaochainoi; p178 © daulon; p179 © phil Holmes; p180 © Ihervas

WJEC examination questions are reproduced by permission from WJEC

Acknowledgements

I am very grateful to the team at Illuminate Publishing for their professionalism, support and guidance throughout this project. It has been a pleasure to work so closely with them.
The author and publisher wish to thank Dr John Ford for his thorough review of the book and expert insights and observations.

Contents

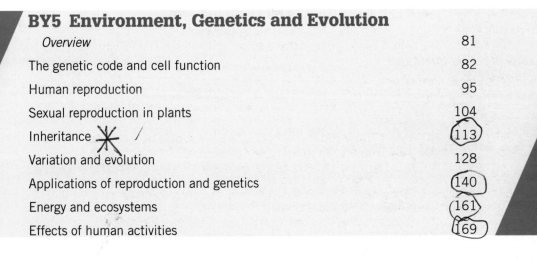

How to use this book

The contents of this book closely match the specification for WJEC A2 Biology and provide you with information and plenty of practice examination questions in order to prepare successfully for the BY4 and BY5 examinations.

This book covers all three of the Assessment Objectives required for your WJEC A2 Biology course. The main text covers AO1 Knowledge and Understanding, which consists of the main factual content of the specification, and AO2 Application of Knowledge and Understanding. The other Assessment Objective, AO3, How Science Works, which covers around 5% of the assessment weighting of the specification, is covered in the form of a margin feature 'How Science Works'. You will not be asked to recall the information given under this heading for the purpose of the examination.

The book content is clearly divided into two Assessment Units, BY4 and BY5:

- BY4 covers Metabolism, Microbiology, Populations, Homeostasis and Co-ordination.
- BY5 covers Environment, Genetics and Evolution.

At the start of each unit there is an overview page. Each unit is divided into a number of topics. Topic openers give a summary of the content to be covered together with a list of learning objectives.

Exam practice questions

At the end of each topic there are a number of practice exam questions from past WJEC A Level Biology exam papers. These are designed to help you practise for the exams and reinforce what you have learned. Please see page 7 for more information. Answers are included at the end of the book.

At the end of the book there are also answers to the Knowledge check questions, a glossary of key terms used in the WJEC specification and a detailed index to help you navigate through the book.

The text is supplemented with a number of features. ➜

YOU SHOULD KNOW ›››

››› The learning objectives provided are more specific to the sub-topic being studied than the more general learning objectives listed at the start of the topic.

Key Terms

There are terms that you need to define and understand included in the body of the text. Where terms are not explained within the same topic these are highlighted in bold type within the text and are highlighted in blue as margin features. Terms can also be looked up in the glossary section which appears at the back of the book. The use of key terms is an important feature since examination papers contain a number of terms that need to be defined.

Knowledge check

These are short questions to check your understanding of the subject, allowing you to apply the knowledge that you have acquired. These questions are of two types: filling in blanks in a passage, or matching terms with phrases specific to the topic under study. Answers are supplied at the back of the book.

How Science Works

This feature helps you understand something about science itself, how scientific knowledge has been obtained, how reliable it therefore is and what its limitations are. It may also help you to have a deeper awareness of how science is used to improve our quality of life. You will not be examined on the information provided by this feature.

▼ Study point

As you progress through your studies, advice is provided to help you understand and use the knowledge content. This may provide some extra information not included in the main text or simply point out that the information is relevant but may not be tested in the examination.

Examiner tip

The examiner may provide general or specific advice to help you with your studies and to prepare you for the exam.

‹ Link ›

Links are highlighted in the margin near the relevant text. They are accompanied by a reference to any areas where sections relate to one another. It may be suggested that you recap a topic before beginning to study the current topic.

How Science Works

It is important not only to understand some of the fundamental scientific explanations of the behaviour of the natural world, but also to know something about science itself, how scientific knowledge has been obtained, how reliable it therefore is, and what its limitations are. It is also important to appreciate the impact that scientific knowledge has on society as a whole. In other words, you need to question what is going on in the science that impacts on your life.

In order to do this you should appreciate that:

✓ Data from observations and measurements are of central importance.

✓ A good explanation may allow us to predict what will happen in other situations, enabling us to perhaps control and influence events.

✓ There may be a correlation between a factor and an outcome.

✓ Proposing a theory may provide an explanation for the available data.

✓ Devising and testing a scientific explanation is not a simple and straightforward process. We can never be completely sure of the data. An observation may be incorrect because of the limitations of either the measuring equipment or the person using it.

✓ Thinking up an explanation is a creative step. It is quite possible for different people to arrive at different explanations for the same data.

✓ The search for new data may confirm the theory or require its amendment.

✓ The scientific community has established procedures for testing and checking the findings and conclusions of individual scientists, and arriving at an agreed view. Scientists report their findings at conferences and in special publications.

✓ The application of scientific knowledge, in new technologies, materials and devices, greatly enhances our lives, but can also have unintended and undesirable side-effects.

✓ The application of science may have social, economic and political implications, and perhaps also ethical ones.

'How Science Works' is developed in this book through relevant topics and is highlighted with the margin feature. These features will help you develop the relevant skills necessary for examination purposes and also give you an idea of how scientists work. This will enable you to have a deeper awareness of how science is used to improve our quality of life.

BY4

Analyse and interpret data to look for patterns and trends, to provide evidence and identify relationships.

→ Calvin cycle: page 27

Evaluate methodology, evidence and data, and resolve conflicting evidence.

→ Gause's competitive exclusion principle: page 46

An observation may be incorrect because of the limitations of either the measuring equipment or the person using it.

→ Observations from light and electron microscopy: page 59

Carry out experimental and investigative activities that can involve making accurate measurements, and recording measurements methodically.

→ The action potential: page 71

BY5

Experimental evidence supports a theory.

→ Meselsohn and Stahl experiment: page 82

Proposing a theory may account for the data.

→ Darwin's theory of natural selection: page 133

The application of science may have social, economic and political implications, and perhaps also ethical ones.

→ Ethics and the use of stem cells: page 142

→ Genetic screening: page 148

The A2 examination

WJEC A2 Biology aims to encourage students to:

- Develop their interest and enthusiasm for the subject, including developing an interest in further study and careers in the subject.
- Appreciate how society makes decisions about scientific issues and how the sciences contribute to the success of the economy and society.
- Develop and demonstrate a deeper appreciation of the skills, knowledge and understanding of how science works.
- Develop essential knowledge and understanding of different areas of the subject and how they relate to each other.

Examination questions are written to reflect the assessment objectives as laid out in the specification. Candidates must meet the following assessment objectives in the context of the content detailed in the specification.

Assessment objective AO1:

Knowledge and understanding of science and How Science Works

Candidates should be able to:

- recognise, recall and show understanding of scientific knowledge
- select, organise and communicate relevant information in a variety of forms.

37% of the questions set on the exam paper are recall of knowledge.

Assessment objective AO2:

Application of knowledge and understanding of science and How Science Works

Candidates should be able to:

- analyse and evaluate scientific knowledge and processes
- apply scientific knowledge and processes to unfamiliar situations including those relating to issues
- assess the validity, reliability and credibility of scientific information.

57% of the questions set on the exam paper include application of knowledge.

Assessment objective AO3:

How Science Works

Candidates should be able to:

- demonstrate and describe ethical, safe and skilful practical techniques and processes, selecting appropriate qualitative and quantitative methods
- make, record and communicate reliable and valid observations and measurements with appropriate precision and accuracy
- analyse, interpret, explain and evaluate the methodology, results and impact of their own and others' experimental and investigative activities in a variety of ways.

6% of the questions set on the exam paper include How Science Works.

BY4 and BY5: Written paper (1 hour 45 minutes)

The following is an approximate guide to the structure of the examination papers, BY4 and BY5:

Type of question	Marks per question	Number of questions per paper	
		BY4	BY5
Short structured	2–5	2–4	2–4
Longer structured	7–15	2–5	2–5
Essay (1 out of 2)	10–12	1	1
Total marks		**80**	**80**

You are normally expected to answer seven structured questions and one essay question. The structured questions total 70 marks and the essay question 10 marks. The time allocation is 1 hour 45 minutes.

Synoptic assessment

A synoptic element is included in your A2 examination. Synoptic questions may require you to draw on knowledge, understanding and skills from AS level that underpin the A2 topic which the question is about. This links knowledge, understanding and skills from topics in the A2 theory unit on which the question is set, perhaps in a new context.

The following advice is given in the specification:

'The examination papers for BY4 and BY5 assess the subject content of the units but also include some marks allocated to synoptic assessment. These are largely skills-based questions such as comprehension and data response which require the bringing together of different parts of the course. Essays may also incorporate credit for synoptic aspects in the answers given. Answers including some fundamental concepts and content from AS units may be credited in synoptic questions.'

Synoptic questions, in particular, may incorporate concepts and ideas that are designed to be more challenging for candidates. Such questions may provide credit for extra insight and appreciation of the inter-relatedness of different aspects of the subject and creativity of thought. Such answers are likely to be in relation to data response and extended answer or essay questions.

Read through your AS notes or Study Guide before the final exams and pay particular attention to topics that underpin the knowledge at A2 level. These topics would include in particular Enzymes, Cell structure, Membranes and transport, Nucleic acids and Evolution.

The following general advice is given in the specification:

'The questions are worded very carefully so that they are clear, concise and unambiguous. Despite this, candidates tend to penalise themselves unnecessarily when they misread questions, either because they read them too quickly or too superficially. It is essential that candidates appreciate the precise meaning of each word in the question if they are to be successful in producing concise, relevant and unambiguous responses. The mark value at the end of each part of each question provides a useful guide as to the amount of information required in the answer.'

Using the exam practice questions in this book

At the end of each sub-topic within BY4 and BY5 there are a variety of questions you should attempt to answer before moving on to the next sub-topic. It is essential to practise these questions from past WJEC exam papers and to familiarise yourself with the general style of the questions that you can expect in the exam. Answers to these questions are supplied at the back of the book.

As well as being able to answer questions requiring the recall of biological facts, the naming of structures and a description of their functions, you also need to appreciate the underlying principles of the subject and understand associated concepts and ideas. In other words, you need to develop skills so that you can apply what you have learnt, perhaps to situations not previously encountered. For example, the handling of numerical data and its transfer into graph form; the analysis and evaluation of numerical data or written biological information; the interpretation of data; the explanation of experimental results.

Structured questions may be in several parts usually about a common theme. You will experience an increase in the degree of difficulty as you work your way through the question.

Structured questions can be short, requiring a one-word response, or may include the opportunity for extended writing. The number of lined spaces together with the mark allocation at the end of each part question are there to help you. They indicate the length of answer expected. If three marks are allocated then you would be expected to give three separate points.

It is essential that you take your time and, even more importantly, understand the instructions and highlight the action words used by the examiner. The following are some common key words used in WJEC exam papers.

Complete

You may be required to complete a comparison table. This is generally a straightforward question and, if you know your work, you may pick up easy marks. However, follow the instructions carefully.

For example: Complete the table to show whether each role applies to mitosis, meiosis or both. If the role applies put a tick (✔) or where it does not apply put a cross (✗). Some tables may have more than one correct answer on a line, don't assume that only one tick per line is required.

Describe

This term may be used in a variety of questions where you need to give a step-by-step account of what is taking place. In a graph question, for example, if you are required to recognise a simple trend or pattern then you should use the data supplied to support your answer. At this level it is insufficient to state that the graph goes up and then flattens. You are expected to describe what goes up and illustrate your answer by using figures from the graph.

For example: Describe two functions of lipids in plants.

Explain

A question may ask you to describe and also explain. You will not be given a mark for merely describing what happens – a biological explanation is also needed.

For example: Describe and explain what happens to chromosomes during anaphase of mitosis.

Suggest

This action word often occurs at the end of a question. There may not be a definite answer to the question but you are expected to put forward a sensible idea based on your biological knowledge.

For example: Suggest how the protein in the diagram would be positioned in a plasma membrane.

Name

You must give no more than a one-word answer. You do not have to repeat the question or put your answer into a sentence. This is wasting time.

For example: Name the cell organelle responsible for the production of the spindle fibres in mitosis.

State

Give a brief concise, answer with no explanation.

For example: State the name given to the model of membrane structure proposed by Singer and Nicolson.

Compare

If you are asked to make a comparison, do so.

For example: If you are asked to compare the dentition of a cat and a sheep, don't write out two separate descriptions. Make a comparative statement, such as, 'a cat has carnassials but a sheep does not'.

Annotate

You are required to add a short description of the function or make a relevant point about the structure of a labelled part of a diagram.

For example: Annotate the diagram of the plant cell with the functions of the parts labelled.

Essay questions

Each unit will contain a choice of one out of two essay questions.

For example: Either (a) describe the events that occur during one complete cell cycle including mitosis, in an animal cell.

Or, (b) Describe the similarities and differences in the structure of amino acids and nucleotides.

Don't answer both essay options

All too often candidates rush into one of these questions and possibly make an incorrect choice. You should take time to read the question carefully to discover exactly what the examiner requires in the answer, and then sketch out a plan. This will not only help you organise your thoughts logically but will also give you a checklist to which you can refer when writing your answer. In this way you will be less likely to repeat yourself, wander off the subject or omit important points.

The rubric in the essay section states: 'Any diagrams in your answer must be fully annotated'. If appropriate, you are encouraged to include a diagram in your essay answer but it must be well drawn and annotated. A diagram without annotations, no matter how well drawn, will gain no marks.

Overview: BY4 Metabolism, Microbiology, Populations, Homeostasis and Co-ordination

ATP and respiration p9

- A series of reactions taking place in cells resulting in the release of energy (in the form of ATP) from organic compounds such as glucose.
- ATP is made from ADP and inorganic phosphate by phosphorylation.
- The breakdown of glucose involves four stages: glycolysis, the link reaction, the Krebs cycle and the electron transport chain.
- Glycolysis takes place in the cytoplasm of the cell and involves the splitting of glucose to pyruvate with the release of ATP and reduced NAD.
- The link reaction involves the conversion of pyruvate to acetyl CoA which enters the mitochondrion to join the Krebs cycle.
- The Krebs cycle results in the formation of reduced carriers, ATP and carbon dioxide.
- The electron transport chain uses the energy of electrons to pump protons with the formation of ATP by ATP synthetase.
- The production of ATP in the electron transport system by aerobic respiration is called oxidative phosphorylation.
- Aerobic respiration has the potential to produce 38 molecules of ATP per molecule of glucose whereas anaerobic respiration involves only glycolysis and produces two molecules of ATP.

Photosynthesis p22

- Photosynthesis takes place in the chloroplast and uses light energy to synthesise organic molecules from carbon dioxide and water.
- Photosynthetic pigments are grouped together to form antenna complexes, which funnel photons of light to one of two reaction centres: PSI and PSII.
- The absorption of light energy boosts the electrons within the reaction centre to a higher energy level.
- The electrons are passed through a series of carriers to form ATP by photophosphorylation.
- This light-dependent stage takes place in the thylakoid membrane of the chloroplast with the production of ATP and reduced NADP.
- The synthesis of ATP occurs by cyclic and non-cyclic photophosphorylation.
- The photolysis of water provides electrons to replace those lost from the reaction centre.
- The light-independent stage takes place in the stroma of the chloroplast and involves the fixation of carbon dioxide using the products of the light-independent stage, ATP and reduced NADP, to convert it to carbohydrate.

Microbiology p32

- Bacteria can be classified according to their shape and the Gram stain technique.
- Bacteria reproduce quickly under optimum conditions of nutrients, temperature and pH.
- Bacteria are cultured using sterile techniques.
- Bacteria may be counted using viable counts or total counts.
- Samples need to be diluted by serial dilution to produce results that are countable.
- An important use of large-scale industrial fermentation is the production of penicillin using the fungus, *Penicillium sp.* Penicillin is produced by batch fermentation and is a secondary metabolite produced when nutrients are depleted.

Factors controlling population size p43

- The numbers of individuals in a population are increased by births and immigration and decreased by deaths and emigration.
- The size of a population is determined by environmental resistance and the carrying capacity.
- Population changes may be density dependent or density independent.
- Population shows a pattern of growth and follows an S-shaped curve.
- Pests may be controlled by chemical and biological methods; each method has its relative advantages and disadvantages.
- Decomposers are the organisms involved in the cycling of nutrients in ecosystems.
- Several different species of bacteria play an important role in the cycling of nitrogen.

Homeostasis and kidney function p56

- Homeostasis is the maintenance of a constant internal environment, relying on negative feedback to produce an opposing change.
- Excretion is the removal of metabolic waste products from the body.
- Fish, birds, insects and mammals produce different excretory products.
- The kidneys are the main organs of the urinary system and are made up of numerous nephrons.
- Small molecules pass from the blood by ultrafiltration and useful substances are reabsorbed into the blood as the filtrate passes along the nephron.
- Osmoregulators in the hypothalamus monitor the water potential of the blood, and the reabsorption of water is controlled by the secretion of ADH from the pituitary gland.

Co-ordination p66

- The nervous system controls and co-ordinates actions by detecting stimuli using receptors, and processes the information and initiates responses by effectors.
- A basic reflex arc involves receptors, sensory, relay and motor neurones, effectors.
- Nerve transmission involves changes in permeability of the axon membrane to sodium ions resulting in the production of an action potential.
- The speed of transmission of an impulse is affected by the presence of a myelin sheath and the axon diameter.
- The transfer of information from one neurone to the next involves the secretion of a neurotransmitter across synapses.
- Synaptic transmission is affected by drugs.
- Plant responses are slower than animal responses as they involve only hormones.
- Photoperiodism is the response of a plant to the relative length of daylight and darkness.
- Photoperiodism involves a light-sensitive pigment, phytochrome, which exists in two forms and the plant measures day length by the relative amount of phytochrome existing in each of the two forms.

BY4

ATP and respiration

Green plants carry out the process of photosynthesis to capture sunlight energy in chemical form. The resulting energy-containing molecules are used to store energy but if broken down directly the energy would be released in an uncontrollable way. Instead energy is transferred from molecules, such as glucose, to an intermediate energy source, ATP, which is released in small, manageable quantities. ATP is a reservoir of potential chemical energy and acts as a common intermediate in metabolism, linking energy-requiring and energy-yielding reactions.

Respiration involves a series of oxidation reactions taking place in living cells, resulting in the release of energy from organic compounds such as glucose. Anaerobic respiration takes place in the absence of oxygen and releases far less energy than aerobic respiration.

By the end of this topic you should be able to:

- Describe the structure of ATP.
- Describe the uses and advantages of ATP as a source of energy.
- Describe the role of ATP in biological processes.
- Outline respiration as a series of four distinct, but linked stages: glycolysis, the link reaction, Krebs cycle and the electron transport chain.
- Explain the process of glycolysis as taking place in the cytoplasm involving the breakdown of glucose to pyruvate with the production of ATP and reduced NAD.
- Describe the diffusion of pyruvate into the matrix of the mitochondrion and its conversion to acetyl coenzyme A by means of the link reaction.
- Describe the Krebs cycle as a series of reactions involving intermediates resulting in the formation of reduced coenzymes, NAD and FAD, and ATP and carbon dioxide.
- Explain that these processes involve decarboxylation and dehydrogenation and describe the role of the coenzymes.
- Explain oxidative phosphorylation in terms of the electron transport chain, located in the cristae of the mitochondrion, involving electron carriers, proton pumps and ATP synthetase in the production of ATP.
- Describe how anaerobic respiration involves only glycolysis with the conversion of pyruvate to ethanol in fungi and plants under certain conditions, and lactic acid in animals.
- Understand that anaerobic respiration yields far less energy than aerobic respiration.
- Describe how fats and amino acids may be used as alternative energy sources.

Adenosine triphosphate (ATP)

All living organisms gain their energy by the process of respiration. Respiration involves the gradual release of energy in a number of small steps rather than the rapid release of energy all at once. Glucose is broken down by means of enzymes through a number of intermediate compounds, with the controlled release of small quantities of energy at each stage. These reactions provide the energy to produce a molecule called adenosine triphosphate or ATP.

The structure of ATP

ATP is a nucleotide consisting of an organic base, adenine, a five-carbon sugar, ribose, and a sequence of three phosphate groups linked together.

▲ *The structure of ATP*

Key Terms

Activation energy = the energy needed to start a chemical reaction.

Phosphorylation = the addition of phosphate (P_i) to ADP.

Study point

An energy currency molecule, such as ATP, acts as an immediate donor of energy to meet the metabolic needs of the cell. An energy storage molecule, such as starch, is a long-term store of potential chemical energy.

How ATP stores energy

The bonds between the phosphate groups are unstable and are easily broken, releasing a considerable amount of energy. Usually in living cells it is only the third phosphate that is removed. This reaction is catalysed by the enzyme ATPase.

$$ATP + water = ADP + P_i + Energy$$

The conversion of ATP to ADP is a reversible reaction. Energy can also be used to add the inorganic phosphate to ADP to re-form ATP.

$$Energy + P_i + ADP = ATP + water$$

The addition of phosphate to ADP is called **phosphorylation**. ATP is therefore a means of transferring free energy from energy-rich compounds, like glucose, to cellular reactions where energy is needed.

There are three forms of phosphorylation:

- Oxidative phosphorylation, which occurs on the membranes of the mitochondria during aerobic respiration.
- Photophosphorylation, which occurs on the membranes of the chloroplasts during photosynthesis.
- Substrate-level phosphorylation, which occurs when phosphate groups are transferred from donor molecules to ADP to make ATP.

During both oxidative phosphorylation and photophosphorylation ATP is released during the transfer of electrons along a chain of electron carrier molecules.

Examiner tip

The addition of water is a hydrolysis reaction and the removal of water is a condensation reaction.

The importance of ATP

Energy transfers are inefficient. Whenever energy is transferred some energy is 'lost' as heat. The uncontrolled release of energy from glucose would result in an increase in temperature that would destroy cells. Instead living organisms use the gradual release of energy in small steps to produce ATP. Since energy is taken up in the production of ATP, it is referred to as an endergonic reaction. The amount of energy needed to add the terminal phosphate molecule is 30 kJ mol^{-1}. ATP can be hydrolysed to release energy as required. When ATP is broken down to ADP and phosphate this is referred to as an exergonic reaction since energy is released. The hydrolysis of ATP to ADP is catalysed by the enzyme ATPase and the removal of the terminal phosphate yields 30 kJ mol^{-1} of free energy.

$$ATP \longrightarrow ADP + P_i + 30\,kJmol^{-1}$$

The uses and advantages of ATP as a source of energy

There are several advantages in having ATP as an intermediate source of energy compared with glucose. These include:

- The hydrolysis of ATP to ADP involves a single reaction that releases immediate energy. The breakdown of glucose involves a number of intermediates and it takes much longer for energy to be released.
- Only one enzyme is needed to release energy from ATP, while many are needed in the case of glucose.
- ATP releases energy in small amounts when and where needed whereas glucose contains large amounts of energy that may not be needed immediately.
- ATP provides a common source of energy for many different chemical reactions, increasing efficiency and control by the cell. ATP is the universal intermediary molecule between energy-yielding and energy-requiring reactions in the cell. ATP is in fact known as the 'universal energy currency in living organisms'.

The roles of ATP

ATP provides the necessary energy for:

- Metabolic processes – to build large, complex molecules from smaller, simpler molecules. For example, the synthesis of DNA from nucleotides, and polypeptides from amino acids.
- Active transport – to change the shape of carrier proteins in plasma membranes to allow molecules or ions to be moved against a concentration gradient.
- Movement – for muscle contraction.
- Nerve transmission – sodium–potassium pumps actively transport sodium and potassium ions across the axon plasma membrane.
- Secretion – the packaging and transport of secretory products into vesicles in cells.

Key Terms

Aerobic respiration = requires oxygen and produces carbon dioxide, water and much ATP.

Anaerobic respiration = takes place in the absence of oxygen and produces lactate in animals and ethanol and carbon dioxide in yeast, together with little energy.

Examiner tip

Although glucose is rich in energy it is relatively unreactive. Two ATP molecules are used to release the energy from the bonds in each molecule of glucose.

▼ Study point

In the absence of oxygen the pyruvate produced during glycolysis is converted to either lactic acid or ethanol. This is necessary in order to re-oxidise NAD so that glycolysis can continue.

Examiner tip

Candidates often make the common error that energy is produced in respiration. Energy cannot be produced but it can be changed from one type to another. It can also be transferred from one molecule to another.

Respiration

There are two different forms of cellular respiration depending on whether oxygen is available or not. Most living organisms **respire aerobically**, using oxygen with the release of a relatively large amount of energy. These are called obligate aerobes. Some micro-organisms, such as yeast, respire aerobically but can also survive in its absence; these are called facultative anaerobes. Some species of bacteria cannot grow in the presence of oxygen and are called obligate anaerobes.

Aerobic respiration can be divided into four distinct but linked stages:

- Glycolysis
- The link reaction
- Krebs cycle
- The electron transport chain (oxidative phosphorylation).

These stages are summarised in the diagram.

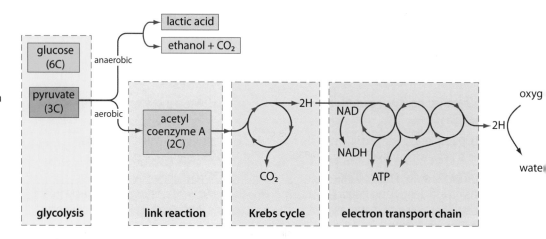

▲ *Summary of respiration*

Glycolysis

Glycolysis, which takes place in the cytoplasm, is the initial stage in both aerobic and **anaerobic respiration.**

- The glucose molecule is first activated by phosphorylation to make it more reactive by the addition of two molecules of ATP. This provides the energy to lower the activation energy for the enzyme-controlled reactions.

- The glucose is converted to 6-carbon hexose phosphate which splits into two molecules of triose phosphate (3-carbon sugar).

- Hydrogen is removed from each of the two triose phosphate molecules and transferred to a hydrogen carrier molecule called NAD to form reduced NAD. In the process the two triose phosphate molecules are converted to pyruvic acid. Two of the steps transfer sufficient energy for the synthesis of ATP. This yields a total of four ATP molecules. The ATP is formed by substrate-level phosphorylation.

- For each molecule of glucose 4 ATPs are made directly by substrate-level phosphorylation. However, 2 ATPs were used to phosphorylate the glucose molecule. Therefore there is a net gain of 2 ATPs from each molecule of glucose.

- Two molecules of reduced NAD are also produced (a potential for an additional 6 molecules of ATP, from the electron transport chain) (see page 14).

A considerable amount of chemical potential energy remains in the pyruvate. If oxygen is available, some of this energy can be released via the Krebs cycle. This energy release takes place in the mitochondria.

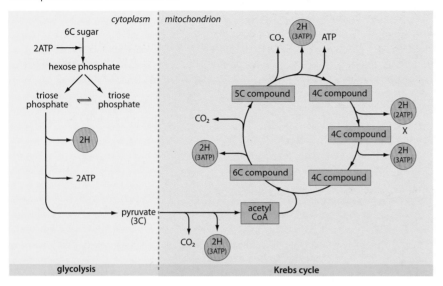

▲ Summary of glycolysis, link reaction and Krebs cycle

The link reaction

The link reaction links glycolysis to the Krebs cycle:

- Pyruvic acid diffuses from the cytoplasm to the mitochondrial matrix.
- The pyruvate is **decarboxylated**.
- The pyruvate is also **dehydrogenated** and the hydrogen released is accepted by NAD to form reduced NAD.
- The 2-carbon acetate formed then combines with coenzyme A to form acetyl coenzyme A, which then enters the Krebs cycle.

Pyruvate + NAD + CoA = acetyl CoA + reduced NAD + CO_2

Krebs cycle

The Krebs cycle is a means of liberating energy from carbon bonds to provide ATP and reduced NAD (and FAD), with the release of carbon dioxide.

Reduced NAD (and FAD) deliver the hydrogen to the electron transport system in the inner mitochondrial membrane so acting as triggers for this system.

- Acetyl CoA enters the Krebs cycle by combining with a 4-carbon acid, to form a 6-carbon compound and the CoA is regenerated.
- The 6-carbon compound undergoes reactions during which carbon dioxide and hydrogen atoms are removed. After the acetate fragment is broken down, the remaining four-carbon residue undergoes conversion to regenerate the four-carbon compound which combines with more acetyl CoA.
- Two of the steps involve decarboxylation, and four of the steps involve dehydrogenation.
- The hydrogen atoms produced are collected by two different carriers with the formation of three molecules of reduced NAD and one molecule of reduced FAD (at point x in the diagram).
- Thus, for each turn of the cycle the overall production is:
  - One ATP (produced as a result of substrate-level phosphorylation).
  - Three reduced NAD and one reduced FAD.
  - Two molecules of carbon dioxide.

Key Terms

Dehydrogenation = the removal of hydrogen.

Decarboxylation = the removal of carbon dioxide.

Examiner tip

The names of the intermediates of glycolysis and Krebs cycle are not required.

Examiner tip

You are only required to know the names of dehydrogenase and decarboxylase enzymes.

▼ Study point

FAD replaced NAD in the carrier system at point x where 2 molecules of ATP are produced rather than 3 molecules.

▼ Study point

In the Krebs cycle it is important that the 4-carbon molecule is regenerated to combine with acetyl Coenzyme A, otherwise the latter would accumulate.

Examiner tip

Don't forget that for each molecule of glucose two molecules of acetyl coenzyme A enter the Krebs cycle. So the cycle turns twice for each glucose molecule.

Link The electron transport chain on page 14 describes how 3 molecules of ATP are produced for each pair of hydrogen ions.

YOU SHOULD KNOW ›››

››› that the electron transport chain is located in the inner membrane of the mitochondria

››› how ATP is synthesised in the electron transport chain

The electron transport chain

The electron transport chain is a series of carriers and pumps, releasing energy in the form of ATP. These are found in the inner mitochondrial membranes.

The carbon dioxide is a waste product of respiration but the hydrogen atoms (or more particularly the electrons they possess) are a potential source of energy. Hydrogen atoms are carried by the **coenzymes** NAD and FAD into the electron transport chain.

If reduced NAD is the initial acceptor, for each pair of hydrogen atoms involved enough energy is released for the synthesis of three molecules of ATP. If reduced FAD replaces reduced NAD as the first carrier, only two molecules of ATP are produced.

The most widely accepted explanation for the synthesis of ATP in oxidative phosphorylation is the **chemiosmotic theory**.

Key Terms

Coenzyme = a molecule required by some enzymes in order to function.

Chemiosmotic theory = a model to explain the synthesis of ATP. The theory proposes that the energy for ATP synthesis originates from the electrochemical gradient of protons across a membrane.

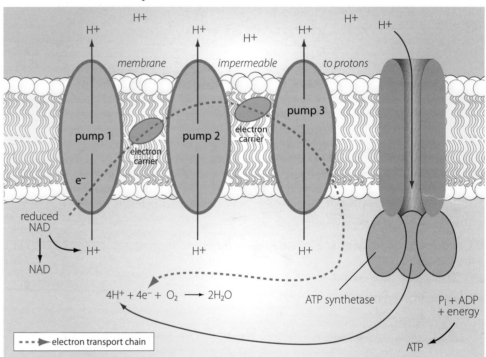

$4H^+ + 4e^- + O_2 \longrightarrow 2H_2O$

▲ *Electron transport chain*

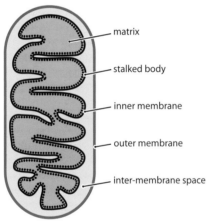

▲ *Mitochondrion*

- matrix
- stalked body
- inner membrane
- outer membrane
- inter-membrane space

▼ Study point

The Krebs cycle releases hydrogen atoms which can be used in oxidative phosphorylation to provide energy to make ATP.

Examiner tip

Some textbooks also refer to ATP synthetase as ATP synthase.

- The hydrogen atoms produced during the Krebs cycle combine with the coenzyme NAD, which is attached to the cristae of the mitochondria.
- Reduced NAD donates the electrons of the hydrogen atoms they are carrying to the first of the series of three electron carriers in the electron transport chain.
- The H+ remains in solution in the mitochondrial matrix.
- The electrons released provide energy for the first proton pump.
- The energy is used to pump protons into the space between the two membranes of the mitochondrion.
- The electrons pass along the chain of carrier molecules providing energy for each pump in turn.
- The protons accumulate in the inter-membrane space as the inner membrane is impermeable to protons.
- The concentration in the inter-membrane space therefore becomes higher than in the matrix, so a concentration gradient is set up.
- In the membrane are special protein channels.
- Associated with each channel is the enzyme ATP synthetase.

- Protons diffuse back into the matrix through these channels and as they do so their electrical potential energy is used to produce ATP.
- At the end of the chain the electrons combine with these protons and oxygen to form water.

Oxygen is referred to as the 'final electron acceptor' in the electron transport chain. Oxygen is essential in the process of the removal of protons and electrons. Without it the protons and electrons would accumulate and cause a 'back-up' along the chain and bring the process to a halt.

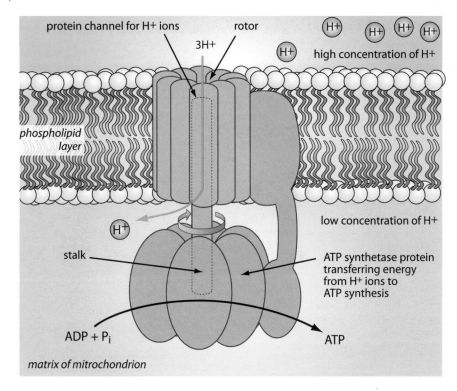

▲ *ATP synthetase complex*

As the protons move down the concentration gradient through the ATP synthetase, the energy released causes the rotor (F_0) and stalk of the ATP synthetase to rotate. The mechanical energy from this rotation is converted into chemical energy as P_i is added to ADP to form ATP in the catalytic head (F_1 domain).

Table showing the number of ATP molecules produced in the electron transport chain per turn of the cycle:

	In the link reaction using reduced NAD	In the Krebs cycle using reduced NAD	In the Krebs cycle using reduced FAD
Number of ATP molecules formed	3	9	2

FAD replaces NAD in the carrier system at the point in the Krebs cycle where two molecules of ATP are produced rather than three molecules of ATP.

FAD passes the hydrogen atoms directly to the 'second' pump. In other words, the carrier system involving NAD has three pumps whereas the carrier system involving FAD has two pumps. This explains why the yield of ATP from the two systems is different.

Examiner tip

The names of the proton pumps and electron carriers in the electron transport system are **not** required.

Examiner tip

Cyanide is a poison that acts as a non-competitive inhibitor of the final acceptor in the electron transport chain resulting in the accumulation of protons and electrons.

How Science Works

To determine the order of the carrier molecules in the electron transport chain an experiment was carried out using a series of different inhibitors.

(2) Knowledge check

Identify the missing word or words.

The first stage in the breakdown of glucose is a process called ••••. This takes place in the •••• of the cell and results in the net production of •••• molecules of ATP and •••• acid. If oxygen is present, this product diffuses into the •••• and is converted to acetyl CoA which then enters the •••• cycle. The final stage of respiration takes place in the cristae of the mitochondrion and is called the •••• •••• ••••

Anaerobic respiration

If there is no oxygen to combine with hydrogen to form water, the electron transport chain cannot function and ATP is not formed by oxidative phosphorylation. Only the first stage of respiration, glycolysis, can take place. The reduced NAD cannot be reoxidised and therefore made available to pick up more hydrogen, and so the link reaction and the Krebs cycle cannot take place. For glycolysis to continue, pyruvate and hydrogen must be constantly removed and NAD must be regenerated. This is achieved by the pyruvate molecule accepting the hydrogen from reduced NAD.

There are two different anaerobic pathways to remove the hydrogen. Both take place in the cytoplasm.

- In animals the pyruvate is converted to lactic acid. This takes place most commonly in muscle tissue. During vigorous exercise the human body cannot get sufficient oxygen to the muscle cells. When deprived of oxygen, pyruvate acts as the hydrogen acceptor and is converted to lactate.

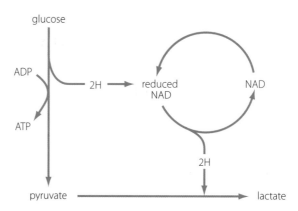

▲ *Anaerobic respiration: lactate formation*

- In various micro-organisms, such as yeast, as well as plant cells under certain conditions, such as root cells in waterlogged soils, pyruvate is converted to ethanol by alcoholic fermentation:

  - The pyruvate is first decarboxylated to produce ethanal.
  - The hydrogen released during glycolysis is passed on to NAD.
  - The reduced NAD then passes the hydrogen to ethanal which is reduced to ethanol.

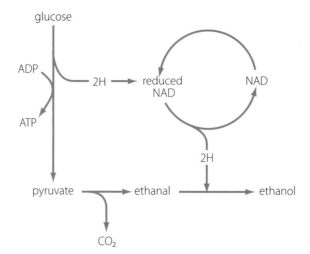

▲ *Anaerobic respiration: fermentation*

The yield of energy from aerobic and anaerobic respiration

The cell produces ATP in two ways:

- Substrate-level phosphorylation takes place in both glycolysis and the Krebs cycle. When an intermediate compound is converted to another with the release of sufficient energy in the presence of P_i and ADP, then ATP is produced.
- Oxidative phosphorylation takes place only in the electron transport chain. The hydrogen atoms from glycolysis, the link reaction and the Krebs cycle that are attached to NAD can be used to indirectly link P_i and ADP to produce ATP.

In glycolysis:

Four ATPs are made directly by substrate-level phosphorylation but two ATPs are used for the activation of glucose.

Net total = 2 ATP

Two reduced NAD (a potential to produce an additional 6 molecules of ATP)

In the link reaction:

Two reduced NAD each capable of producing 3 ATP by oxidative phosphorylation.

Total = 6 ATP

Krebs cycle:

Six reduced NAD each capable of producing 3 ATP by oxidative phosphorylation.

Total = 18 ATP

Two reduced FAD each capable of producing 2 ATP by oxidative phosphorylation.

2 ATPs made directly by substrate-level phosphorylation.

Total = 24 ATP

Table summarising the number of ATP molecules and number of coenzyme molecules produced at each stage in respiration (from one molecule of glucose).

Stage	Number of ATP molecules formed	Number of molecules of reduced NAD	Number of molecules of reduced FAD
Glycolysis	2	2	0
Link reaction	6	2	0
Krebs cycle	24	6	2

In anaerobic respiration pyruvate does not enter the mitochondrion and is not available for the Krebs cycle. Therefore only the two ATPs formed by glycolysis are made available by anaerobic respiration. This is a small amount compared with the 32 molecules of ATP produced during aerobic respiration.

YOU SHOULD KNOW ›››

››› the difference between substrate-level and oxidative phosphorylation

››› the yield of ATP from glycolysis, link reaction and Krebs cycle

››› the difference in ATP yield between aerobic and anaerobic respiration

››› the reason for the difference in yield of ATP from reduced NAD and reduced FAD

Examiner tip

Don't forget that for each molecule of glucose, two molecules of acetyl coenzyme A enter the Krebs cycle. So the cycle turns twice for each glucose molecule.

▼ Study point

Many cells can only use glucose as their respiratory substrate, but others break down fatty acids, glycerol and amino acids in respiration.

Examiner tip

One gram of fat releases more than twice as much energy as one gram of carbohydrate.

▼ Study point

Most metabolic pathways lead to acetyl CoA, which is a kind of crossroads in metabolism. As well as its formation during the oxidation of carbohydrates, it is formed during the oxidation of fats and proteins and represents a common pathway by which the products of all three are fed into the Krebs cycle.

▼ Study point

Protein is very rarely used as a respiratory substrate, usually only when all reserves of carbohydrate and fat have been depleted.

Alternative respiratory substrates

In addition to glucose, under certain circumstances, fats and proteins can be used as respiratory substrates.

Lipids

- Fat provides an energy store and is used as a respiratory substrate when carbohydrate levels are low. First it has to be split into its constituent molecules of glycerol and fatty acids by hydrolysis.

- Then the glycerol is phosphorylated with ATP, dehydrogenated with NAD and converted into a 3-carbon sugar, triose phosphate, which enters the glycolysis pathway.

- The long fatty acid chain molecules are split into 2-carbon fragments which enter the Krebs cycle as acetyl CoA. Very large numbers of ATP molecules are built up during the process, the precise number depending on the length of the hydrocarbon chain of the fatty acid. This is because the hydrogen ions released are picked up by NAD and fed into the electron transport chain.

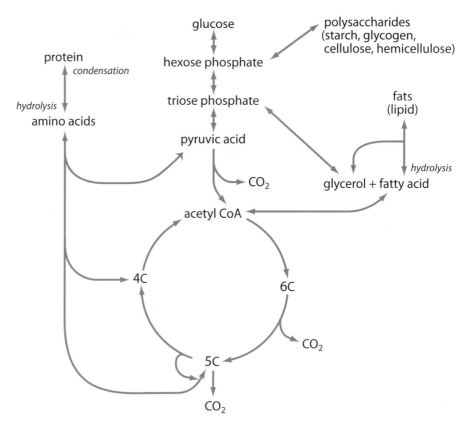

▲ *Alternative energy substrates and pathways*

Protein

Protein can be used as a respiratory substrate in the extreme circumstance of prolonged starvation. In this situation the tissue protein is mobilised to supply energy and, whenever dietary energy supplies are inadequate, the protein component of the food is diverted for energy purposes. The protein is hydrolysed into its constituent amino acids and then it is deaminated in the liver. The amino group is converted into urea and excreted and the residue is converted to either acetyl CoA, pyruvic acid or some other Krebs cycle intermediate, and oxidised

ATP and respiration

1 The diagram below represents a molecule of adenosine triphosphate (ATP).

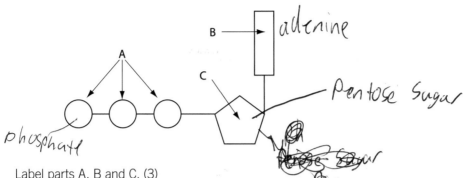

B → adenine

C → Pentose Sugar

pentose Sugar ~~Pentose Sugar~~

phosphate

(a) Label parts A, B and C. (3)

(b) Name two processes in the cell that require energy. (2) — active transport, muscle contraction

(c) ATP is often described as 'universal energy currency'. Explain why it is described in this way. (2) – used in every reaction and in every cell (supplies energy)

(d) Give three advantages of ATP in its function as a source of energy. (3) easily hydrolysed, only 1 enzyme needed, releases energy when and where needed

WJEC BY4 JAN 2010

2 The diagram outlines the stages involved in respiration.

(a) ATP is produced by phosphorylation during both anaerobic and aerobic respiration. Name the two different types of phosphorylation which take place at the points labelled A and B. (2)

(b) State the type of enzyme responsible for the removal of:

(i) Carbon dioxide. (1)

(ii) Hydrogen. (1)

(c) There are four places where hydrogen acceptors remove hydrogen in the Krebs cycle.

(i) Name the hydrogen acceptors at X and Y. (2) NAD, FAD

(ii) Explain why these two hydrogen acceptors lead to the production of different numbers of ATP molecules. (1) NAD has 3 pumps FAD has 2

(d) Complete the table to show the number of ATP molecules formed from one molecule of glucose. (4)

Stage	Number of ATP molecules formed from reduced hydrogen acceptor	Number of ATP molecules formed directly	Total number of ATP molecules formed from each
Link reaction	6	0	6
Krebs cycle	22	2	24

(e) (i) Identify the molecule labelled Z. (1) Acetyl COA

(ii) State the number of carbon atoms from this molecule that enter the Kreb cycle. (1) 2

(iii) Describe the formation of molecule Z. (2)

Pyruvate is decarboxylated (loses CO_2)

$3C \rightarrow 2C$

Diagram labels: 6C sugar; 2ATP → hexose phosphate; triose phosphate ⇌ triose phosphate; glycolysis; 2H; X; 2ATP; A; pyruvate (3C); cytoplasm; mitochondrion; CO_2; 2H (3ATP); B; X; Z; 4C compound; 6C compound; B; 2H (3ATP); X; 4C compound; 2H (3ATP); X; 2H (2ATP); Y; 4C compound; 5C compound; 4C compound; CO_2; A; ATP; 2H (3ATP); CO_2; X; X

WJEC BI4 JAN 2009

3 (a)   The diagram represents an outline of the stages involved in respiration of a yeast cell.

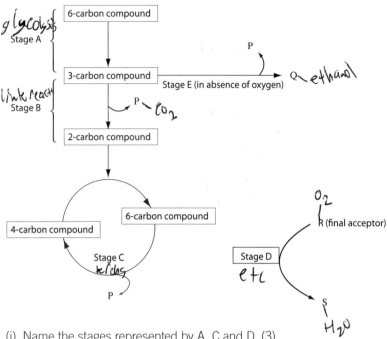

glycolysis
Stage A

link reach
Stage B

6-carbon compound

3-carbon compound   Stage E (in absence of oxygen) → Q *ethanol*

P ~ CO_2

2-carbon compound

4-carbon compound   6-carbon compound

Stage C   *krebs*

P

O_2
R (final acceptor)

Stage D   *etc*

S
H_2O

(i)   Name the stages represented by A, C and D. (3)

(ii) Name the compounds represented by P, Q, R and S. (4)

(iii) Name the carrier molecule that, in its reduced form, delivers hydrogen atoms from stages A, B and C to stage D. (1)

(b)   During stage D an electrochemical gradient is created across the inner mitochondrial membrane.

(i)   Describe how components of the membrane use the hydrogen atoms delivered by the carrier molecule to create an electrochemical gradient. (2)   *H atoms split to e⁻ and protons, e⁻ provides energy for pumps to pump protons across membrane*

(ii) Using letters from the diagram show a process that takes place in the matrix and also helps maintain the electrical gradient. (1)   *R−S (ETC)*

(iii) Explain why the process you described in part (ii) affects the electrochemical gradient across the membrane. (1)   *It takes up H to form water*

(iv) Explain how the electrochemical gradient subsequently leads to the formation of ATP. (3)   *ADP + Pi → ATP*

WJEC BI4 JUNE 2005

4 (a)   The diagram represents an overview of the main stages in the breakdown of a glucose molecule in an animal cell when oxygen is freely available.

(i)   Identify the molecules which are represented by boxes A–F. (6)

(ii) State a reason why ATP is used in the process of glycolysis. (1)

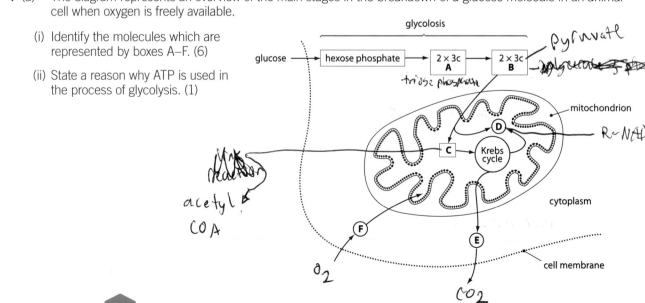

glycolysis

glucose → hexose phosphate → 2 × 3c **A** → 2 × 3c **B** → *Pyruvate*

triose phosphate

mitochondrion

R ~ NAD

D

reaction

C   Krebs cycle

acetyl COA

cytoplasm

F

E

O_2

cell membrane

CO_2

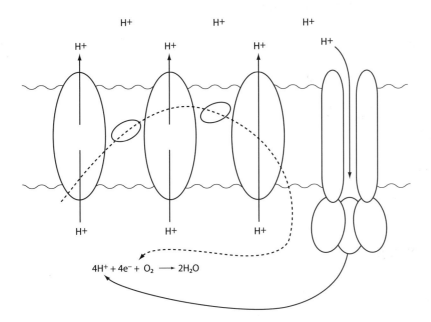

$$4H^+ + 4e^- + O_2 \longrightarrow 2H_2O$$

(b)   The diagram represents the electron transport chain in an animal cell.

   (i) State precisely where this process takes place in a cell. (1) *iner mitochondrial membrane /Cristae*

   (ii) What is the origin of the electrons which are passed along the chain? (1) *H*

   (iii) As electrons are transferred along the electron transport chain, energy is made available for ATP production. Using the information in the diagram explain how this energy is used to make ATP. (4)

WJEC BI4 JUNE 2006

---

5   The table summarises the stages in aerobic respiration.

Stage	Start point	End point	ATP	Reduced NAD	Reduced FAD	Carbon dioxide
				Products		
Glycolysis	Glucose	Pyruvate	✓	✓		
Link reaction	Pyruvate	Acetyl CoA		✓		✓
Krebs cycle	Acetyl CoA	4 carbon compound	✓	✓	✓	✓
Electron transport chain (oxidative phosphorylation)	Reduced NAD or reduced FAD	Water	✓			

(a)   Place a tick in each of the appropriate boxes to indicate the product or products of each stage. (4)

(b)   Which stage takes place on the cristae or inner membrane of the mitochondria? (1) *ETC*

(c)   Describe the main difference between the way in which ATP is produced by oxidative phosphorylation and the way in which it is produced in photosynthesis. (1)   *· light is energy source for photo*

(d)   Describe precisely what happens to the pyruvate in the absence of oxygen in: *· glucose provides the energy for oxidative*

   (i) Animals. (1)   *lactic acid*

   (ii) Yeast. (2)   *ethanol*

WJEC HB4 JUNE 2010

---

6   Describe the process of glycolysis. Explain what happens to the products of glycolysis in an animal and yeast cell under anaerobic conditions. (10)

WJEC BI4 JUNE 2009

BY4

Photosynthesis

The process of photosynthesis takes place in the chloroplasts. These are found in the mesophyll cells and guard cells of green leaves. In the chloroplasts the energy of sunlight is trapped by the pigment chlorophyll.

The biochemical process of photosynthesis may be divided into two parts, the light-dependent stage and the light-independent stage. The light-dependent stage takes place in the thylakoid membrane of the chloroplast. It involves the photolysis of water and results in the production of ATP and reduced NADP with the release of oxygen as a waste product. The light-independent stage or Calvin cycle takes place in the stroma of the chloroplast. Here carbon dioxide combines with a 5-carbon acceptor and the products of the light-dependent stage are used to produce glucose.

Topic contents

By the end of this topic you should be able to:

- State that the photosynthetic pigments include chlorophyll a, chlorophyll b, carotene and xanthophylls.

- Understand that these pigments are grouped together to form antenna complexes which act as funnels bringing photons of light to the reaction centre.

- Understand that there are two types of reaction centres: photosystem I and photosystem II.

- Explain that both cyclic and non-cyclic photophosphorylation involve the production of ATP from ADP and P_i.

- Describe how the different pigments absorb different wavelengths of light.

- Describe the difference between an absorption spectrum and an action spectrum.

- Draw the absorption spectrum and action spectrum for photosynthesis on the same graph.

- State that the light-dependent stage takes place on and across the thylakoid membrane of the chloroplast.

- Describe the light-dependent stage as the photoactivation of chlorophyll and energy transfer to produce to produce ATP and reduced NADP.

- State that the light-independent stage takes place in the stroma of the chloroplast.

- Explain that the reduced NADP and ATP are used in the light-independent stage, when carbon dioxide is fixed and then reduced to glucose.

An overview of photosynthesis

The overall equation for photosynthesis is:

$$6CO_2 + 6H_2O \xrightarrow[\text{Chlorophyll}]{\text{Light energy}} C_6H_{12}O_6 + 6O_2$$

The diagram on the right shows that this process involves two stages: the light-dependent and light-independent.

The light-dependent reaction involves the conversion of light energy to chemical energy. The reactions include the photolysis of water to provide protons and electrons. The protons are used to reduce NADP. Energy from the electrons is used to make ATP by **photophosphorylation**.

In the light-independent reaction the reduced NADP and ATP are used to reduce carbon dioxide to produce energy-containing glucose.

▶ *Photosynthesis*

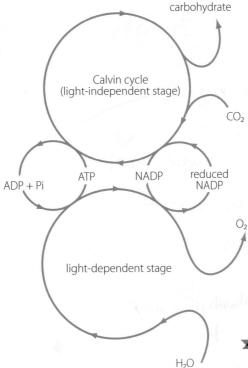

Key Term

Photophosphorylation = the synthesis of ATP from ADP and P_i using light energy.

How Science Works

The results of Englemann's experiments are an example of How Science Works.

Englemann's experiment

The site of photosynthesis was detected in 1887 by a botanist called Englemann. He devised an experiment to determine which wavelengths of light were the most effective in carrying out photosynthesis using a filamentous green alga, each cell of which contains a ribbon-like chloroplast shaped in the form of a spiral. He placed the algae in a suspension of motile, aerobic bacteria which were evenly distributed and exposed the algal cells to a range of wavelengths. After a short period of time he noticed that the bacteria clustered near to the chloroplasts at the blue and red wavelengths. This was because these wavelengths resulted in increased photosynthesis, which produced more oxygen and so attracted more of the bacteria.

▼ *Englemann's experiment*

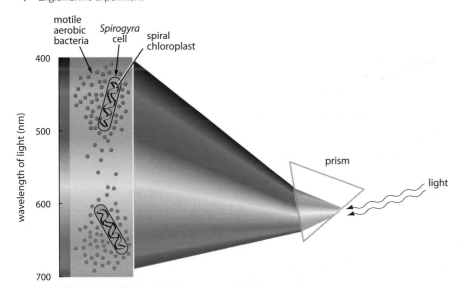

Study point

The role of photosynthetic pigments is to absorb light energy and to convert it to chemical energy.

Examiner tip

It is incorrect to state that 'pigments absorb light'. They absorb light energy.

The structure and role of chloroplasts

Photosynthesis takes place in the chloroplasts. These organelles are surrounded by a double membrane. Inside the chloroplast are:

- Grana – stacks of up to 100 disc-like structures called thylakoids. This is where the reactions of the light-dependent stage of photosynthesis take place and where the photosynthetic pigments are located.
- Stroma – this is the fluid-filled interior where the light-independent reactions take place.

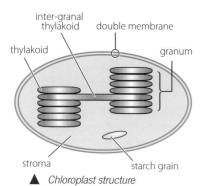

▲ *Chloroplast structure*

Photosynthetic pigments

Light energy is trapped by photosynthetic pigments. In photosynthesis different wavelengths of light are trapped by different pigments. In flowering plants there are two main types of pigments: chlorophylls and carotenoids. Chlorophylls absorb light energy mainly in the red and blue-violet regions of the spectrum, whereas the carotenoids absorb the light energy from the blue-violet region of the spectrum. The two main types of carotenoids, the carotenes and the xanthophylls, act as accessory pigments.

Examiner tip

Accessory pigments are important as they absorb wavelengths of light not absorbed by the primary pigments. This ensures a greater range of wavelengths absorbed and so a greater degree of efficiency of photosynthesis.

Absorption and action spectra

Experimentally, the different pigments can be shown to absorb different wavelengths by making separate solutions of each pigment and shining light through them.

This absorption spectrum can be represented as a graph that indicates how much light a particular pigment absorbs at each wavelength. For example, chlorophyll absorbs wavelengths in the blue and red parts of the spectrum. However, this does not indicate whether the wavelengths are actually used in photosynthesis.

The action spectrum is a graph that shows the rate of photosynthesis at different wavelengths of light. That is, the amount of carbohydrate synthesised by plants exposed to different wavelengths of light. If one graph is superimposed on the other it can be seen that there is a close correlation between the absorption spectrum and the action spectrum. This suggests that the pigments are responsible for absorbing the light used in photosynthesis.

▼ Study point

The shorter the wavelength, the more energy light contains.

▼ *Graph showing the relationship between the absorption spectrum and the action spectrum*

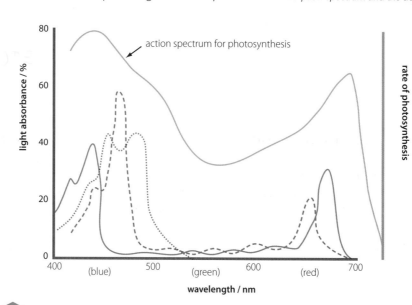

Light harvesting

The chlorophylls and accessory pigments in the thylakoid membranes of the chloroplast are grouped in clusters of several hundred molecules. Each cluster is called an antenna complex. Special proteins associated with these pigments help to funnel photons of light energy entering the chloroplast. That is, the pigment molecules pass absorbed light energy from one molecule to the next. Photons of light are thus transferred through the antenna complex until they reach chlorophyll a, which is a primary pigment molecule and is known as the reaction centre.

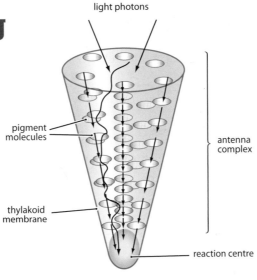

▲ *Antenna complex*

There are two types of reaction centre:

- Photosystem I (PSI) is arranged around a chlorophyll a molecule with an absorption peak of 700nm. (The reaction centre is also called P700.)
- Photosystem II (PSII) is arranged around a chlorophyll a molecule with an absorption peak of 680nm. (The reaction centre is also called P680.)

The light-dependent stage of photosynthesis

The reactions of the light-dependent stage occur in the thylakoid membranes of the chloroplasts. They involve:

- **Photolysis**, the splitting of water molecules by light, to produce hydrogen ions and electrons.
- The synthesis of ATP from ADP and P_i. This type of phosphorylation is known as photophosphorylation, as light energy is involved.
- The combination of hydrogen ions with NADP to produce reduced NADP.

When light strikes a molecule at the reaction centre an electron is raised to a higher energy level, thus setting up a flow of electrons. This electron flow is referred to as the 'Z scheme'.

There are two ways in which ATP can be synthesised:

- Non-cyclic photophosphorylation.
- Cyclic-photophosphorylation.

Non-cyclic photophosphorylation involves both photosystem I and photosystem II:

- Photons of light are absorbed by photosystem II and passed to chlorophyll a in the reaction centre.
- This causes the displacement of two 'excited' (high energy) electrons, which are raised to a higher energy level where they are picked up by electron acceptors. These electron acceptors pass the electrons along a chain of carriers through a proton pump and to photosystem I.
- The energy lost by the electrons is used to convert ADP to ATP.

Key Term

Photolysis = the splitting of water molecules by light.

▼ Study point

Each photosystem is a collection of accessory pigments which pick up light energy at various wavelengths and funnel this energy to the reaction centre.

▼ Study point

Textbooks differ in their use of the term 'reduced NADP'. Some use $NADPH_2$, others $NADPH^+H^+$. Throughout this book the term 'reduced NADP' will be used.

4 Knowledge check

Identify the missing word or words.

The light-dependent reactions of photosynthesis take place in the ···· ·····. Light ···· is absorbed by pigments located in the ···· ·····. The pigment ···· ····· is located in the reaction centre of this unit. Here 'excited' electrons are raised to a higher energy level where they are picked up by electron ·····.

- Photons of light are absorbed by photosystem II and passed to chlorophyll a in the reaction centre.

- This in turn causes two electrons to be emitted and raised to a higher energy level where they are picked up by another electron acceptor.

- Photosystem II is now unstable as it has lost electrons. These are replaced when electrons become available from the splitting of water by photolysis.

- During photolysis, the water molecule dissociates into electrons, hydrogen ions and oxygen.

- The second electron acceptor, which receives electrons from photosystem I, passes some of these electrons to hydrogen ions on the outside of the thylakoid membrane, where they reduce NADP.

- Since these electrons are not recycled back into the chlorophyll, this method of ATP production is called non-cyclic photophosphorylation.

Examiner tip

The carrier system in photosynthesis has only one proton pump but in respiration there are three.

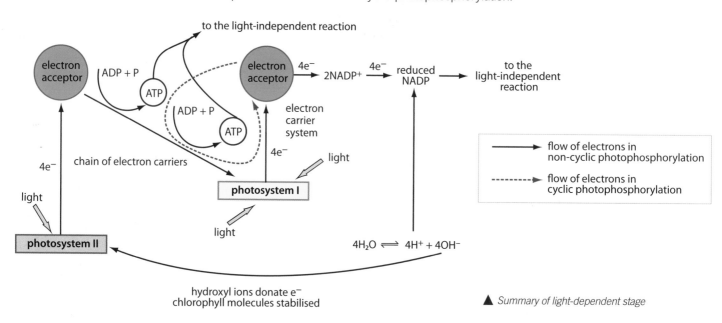

▲ *Summary of light-dependent stage*

Photolysis of water

How Science Works

The Hill reaction demonstrates how chloroplasts have the reducing power to reduce fixed carbon dioxide to carbohydrate. They produce hydrogen ions. This is observed by their reduction of a coloured redox reagent to colourless.

When light strikes a molecule at the reaction centre of photosystem II an electron is raised to a higher energy level, leaving the chlorophyll molecule short of electrons. If the chlorophyll molecule is to continue absorbing light energy, these electrons must be replaced. The replacement electrons are provided from water molecules that are split using light energy. The protons combine with electrons from photosystem I and NADP to give reduced NADP. The photolysis of water can be demonstrated using the Hill reaction.

In 1939 Robert Hill used isolated chloroplasts to demonstrate that they have the reducing power to evolve oxygen from water in the presence of an oxidising agent. It is possible to replicate his experiment in the laboratory using the blue dye DCPIP, which acts as a substitute for the plant's NADP. Chloroplasts may be extracted from a plant, such as lettuce, and placed in a buffer solution with DCPIP. In the presence of light, the DCPIP becomes colourless when reduced.

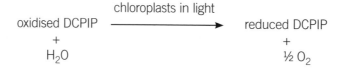

Cyclic photophosphorylation involves only photosystem I:

- Light energy is absorbed by PSI and passed to chlorophyll a at the reaction centre.
- The electrons are passed to a higher energy level where they are received by the second electron acceptor.
- Those electrons which are not taken up in the production of reduced NADP then pass along a chain of electron carriers before they are returned to PSI.
- As the electron passes along the chain of carriers sufficient energy is generated to make ATP.
- No reduced NADP is produced during this process.

The reactions of the light-dependent stage of photosynthesis take place in the thylakoid membranes of the chloroplast. As electrons flow along the chain of electron carriers from photosystem II to photosystem I they provide energy to pump hydrogen ions from the stroma, across the thylakoid membrane and into the thylakoid space. This sets up an electrochemical gradient, since there are more hydrogen ions inside the thylakoid space than there are outside in the stroma. Hydrogen ions flow along this gradient out across the thylakoid membrane through the protein channels. This produces sufficient energy for the formation of ATP by ATP synthetase.

YOU SHOULD KNOW ›››

››› how carbon dioxide is incorporated into organic molecules

››› the roles of ATP and reduced NADP in the light-independent reaction

››› the importance of the regeneration of the carbon dioxide acceptor

Examiner tip
Compare chemiosmosis in photosynthesis with that in respiration.

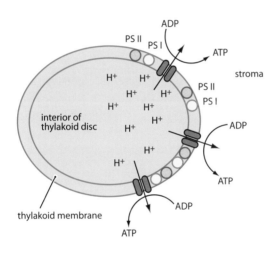

▲ *ATP production in the chloroplast by chemiosmosis*

The light-independent stage

The light-independent stage occurs in the stroma of the chloroplast and involves many reactions each catalysed by a different enzyme. The reactions use the products of the light-dependent stage, ATP and reduced NADP. ATP acts as a source of energy, and reduced NADP acts as the source of the reducing power to reduce carbon dioxide and synthesise hexose sugar.

The ATP and reduced NADP produced from the light-dependent stage are used in the light-independent stage as follows:

- A five-carbon acceptor molecule, ribulose bisphosphate (RuBP), combines with carbon dioxide (catalysed by the enzyme Rubisco) forming an unstable six-carbon compound.
- The six-carbon compound immediately splits into two molecules of a three-carbon compound called glycerate-3-phosphate (GP).
- GP is phosphorylated by ATP and then reduced by reduced NADP to triose phosphate.

 How Science Works

The sequence of events in the light-independent stage of photosynthesis was worked out by Calvin and his associates using C^{14}, a radioisotope of carbon, and the unicellular algae, *Chlorella*. It is known as the Calvin cycle. In the experiment radioactive hydrogencarbonate was added to a flat 'lollipop' vessel. The algae then photosynthesised and at 5-second intervals, samples were dropped into hot methanol to stop any further chemical reactions. After a period of 30 seconds all the compounds produced by the algae were separated out and identified.

5

Knowledge check

Identify the missing word or words.

In the light-independent reaction, carbon dioxide combines with the 5-carbon acceptor, ···· ······. ATP and reduced ···· from the ···· ······ stage are used to produce ·····.

- Some of this three-carbon sugar can be built up into glucose phosphate and then into starch by condensation.
- In order that the cycle continues, most of the triose phosphate formed enters a series of reactions driven by ATP which results in the regeneration of RuBP.
- The NADP is reformed and goes back to the light-dependent reaction to be reduced again.

Study point

For every six molecules of triose phosphate formed, five are used to regenerate ribulose bisphosphate and only one molecule is converted to glucose.

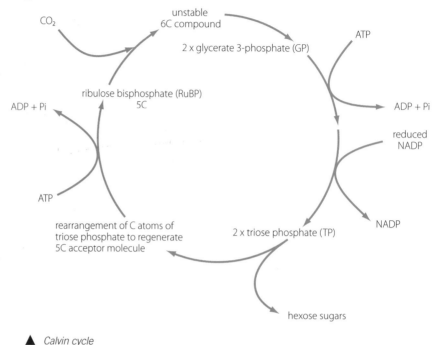

▲ *Calvin cycle*

Product synthesis

Study point

You are not required to provide chemical details of the manufacture of the products of photosynthesis.

Study point

A knowledge of nitrogen and magnesium only are required by the specification.

Following the metabolism of triose phosphate to carbohydrates, lipids and amino acids and the absorption of mineral ions from the soil, the plant is able to manufacture all the other products needed for life.

Various inorganic nutrients are needed by plants and may be limiting factors to metabolism if in short supply. Mineral ions are also required for the synthesis of compounds needed for the growth of the plant.

Macronutrients, for example potassium, sodium, magnesium, calcium, nitrate and phosphate, are required in substantial quantities but the micronutrients, for example manganese and copper, are needed in much smaller amounts.

Nitrogen is taken up by the roots as nitrates. It is transported as nitrates in the xylem and as amino acids in the phloem. It is used for the synthesis of proteins and nucleic acids. Symptoms of nitrogen deficiency are reduced growth of all organs, and chlorosis, a yellowing of the leaves due to inadequate chlorophyll production. Chlorosis first appears in the older leaves.

Magnesium is absorbed as Mg^{2+} and its function is in chlorophyll production and activation of ATPase. Magnesium is required by all tissues but especially leaves and is transported as Mg^{2+} in the xylem.

Magnesium forms part of the chlorophyll molecule. Pronounced chlorosis begins between the veins of older leaves and is the main symptom of magnesium deficiency. This is because existing magnesium in the plant is mobilised and transported to newly formed leaves.

Photosynthesis

1 The diagram outlines the biochemical pathways involved in photosynthesis.

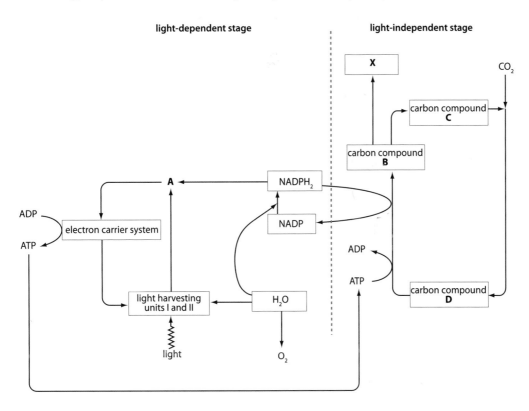

light-dependent stage   light-independent stage

(a) Where precisely in the chloroplast, does the light-dependent reaction take place? (1)

(b) Name the light-harvesting units I and II. (1)

(c) Name the process by which ATP is produced in the light-dependent stage. (1) *thylakoid membrane*

(d) During the light-dependent stage, water molecules are broken down to produce oxygen, electrons and protons (hydrogen ions). With reference to the diagram:

  (i) Name the process by which water molecules are broken down. (1) *photolysis*

  (ii) What happens to the electrons produced in this process? (1) *they replace the e⁻ lost in PS2*

  (iii) What happens to the protons produced in this process? (1) *accepted by NADP which is reduced*

  (iv) What is the function of A? (1) *accept electrons*

(e)(i) In the light-independent stage name the biochemical pathway which includes compounds B, C and D. (1) *Calvin Cycle*

  (ii) Where in the chloroplast do these reactions take place? (1) *stroma*

(f)(i) In the chain of chemical reactions which of the letters B to D indicates a 5-carbon compound? (1) *C*

  (ii) Name the end product of photosynthesis, labelled X. (1) *glucose*

WJEC BI4 JAN 2009

2 The important pigments in most chloroplasts are chlorophyll a, chlorophyll b, and carotene.

The graph shows the absorption spectrum of these pigments along with the action spectrum for photosynthesis.

(a) Describe the function of chlorophyll a. (1) *absorb light*

(b)(i) State the wavelength which is most effectively absorbed by chlorophyll a. (1) *435-340 nm*

(ii) Use the information in the graph to explain why it is an advantage for a leaf to contain more than one pigment. (2) *addition pigments increase range of wavelengths absorbed*

(c) Why do most leaves characteristically have a green colour? (1) *green wavelength is reflected*

(d) The graph also shows the 'action spectrum' for photosynthesis.

Describe the relationship between the absorption spectrum and the action spectrum and explain what this relationship tells us about light absorption and photosynthesis. (2)
similar trend, wavelengths responsible for light absorption, are used in photosythsis

(e) The following diagram represents a photosystem.

(i) Identify regions A and B on the diagram. (2)

(ii) In which region would you find chlorophyll a? (1) *reaction centre*

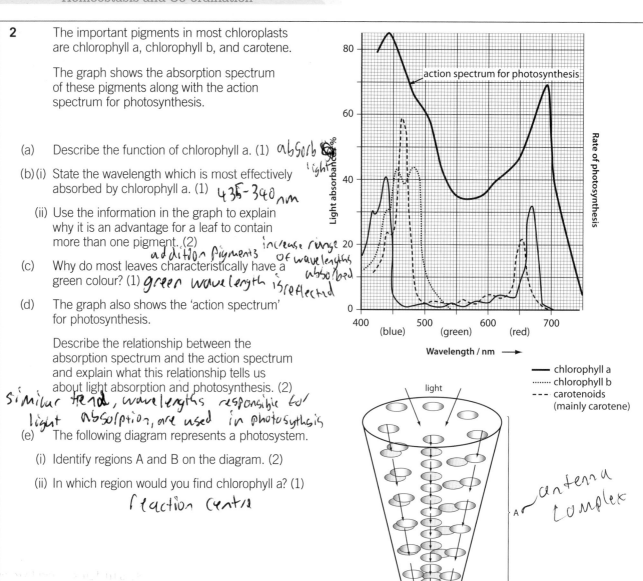

A — antenna complex

B — reaction centre

action spectrum for photosynthesis

Rate of photosynthesis

Light absorbance %

400 (blue) 500 (green) 600 (red) 700

Wavelength / nm →

light

—— chlorophyll a
······· chlorophyll b
--- carotenoids (mainly carotene)

WJEC BY4 JAN 2011

3 The diagram summarises the light-independent reactions of photosynthesis.

(a) Name the molecule which enters the cycle at point A. (1) *CO₂*

(b) State the two products of the light-dependent stage that are required in the Calvin cycle. (2) *ATP reduced NADP*

(c) Using the letters in the diagram indicate where the chemicals named in (b) are required. (3)

(d) State one possible fate of the hexose sugar produced. (1)

energy source / starch

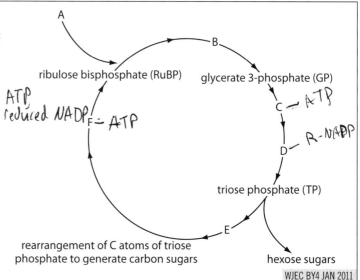

A

B

ribulose bisphosphate (RuBP)   glycerate 3-phosphate (GP)

F — ATP   *C — ATP*

D — R-NADP

triose phosphate (TP)

E

rearrangement of C atoms of triose phosphate to generate carbon sugars

hexose sugars

WJEC BY4 JAN 2011

4 An experiment was carried out to investigate the conditions required for photosynthesis. Chloroplasts of nettle leaves were extracted and suspended in buffer solution containing the dye, methylene blue. The solution was divided into four equal parts and treated as shown in the table of results below. The methylene blue acts as an artificial hydrogen acceptor and becomes colourless (or pale green in this experiment) when reduced.

Experiment	Conditions	Colour of solution	
		After 5 minutes	After 45 minutes
1	Dark at 5°C	Blue-green	Blue-green
2	Dark at 25°C	Blue-green	Blue-green
3	Light at 5°C	Blue-green	Pale-green
4	Light at 25°C	Pale-green	Pale-green

(a) Explain how the hydrogen is being formed during photosynthesis. (1)

(b) What would be the normal hydrogen acceptor in the chloroplast? (1)

(c) What conclusions may be drawn from the results? (3)

(d) Suggest an explanation for the conclusions. (1)

WJEC BI4 JUNE 2004

5 Complete the table comparing ATP synthesis in mitochondria and chloroplasts. (6)

	Oxidative phosphorylation	Cyclic photophosphorylation	Non-cyclic photophosphorylation
Requires light	no	yes	yes
Requires oxygen	yes	no	no
Produces oxygen	no	no	yes
Number of proton pumps involved	3	1	1
Source of electrons	R-NAD/R-FAD	PS1	PS2/water
Final electron acceptor	Oxygen	PS1	NADP

WJEC BI4 JUNE 2009

6 The diagrams compare the structure of a mitochondrion with that of a chloroplast (structures C and I are only shown in part of the diagrams).

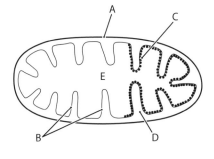
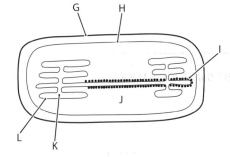

Using a letter from each of the diagrams, identify the regions or structures in which:

(a) There is a high concentration of protons. (2) D, K

(b) Carbon dioxide is either taken up or released. (2) E, J

(c) The electron transport chain occurs. (2) B, L or C, I

(d) Most of the synthesis of ATP takes place. (2) C and I

WJEC BI4 JAN 2003

7 Describe the light-dependent stage of photosynthesis. (10)

WJEC BI4 JAN 2004

BY4

Microbiology

Micro-organisms include bacteria, fungi, viruses and protoctista. This section describes the classification, growth and methods of counting bacteria. Particular emphasis is placed on the principles of aseptic technique. The principles involved in the batch culture fermenter are studied together with its application in the production of the antibiotic penicillin on a commercial scale using the fungus *Penicillium*. Apart from the latter, this section deals mainly with bacteria.

Topic contents

By the end of this topic you should be able to:

- Describe that bacteria may be classified according to their shape and also by the Gram stain technique.

- Explain how bacterial growth is affected by temperature, pH, oxygen and nutrients.

- Explain the importance of taking certain safety precautions when working with micro-organisms.

- Describe how the growth of bacteria may be monitored by a number of methods but with particular reference to the technique of counting colonies.

- Describe how a batch fermenter is used in the industrial production of the antibiotic penicillin.

Microbiology

Bacteria and fungi are extremely important in the decay of dead organisms releasing and recycling nutrients. Certain bacteria, viruses and fungi can cause disease in humans, crops and domestic animals. Bacteria reproduce asexually by binary fission, although certain bacteria can also reproduce sexually. Some bacteria are pathogens and some cause deterioration of stored food, but it is important to remember that many are beneficial to humans.

Classification of bacteria

This section deals with bacteria in particular. Bacteria vary considerably in size. The diagram shows a comparison of sizes for a number of different cells.

Key Term

Gram stain = a method of staining bacteria as an aid to their identification.

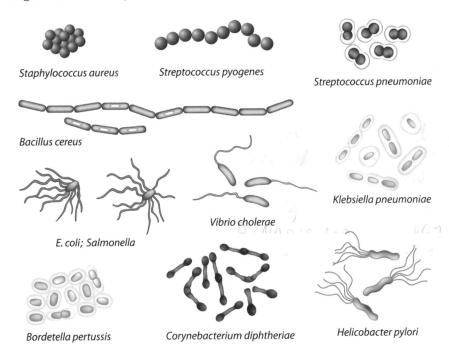

Staphylococcus aureus

Streptococcus pyogenes

Streptococcus pneumoniae

Bacillus cereus

Klebsiella pneumoniae

Vibrio cholerae

E. coli; Salmonella

Bordetella pertussis

Corynebacterium diphtheriae

Helicobacter pylori

Examiner tip

Bacteria, in common with all living organisms, are named according to the binomial system. For example, *Staphylococcus aureus*. Their name may also indicate their shape.

Microbiologists classify bacteria according to their shape and by the Gram stain technique.

Classification by shape

There are three main shapes of bacteria according to species:

- Bacillus or rod-shaped.   e.g. *Escherichia*
- Cocci or spherical. e.g. *Staphylococcus*
- Spiral or corkscrew-shaped. e.g. *Spirillum*

Further differentiation is often possible according to the way bacteria tend to be grouped. They may be single, in pairs, forming chains or in clusters.

Classification by the Gram stain reaction

This enables microbiologists to distinguish between Gram-positive and Gram-negative bacteria. The different staining properties are due to differences in the chemical composition of their cell walls.

Before staining, all bacteria are colourless. At the end of the procedure the Gram positive bacteria will be stained violet and the Gram negative red. The procedure involves a process of counterstaining.

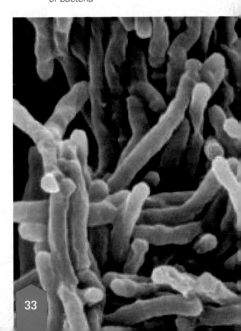

▼ Scanning electron microscope image of bacteria

▶ *Diagrammatic representation of Gram stain technique*

| before staining all bacteria are colourless | after basic stain (*crystal violet*) all bacteria are stained violet | after mordant (*Lugol's iodine*) stain is fixed more firmly into the cell | after decolouriser (*acetone-alcohol*) some bacteria are colourless (Gram negative) while others are still violet (Gram positive) | after counterstain (*safranin*) colourless bacteria (Gram negative) have taken up stain and appear red; Gram positive bacteria remain violet |

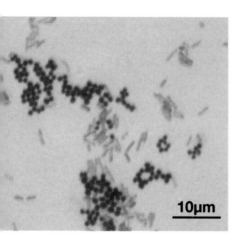

10µm

▲ *Photomicrograph of Gram stain*

The cell wall of all bacteria consists of a mixture of polysaccharide and polypeptides, known as peptidoglycan (murein). The cross-linking provides strength, gives the cell its shape, and the wall protects against swelling and bursting or lysis due to osmosis. Gram positive bacteria possess this basic cell wall structure but Gram negative bacteria possess an additional outer layer of lipopolysaccharide.

Gram positive bacteria

After staining, they appear violet or purple under the microscope. These bacteria are more susceptible to the antibiotic, penicillin, and the enzyme, lysozyme, than Gram negative bacteria. Gram positive bacteria include *Bacillus, Staphylococcus* and *Streptococcus* species.

Penicillin works by interfering with interpeptide linking of peptidoglycan, the strong, structural molecule found specifically in bacterial cell walls. Cell walls without intact peptidoglycan cross-links are structurally weak, prone to collapse and disintegrate when the bacteria attempts to divide. Since the eukaryotic cells of humans do not have cell walls, our cells are not damaged by penicillin.

Gram negative bacteria

These have more chemically complex walls where the peptidoglycan is supplemented by large molecules of lipopolysaccharide which protect the cell. They do not retain dyes like crystal violet and appear red or pink when viewed under the microscope. Gram negative bacteria include *Salmonella* species. They are not affected by the antibacterial enzyme, lysozyme, which occurs in human tears, and are resistant to penicillin. They require a different class of antibiotics that interfere with the cell's ability to make proteins. Although human cells also make proteins, the protein-making cellular machinery is different in eukaryotic cells, so it is not harmed by these antibiotics.

6

Knowledge check

Match the terms 1–3 with the statements A–C.

1. Peptidoglycan.
2. Bacillus.
3. Lipopolysaccharide.

A. Rod-shaped bacteria.
B. Found in all bacterial cell walls.
C. Found only in Gram negative bacteria.

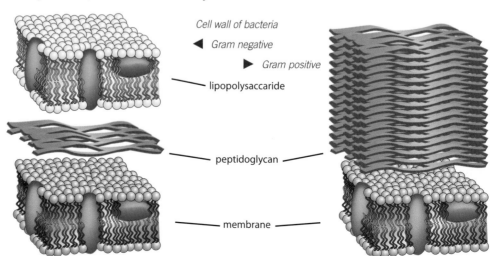

Cell wall of bacteria
◀ *Gram negative*
▶ *Gram positive*

— lipopolysaccharide

— peptidoglycan —

— membrane —

Conditions necessary for culturing bacteria

Micro-organisms reproduce quickly given a suitable environment. For example, bacteria are able to divide every twenty minutes under optimum conditions. In the laboratory, bacteria can be grown on a wide variety of substrates providing they are supplied with suitable physical conditions, nutrients and water. Micro-organisms vary in their requirements and usually grow over a range of temperatures and pH values, with an optimum within the range.

Micro-organisms require the following conditions for growth:

- Nutrients – in the laboratory nutrients are supplied in nutrient media, such as agar, and include: carbon, usually in the form of glucose; nitrogen, in organic and inorganic form; growth factors such as vitamins and mineral salts. Nitrogen is needed to produce amino acids during protein synthesis.

- Temperature – as all growth is normally regulated by enzymes, the range of 25–45°C is favourable for the majority of bacteria. The optimum for mammalian pathogens is around 37°C.

- pH – most bacteria are favoured by slightly alkaline conditions (pH 7.4), whereas fungi grow better in neutral to slightly acid conditions.

- Oxygen – many micro-organisms require oxygen for metabolism and are referred to as obligate aerobes. Some, while growing best in the presence of oxygen, can nevertheless survive in its absence; these are called facultative anaerobes. Others cannot grow in the presence of oxygen and are called obligate anaerobes. *Clostridium* bacteria are obligate anaerobes that produce toxins or poisons in a wound. These bacteria destroy body tissue and the condition is called 'moist gangrene'.

Key Term

Aseptic = a procedure performed under sterile conditions.

▼ **Study point**

Two potential problems which must be prevented when working with bacteria are: the contamination of supplied cultures from the environment, and the contamination to the environment.

Principles of aseptic technique

Bacteria (*and fungi*) are cultured on, or in, media that are designed to supply the cell with all its nutritional requirements. **Aseptic** techniques (also known as sterile techniques), in which the apparatus and equipment are kept free of micro-organisms, are used to prevent contamination of bacterial cultures and the surrounding environment.

To prevent the contamination of pure cultures and apparatus by bacteria from the environment:

- Sterilise all apparatus and media before use to prevent initial contamination.

- Handle cultures carefully and use equipment such as sterile loops to prevent subsequent contamination.

To prevent contamination to the environment by the bacteria being used in experiments:

- Sterilise the work surface before and after an experiment using a disinfectant, for example, Lysol used as a 3% solution.

- Use the correct handling techniques to prevent the contamination of personnel and the immediate environment by the organisms being cultured.

For example, when carrying out the process of inoculation:

- Grasp the culture bottle in one hand; remove the cap with the little finger of the other hand – do not place the cap down on the work surface.

- Flame the mouth of the bottle for 2 or 3 seconds.

- Pass the inoculating loop through a flame until red hot.

- Lift the lid of the Petri dish just enough to allow entry of the inoculating loop.

Key Term

Pathogen = a disease-causing micro-organism.

- Secure the Petri dish lid with adhesive tape. Use two pieces of tape to fasten the lid, but do not seal all the way round as this could create anaerobic conditions and encourage the growth of possible **pathogenic** micro-organisms.

- Incubate at around 25°C (cultures should not be cultured at 37°C as this is an ideal temperature for the growth of many pathogenic species).

- Do not open Petri dishes after incubation.

- In a laboratory the preferred method of sterilisation is to use an autoclave. This is a sealed container in which glass and metal equipment is heated at 121°C in steam under pressure for 15 minutes after the required pressure has been reached. This is essential as, under certain unfavourable growth conditions a few bacteria such as *Clostridium*, are capable of producing an internal resting cell known as an endospore. This is a means of protecting the nuclear material. Endospores are resistant to heat, drying, pH change and use of disinfectant. When favourable conditions return, endospores can reform into a bacterial cell.

- Disposable materials, such as plastic Petri dishes, can be sealed inside autoclavable plastic bags and placed in a dustbin after having been autoclaved.

- Radiation, e.g. gamma rays, is used commercially to sterilise plastic equipment.

Examiner tip

An examiner will be impressed if you can incorporate your practical experience into your exam answers and be aware of the safety issues and potential hazards associated with practical techniques.

8

Knowledge check

State which of the following six statements regarding aseptic techniques are false.

1. Flame the mouth or neck of the culture bottle.

2. Leave the lid off the Petri dish for a few minutes after inoculation.

3. Incubate at 37°C.

4. Seal the Petri dish and lid all the way round.

5. Sterilise all equipment in boiling water for 15 minutes.

6. Sterilise the work surface before and after an experiment using a disinfectant.

▼ *Sterile techniques*

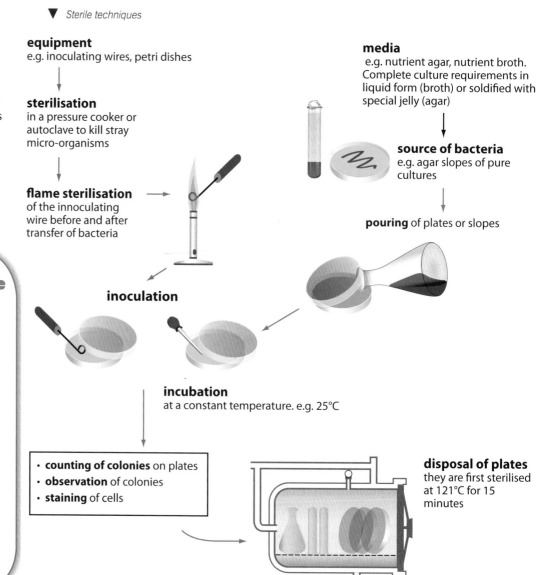

equipment
e.g. inoculating wires, petri dishes
↓
sterilisation
in a pressure cooker or autoclave to kill stray micro-organisms
↓
flame sterilisation
of the innoculating wire before and after transfer of bacteria

media
e.g. nutrient agar, nutrient broth. Complete culture requirements in liquid form (broth) or soldified with special jelly (agar)
↓
source of bacteria
e.g. agar slopes of pure cultures
↓
pouring of plates or slopes

inoculation

incubation
at a constant temperature. e.g. 25°C

- **counting of colonies** on plates
- **observation** of colonies
- **staining** of cells

disposal of plates
they are first sterilised at 121°C for 15 minutes

Methods of measuring growth

Estimating the growth of bacteria is extremely important. Environmental health officers regularly inspect food premises and take samples for analysis. Water authorities check water supplies daily. Many products are produced using bacteria grown in **fermenters**. Measuring their growth is an important part of the process.

The size of a population of micro-organisms in liquid culture may be measured by counting cells directly, or by taking some indirect method such as the turbidity (cloudiness) of the culture. Direct cell counts may be divided into:

- Total counts, which include both living and dead cells.

- Viable counts, which count living cells only.

There are several different methods of measuring growth.

Measuring growth directly

Rough estimates of growth rates can be made by regularly measuring the diameter of a bacterial or fungal **colony** as it spreads from a central point to cover the surface of a solid growth medium.

Plating and counting colonies

In practice, it is never possible to count whole populations of micro-organisms. Instead, the cells in a very small sample of culture are counted, and the result multiplied up to give a population density in organisms per cm³ of culture. Even then the population density is likely to be so high that cell counts are usually made in known dilutions of the culture, usually in 10-fold steps. This is known as serial dilution.

◀ *Serial dilution*

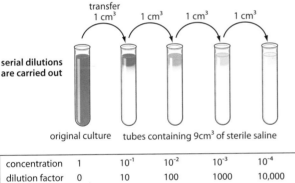

serial dilutions are carried out

transfer 1 cm³   1 cm³   1 cm³   1 cm³

original culture   tubes containing 9cm³ of sterile saline

concentration	1	10^{-1}	10^{-2}	10^{-3}	10^{-4}
dilution factor	0	10	100	1000	10,000

when a sample is plated, each colony that grows represents a single cell or spore in the original sample

plate onto sterile agar plates

incubate

clumping   count colonies   count colonies

colony count multiplied by dilution factor

It may be necessary for a water authority to estimate the number of bacteria in a sample of water. The sample must first be diluted using the serial dilution technique; 1cm³ of the diluted sample is then added to a sterile agar plate. This is placed in an incubator at 25°C for two days to allow time for bacteria to grow. The dish containing the colonies that are distinct and separate is chosen and the colonies counted. To find the total viable cell count the number of colonies is multiplied by the appropriate dilution factor.

If the dilution is insufficient then colonies will merge, referred to as 'clumping', and counting is inaccurate, resulting in an underestimate of numbers.

YOU SHOULD KNOW ›››

››› the difference between total and viable counts

››› the estimation of bacterial numbers using the technique of plating and counting colonies

››› the technique of serial dilution

Key Terms

Colony (of bacteria) = a cluster of cells or clone which arises from a single bacterium by asexual reproduction.

Fermenter = vessel used to culture micro-organisms, usually on an industrial scale.

Study point

The separate colonies of bacteria are counted with the assumption being made that each colony has arisen from a single cell from the original culture which has divided asexually.

▼ *Plate showing colonies*

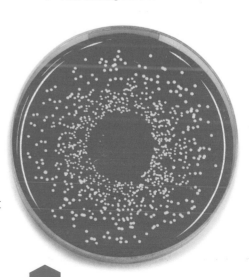

YOU SHOULD KNOW ›››

››› the principles underlying the use of a batch culture fermenter

››› the production of penicillin using a batch culture fermenter

Examiner tip
You are not required to describe or use a haemocytometer or colorimeter.

Using a haemocytometer

This is a more accurate method using a specialised microscope slide. Using the haemocytometer gives total cell counts as it is not possible to distinguish between living and dead cells.

Turbidimetry

A colorimeter is used to measure the cloudiness or turbidity of the culture as cell numbers increase. Results are derived by comparison with a standard graph of light absorbance plotted against known cell numbers.

Batch culture fermentation

Industrial fermentation is widely used to culture bacterial and fungal cells.

An important use of large-scale industrial fermentation is the production of antibiotics such as penicillin.

There are a number of advantages to growing micro-organisms in fermenters. The microbes grow rapidly and enzymes do not have to be supplied. This means that fermentation can take place at lower temperatures than normally used in industrial processes and therefore production is cheaper.

Fermenter design

The following describes the main principles of batch fermentation:

- A pure culture of an organism is needed for the formation and harvesting of a pure product during and after growth in a fermenter vessel. The organism must be supplied with suitable conditions for growth and without competition for maximum efficiency.

- The vessel should be sterilised beforehand and an appropriate sterile medium used. During use the vessel openings must be protected from contamination by filters, and aseptic conditions and handling are required to maintain purity.

- Forced aeration may be needed, for maximum growth of aerobes, which may also mix the culture to improve contact with nutrients. Mixing may be improved by a separate mixer.

- Temperature monitoring and control are required to maintain constant conditions, and water-jackets remove excess heat produced during the culture process.

- Commercially, sophisticated monitors are used to improve control of temperature and pH, and air inlets may use spargers or other devices to improve aeration.

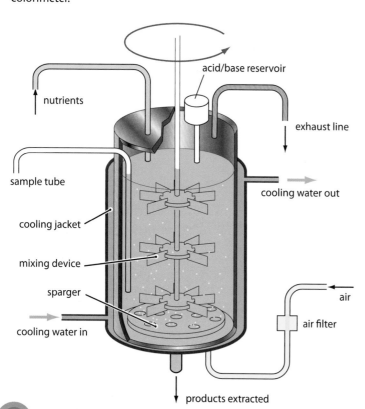

▲ *Fermenter*

9

Knowledge check

Link the parts of the fermenter with their functions A–D.

1. Cooling jacket.
2. Air filter.
3. Sparger.
4. Acid-base reservoir.

A. Bubbles air through the medium.
B. To remove heat generated by the metabolism of microbes.
C. To prevent contamination by airborne bacteria.
D. To maintain a constant pH.

Production of penicillin

- The fermenter is inoculated with a culture of *Penicillium notatum*, which then grows under the optimum conditions provided in the fermenter.

- It takes about 30 hours for penicillin production to begin. The penicillin is secreted by the fungus and accumulates in the medium. The delay in production occurs because penicillin is a secondary metabolite.

- After about six days the culture fluid mixture is filtered and the penicillin is extracted and purified. That is, the culture medium, after filtering, is retained and processed.

- This type of fermentation is known as a batch culture. This method has the disadvantage that the fermenter has to be emptied, cleaned and sterilised, ready for the next batch.

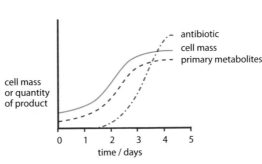
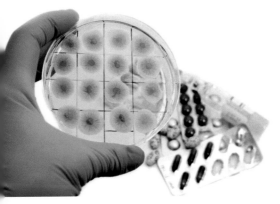

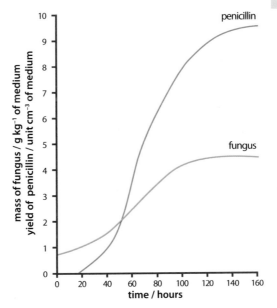

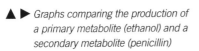 *Graphs comparing the production of a primary metabolite (ethanol) and a secondary metabolite (penicillin)*

Primary metabolism is the norm, when the fungus is metabolising glucose to release energy and increasing its own biomass. Continuous cultivation is suitable for products known as primary metabolites. This allows production to continue for much longer, as nutrients are added throughout the process and the products are continuously being removed. Many products including alcohol and insulin are produced in this way.

However, penicillin is a **secondary metabolite** and is only produced when food supplies are becoming scarce. That is, the antibiotic is produced at a period in the life of the fungus when there is a change away from its optimum conditions. This explains why penicillin has to be produced using a batch fermenter, where nutrients are added at the start and the process is allowed to continue without the further addition of nutrients.

Microbiology

1   Three students carried out an experiment involving culturing bacteria in a liquid. A sample of the bacteria was stained using the Gram stain.

(a)(i) The bacteria stained pink and the students concluded that the bacteria were Gram negative. Give two features of a Gram negative bacterial cell wall. (2)

  (ii) Give one advantage to the bacteria of having this cell wall structure. (1)

(b)   The students decided to monitor population growth each using a different method.

  (i) One student decided to use a viable count. What assumption must be made when using this method? (1)

  (ii) State one limitation of using this method. (1)

(c)   Another student used a total count method. He counted all the bacteria in the field of view of the microscope. Suggest why this method gave a higher estimate of the population than the viable count. (1)

(d)   In both methods the original culture must be diluted before a count can be made. The diagrams below show how a dilution was carried out and the result of incubating $1\,cm^3$ of the diluted sample on a nutrient agar plate for 24 hours.

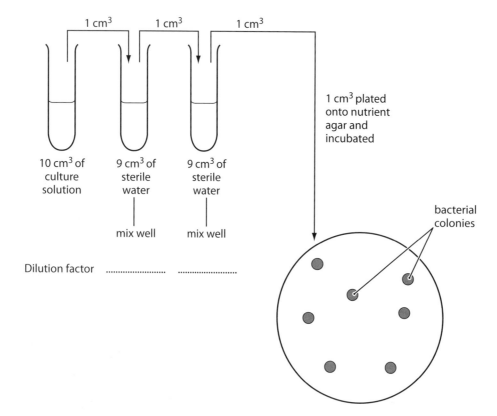

Using the information, complete the dilution factors and calculate the estimated total population in $1cm^3$ of the original culture. (3)

(e)   Explain why during the experiment:

  (i) Sterile equipment was used. (1)

  (ii) The dishes were incubated at 25°C. (1)

  (iii) The lids of the dishes were taped down following the addition of the culture. (1)

(f)   After the experiments were completed explain why the dishes were autoclaved at 121°C for 15 minutes. (1)

WJEC BI4 JAN 2005

2 (a)   State three conditions necessary for growing bacteria in the laboratory. (1)

(b)   Bacteria may be classified or grouped according to the shape of their cells. State the names of two different-shaped bacteria. (2)

(c)   The diagrams show parts of two bacterial cells.

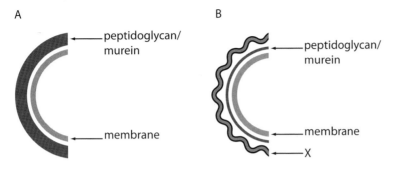

A

peptidoglycan/
murein

membrane

B

peptidoglycan/
murein

membrane

X

(i)   Complete the following table to show the colour each cell would be stained by the test and whether it is positive or negative. (2)

Cell	Colour after staining	Positive or negative
A		
B		

(ii)   Name two chemical components of the structure labelled X in cell B. (2)

WJEC BI4 JUNE 2007

3   The diagram shows an industrial fermenter which could be used in the early stage during the manufacture of penicillin.

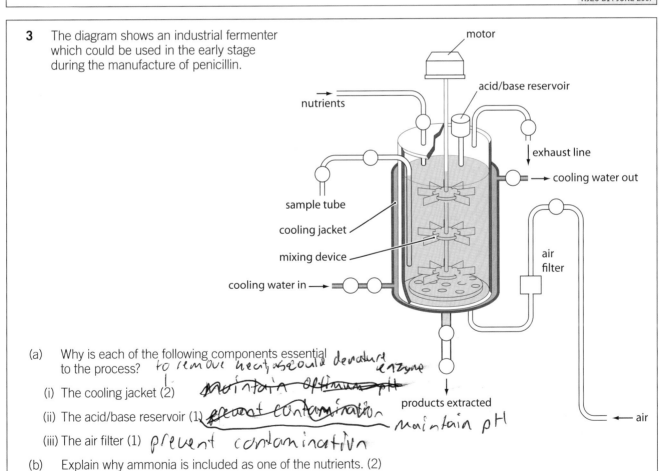

motor

acid/base reservoir

nutrients

exhaust line

cooling water out

sample tube

cooling jacket

mixing device

cooling water in

air
filter

products extracted

air

(a)   Why is each of the following components essential to the process?   *to remove heat, as could denature enzyme*

(i)   The cooling jacket (2)   *maintain optimum pH*

(ii)   The acid/base reservoir (1)   *prevent contamination   maintain pH*

(iii)   The air filter (1)   *prevent contamination*

(b)   Explain why ammonia is included as one of the nutrients. (2)

(c) The graph shows the characteristics of batch production of *Penicillium notatum* cells over time.

(i) At what point on the graph will penicillin production begin? (1)

(ii) Give an explanation of your answer. (1)

(iii) Show how this reflects the need of the organism when free-living. (1)

(d) Give two reasons why aseptic conditions should be maintained during batch culture of microbes. (2)

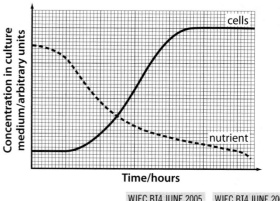

WJEC BI4 JUNE 2005   WJEC BI4 JUNE 2002

---

4 (a) Many bacteria have precise metabolic requirements for oxygen. Aerobic and anaerobic bacteria can be identified by growing them in liquid culture. The results of one such experiment are shown below. The growth media was the same in all tubes.

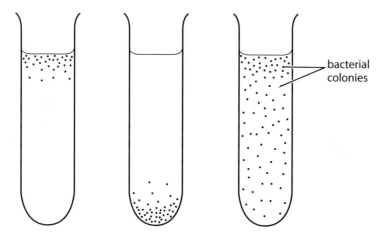

bacterial colonies

Give the correct biological term for each of these types of bacteria from their position in the growth tubes and give a reason for each answer. (6)

(b) Some anaerobic bacteria, such as *Clostridium perfringens*, produce toxins which are highly dangerous to humans if a wound becomes infected (gangrene). Hyperbaric oxygen therapy is one method used in the treatment of such infections. This involves two to four daily sessions with the whole body exposed to oxygen in a chamber for 150 minutes at 3 atmospheres pressure. Suggest how this treatment is successful for treating these infections. (2)

WJEC BY4 JUNE 2010

BY4
Controlling population size

Organisms live as part of populations and communities. It is advantageous for animals to live in groups because they gain protection from predators, enabling them to breed and rear young more successfully. However, certain factors can limit the growth of a population and a balance between birth rate and death rate has to be maintained. Organisms competing with humans for food are regarded as pests. It is essential to control these pests in order to feed the human population and reduce disease. There are relative advantages and disadvantages to the control of pests using chemicals and biological agents, so it may be advisable to use a combination of these two methods.

All living organisms require nutrients, particularly carbon and nitrogen. All organic molecules contain carbon, and nitrogen is needed to make proteins and nucleic acids. These elements are in limited supply on Earth. Micro-organisms play a key role in the process of decay, releasing these elements back into the ecosystem through the carbon and nitrogen cycles.

By the end of this topic you should be able to:

- Describe and explain how bacterial populations show a pattern of growth which follows an S-shaped growth curve.

- Explain that the size of a population at a particular time is determined by a number of factors, including biotic potential, environmental resistance factors and the carrying capacity.

- Explain that, in general, the size of the population is regulated by the balance between the birth rate and the death rate.

- Explain that population changes may be density dependent due to biotic factors, such as competition for food, or density-independent factors, such as adverse flood or fire.

- Distinguish between intraspecific competition and interspecific competition.

- Describe that chemical control involves the use of pesticides, whereas biological control uses predators, parasites or pathogens to control the numbers of a pest.

- Describe the relative advantages and disadvantages of the two methods of pest control.

- Understand that decomposers are the key organisms involved in the cycling of nutrients.

- Describe the carbon cycle with reference to the increase in carbon dioxide levels in the atmosphere due to human activity.

- Describe the nitrogen cycle and the role of bacteria.

YOU SHOULD KNOW ›››

››› the factors that determine the size of a population

››› the stages in the population growth curve

››› carrying capacity and environmental resistance

››› the difference between density-dependent and density-independent factors

Key Terms

Population = a group of organisms of a single species interbreeding and occupying a particular area.

Birth rate = the reproductive capacity of the population.

Immigration = the movement of individuals into a population.

Factors controlling population growth

The growth of a particular **population** at a particular time is determined by the **birth rate** and death rate. In addition, individuals can **immigrate** to or emigrate from an area.

The following describes what happens when a species colonises a new area under favourable conditions.

The usual pattern of growth for a population of bacteria consists of four phases:

- The lag phase – this may last from a few minutes to several days. It is a period of adaptation or preparation for growth, with intense metabolic activity, notably enzyme synthesis. Then there is a period of slow growth as the individuals are few at the start, but when they start to reproduce, numbers slowly build.

- The exponential phase – as numbers increase, providing there is no factor limiting growth, more individuals become available for reproduction. In the case of bacteria, the cells begin to divide at a constant rate with the population doubling per unit time. The cell population increases geometrically. This rate of increase cannot be maintained indefinitely.

- The stationary phase – population growth enters this phase when the birth rate of new individuals is equal to the death rate of older ones. Certain factors limit the population growth. The population has reached its maximum size. This is known as the carrying capacity for the particular environment in which the population occurs. This describes the limit to the number of individuals that an area can support.

- The death phase – when death rate is greater than birth rate. This may occur when all the food in a nutrient solution has been used up.

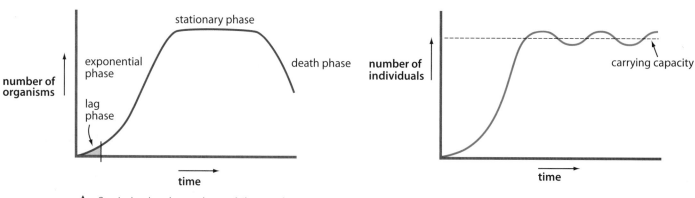

▲ *Graph showing changes in population growth*   ▲ *Graph showing carrying capacity*

Consider a sample of a particular species of micro-organism placed in a flask of water. If the temperature is around 25°C and mineral nutrients have been added, it will divide rapidly because all the factors needed for the growth of the population are present. There are no limiting factors. However, over time the situation will change:

- Nutrients will be used up.

- Toxic waste will build up.

- Space may become limiting.

- Disease may occur as a result of overcrowding.

The S-shaped curve is typical of any animal species when it occupies a new habitat. There is a period of slow growth as the species adapts to the habitat, followed by a period of rapid growth with little environmental resistance. The graph then levels off as the population reaches its carrying capacity. If one factor becomes in short supply, then this can limit the growth of the population, which then goes into decline.

▼ **Study point**

Environmental resistance slows down population growth.

A term used to describe all the factors that may limit the growth of a population is environmental resistance. In the situation in the flask these factors include available food, disease, overcrowding, competition and the accumulation of toxic waste. However, in a less artificial situation other factors may play a part. These additional **biotic** factors include predation, parasitism, competition from other species for food, disease. Factors such as temperature, pH and light may also play a role in affecting population size. These factors are called **abiotic** factors.

Factors that regulate population increase

It is possible to distinguish between those factors that will slow down population growth rate and those that might cause a population crash.

- Some factors are density dependent, that is, their effect increases as the density of the population increases. For example, accumulation of toxic waste, disease, parasitism and depletion of food supply. The carrying capacity is dependent on the resources provided by the environment (which therefore act as density-dependent factors).
- Other factors are density independent. The effect of these factors does not depend on the population density. All the plants and animals are affected no matter what the population size. The effect is the same regardless of the size of the population. It is usually due to a sudden or violent change in an abiotic factor, e.g. freezing, flood or fire.

Populations fluctuate in numbers

In general the size of a population is regulated by the balance between the birth rate and the death rate. However, populations fluctuate; they do not remain constant in size, although these fluctuations are not usually large and erratic. The numbers of most species lie near an equilibrium point known as the set point. For a given species in a particular environment, there is a certain equilibrium population that the environment can support. If the population rises above the set point, a density-dependent factor increases mortality or reduces breeding to such an extent that the population declines. If the population falls below the set point, environmental resistance is temporarily relieved so that the population rises again.

The size of a population may fluctuate on a regular basis. This may be the consequence of weather patterns such as temperature or rainfall.

Population oscillations are regulated by a process known as negative feedback.

▼ *Negative feedback control of population*

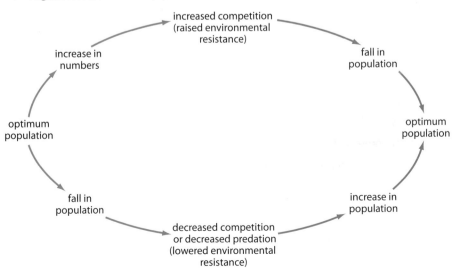

Key Term

Niche = the ecological role and space that an organism fills in an ecosystem.

Examiner tip

Which of two species in a niche has the competitive advantage depends on the conditions at any point in time. For example, when food is in short supply, if one species is smaller than another, it may need less food in order to survive.

How Science Works

Measuring the population numbers of *Paramecium* species cultured together and separately enabled Gause to formulate a general principle known as the competitive exclusion principle.

Competition

In nature, plants and animals have to struggle to survive. Plants compete for resources such as light, space, water and nutrients. Animals compete for food, shelter, space and reproductive partners.

There are two types of competition:

- Intraspecific competition is competition between individuals of the same species. This type of competition is density dependent since, as the population increases, a greater proportion of the population fails to survive. This has value to a population since organisms tend to produce more offspring than the habitat can support. Those organisms that are best adapted have a better chance of survival.

- Interspecific competition is competition between individuals of different species. Each species occupies a particular place, or **niche**, in an ecosystem. This is not only the particular physical space it occupies but also the role it carries out within the community. In the long term, two species cannot occupy the same niche in a specific habitat.

▼ *Competition between two species of* Paramecium

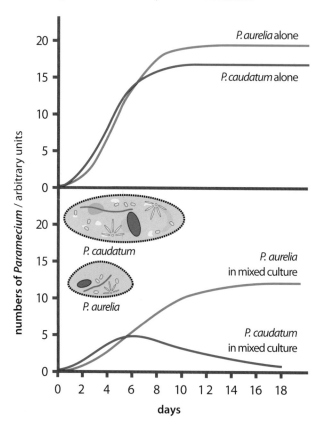

The Russian scientist, Gause, carried out an experiment whereby he cultured two different species of *Paramecium* in the laboratory with yeast as a source of food. When grown separately under identical conditions *P. aurelia* and *P. caudatum* showed similar and typical S-shaped growth curves. When grown together, after a short period of time, the smaller, faster-growing species, *P. aurelia* out-competed the larger, slower-growing *P. caudatum*. The latter eventually died as it could not occupy the same niche as its competitor.

Pest control

Pests attack animals and crop plants causing a reduction in yield and a massive economic loss for farmers. Pests can cause damage by:

- Feeding on crops and animals.
- Competing with crop organisms for resources.
- Directly causing disease in crop organisms.
- Making infection by pathogens more likely.
- Spoiling food when it is being stored or transported.

The economic injury level is when pest numbers are causing so much economic damage then it becomes worthwhile spending money on controlling the pest. The farmer has the option of using chemical or biological control.

▼ *Graph showing economic threshold*

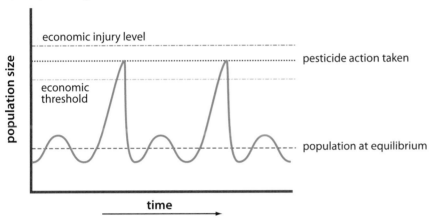

Chemical control

Chemical control involves using **pesticides**. These include herbicides, fungicides and **insecticides**. The chemicals can be sprayed onto the crop, applied as powders or smokes in enclosed areas, sprayed onto animals or added to animal feed.

Ideally an insecticide should be specific, non-persistent and should not accumulate and be passed along food chains. Organo-chlorine chemicals, such as DDT, were persistent and remained in the environment for long periods, a property which is regarded as undesirable in a modern pesticide. The overuse of pesticides has also led to the development of **resistance** among many species of insects.

▼ *Spraying insecticides on a small and large scale*

Key Terms

Pest = any organism that competes with or adversely affects a population of organisms that are of economic importance.

Pesticides = poisonous chemicals used to control organisms considered harmful to agriculture or organisms involved in disease transmission.

Insecticides = chemicals used to kill insects.

Resistance = the ability of an organism to survive exposure to a dose of that poison which would normally be lethal to it.

Study point

The use of many early insecticides, such as organo-chlorines, has long been banned.

Study point

An effective pesticide should be specific, not accumulate, be biodegradable and be cost-effective.

Key Term

Biological control = the control of a pest by using organisms that are either predators or parasites of the pest organism.

Examiner tip

In an exam question it is insufficient to describe a graph as 'one goes up and the other goes down'. You are expected to use figures and refer to the specific line of a graph in order to gain credit.

The advantages and disadvantages of chemical control

Advantages:

- It is a very effective means of control.
- Pests are eradicated quickly and relatively cheaply.
- Chemicals can be applied on a small scale, such as to a single field.
- Application does not require a high level of skill.

Disadvantages:

- The chemicals are not specific and can eradicate beneficial insects. For example, pollinating insects, such as bees; biological control agents. With the removal of the insect predators of the pest there may be a resurgence (build-up in numbers) of the pest.

▼ *Graph showing pest resurgence after application of insecticide*

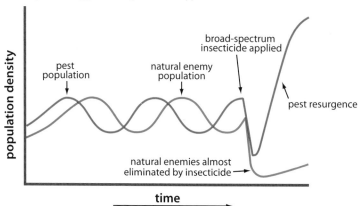

- Pests may become resistant to the pesticide.
- Some pesticides may kill fish, birds or mammals by contaminating their food, for example seed dressings.
- Long-term over-exposure to pesticides can cause harm to humans, For example, farmers using pesticides in sheep-dipping have developed cancers.

Biological control

Biological control is a specific type of interspecific competition that involves the relationship between the predator and its prey. The graph below illustrates the cyclic fluctuations in populations of a typical predator and prey relationship.

▼ **Study point**

An effective biological control agent should be species specific, effective long term.

▼ *Graph showing predator–prey relationship*

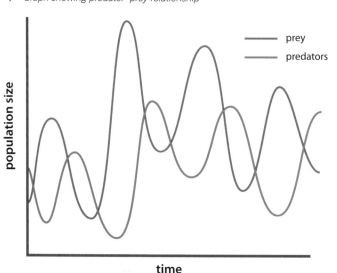

Predators kill other animals (their prey) for food. Predators are normally larger than their prey and tend to kill before they eat. The abundance of prey is a factor limiting the numbers of the predator. Within a food chain, a predator–prey relationship causes both populations to oscillate and these oscillations are regulated by **negative feedback**.

An early example of successful biological control involved the prickly-pear cactus, *Opuntia stricta*. This species was introduced from North America to Australia in 1900. As it had no natural predator it flourished and soon spread to grassland. Within 25 years it covered millions of acres and became a serious pest. In its natural habitat the cactus population is kept down by the burrowing of the larva of a moth, *Cactoblastis*. When the moth was introduced into Australia from Argentina in 1925, the caterpillars soon stopped the spread of the cactus and within a few years most of the farmland was reclaimed.

Since then the effect of the predator–prey relationship in regulating populations has been exploited by humans as a method of controlling pests. That is, biological control methods exploit natural enemies to regulate the population of pest species. A beneficial organism (the agent) is deployed against an undesirable one (the target). The aim is to reduce the pest population to a tolerable level by artificially increasing the populations of the agent. That is, to keep the numbers of the pest below the economic damage threshold for a particular crop. Some of the most successful results have been achieved using insect parasites. More recently, micro-organisms have been used as specific insect pathogens.

▼ *Graph showing principle of biological control*

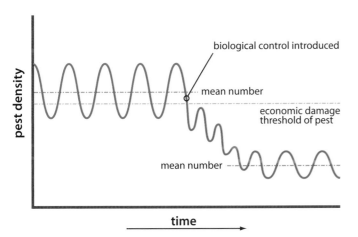

To eradicate the pest completely could be counter-productive. This would not leave any food source for the predator, which would then die out. Should the pest re-invade at a later date it would soon increase its numbers to an economically damaging level.

Pests are normally regulated by their natural predators. Modern agriculture can upset the natural system. For example, increasing field size has resulted in the destruction of hedgerows reducing the natural habitat of predators. Some of the most successful examples of biological control have involved the introduction of insects from another country to control the indigenous pest. However, there have been cases where the predator, having eradicated the pest, has turned to an alternative food supply and has itself become a pest.

Key Term

Negative feedback = when there is a change in a monitored variable a response is triggered to counteract the initial fluctuation.

▲ *Prickly-pear cactus*

▼ Study point

There are only a limited number of instances of successful biological control. The advantage of regulating populations in this way is that the control is very specific, so that useful organisms are unaffected. In contrast, pesticides kill both the target organism and desirable species.

The advantages and disadvantages of biological control

Advantages:

- It is usually highly specific to one pest. That is, it must target the pest only.

- It can provide long-term control if population equilibrium is established.

- Initial research costs mean that it is expensive to introduce. However, biological control is relatively inexpensive in the long term.

- There is no environmental contamination.

- It can be used in the glasshouse situation.

Disadvantages:

- Biological control agents are slow to build up in number to react to a sudden increase in pest numbers.

- Successful examples are relatively few in number. Biological agents are not known for most pest problems.

- A detailed knowledge of the life cycle is required involving a high level of skill and research. This can be expensive.

- There is the potential for the release of exotic organisms with unknown ecological effects.

- A frequent input is needed to attain a population balance.

- The introduction of biological control has been particularly successful in the confined area of commercial glasshouses. However, on a large scale in the open it is more difficult to eradicate pests.

▼ *Table comparing chemical and biological control*

Chemical control	Biological control
Affects non-target species	Very specific
Must be reapplied at intervals	Once established, permanent control
Expensive	Initially expensive, but once established no further expense
Pests may become resistant	No pest resistance

Integrated pest control

Despite the development of improved pesticides such as organophosphates and synthetic pyrethroids, it is now considered that pest control is best achieved by combining various methods. These include the use of biological control agents, producing pest-resistant crops, varying cultivation techniques and where necessary, the minimal, well-targeted application of highly selective pesticides. This is known as integrated pest management.

▶ *Integrated control*

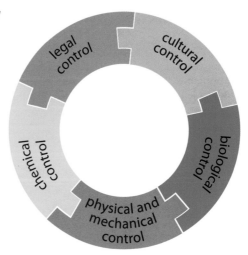

Recycling nutrients
Carbon cycle

Carbon is a major component of all organic molecules such as carbohydrates, fats and protein. During the day plants remove carbon dioxide from the air by the process of photosynthesis and convert it into carbohydrate. All organisms return it to the air by the process of respiration. The global level of atmospheric carbon dioxide has remained relatively constant for millions of years but over the past few hundred years the level has increased. This increase has mainly been caused by two human activities:

- The burning of fossil fuels has released to the atmosphere carbon dioxide that was previously locked up within these fuels.

- Deforestation has removed large quantities of photosynthesising biomass and so less carbon dioxide is being removed from the atmosphere.

The basis of the carbon cycle involves:

- Carbon dioxide is added to the air by the respiration of animals, plants and micro-organisms and by the combustion of fossil fuels.

- Photosynthesis takes place on so great a scale that it re-uses on a daily basis almost as much carbon dioxide as is released into the atmosphere.

- The production of carbohydrates, proteins and fats contributes to plant growth and subsequently to animal growth through complex food webs. The dead remains of plants and animals are then acted upon by **saprobionts** in the soil which ultimately release gaseous CO_2 back to the atmosphere.

▼ *Carbon cycle*

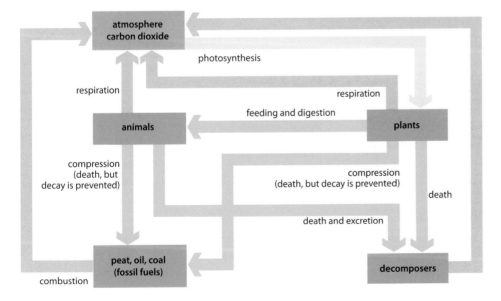

YOU SHOULD KNOW ›››

››› how carbon enters and leaves the living component of an ecosystem

››› how carbon enters the non-living component of the ecosystem

››› the role played by saprobionts in the carbon cycle

Key Term

Saprobiont (also saprophyte) = a micro-organism that obtains its food from the dead or decaying remains of other organisms.

▼ Study point

If decay is prevented by anaerobic conditions then organisms may become fossilised into coal, oil or peat.

Link Deforestation is studied in detail on page 174.

The effect of human activities on the carbon cycle is studied on page 178.

The nitrogen cycle

The nitrogen cycle is the flow of organic and inorganic nitrogen within an ecosystem where there is an interchange between nitrogenous compounds and atmospheric nitrogen.

Living organisms need nitrogen to make amino acids, proteins and nucleic acids. Plants and animals are unable to use nitrogen gas. Instead plants take in nitrates in solution through their roots. The organic nitrogen compounds produced by plants are transferred through the food chain when consumers eat plants. When plants and animals die, the minerals locked in their bodies, together with the excretory products of animals, must be decomposed in order to release the minerals back into the soil.

Bacteria are the key organisms involved in the process.

▼ *Nitrogen cycle*

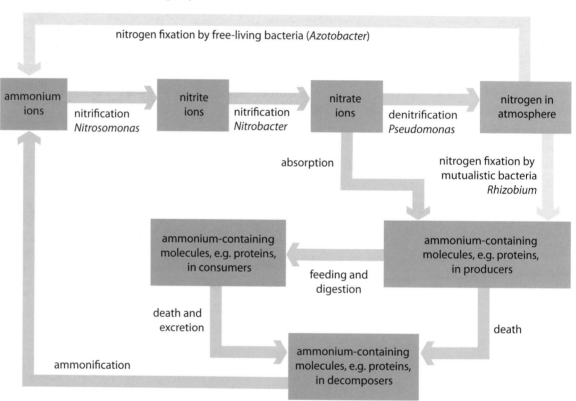

Study point

Nitrogen is found in all amino acids and the proteins which are formed from them. Nitrogen is taken up by plants through the roots as nitrate ions.

Examiner tip

You must learn the generic names of the bacteria involved in the nitrogen cycle.

The main processes involved are as follows.

Ammonification

Bacteria and fungi are called decomposers and result in the decay of dead plants and animals, faeces and urine into ammonium ions. This process is also called putrefaction.

Nitrification

The ammonia formed in putrefaction is converted by nitrification via nitrites to nitrates. Various bacteria are involved. For example, ammonia is converted to nitrite by *Nitrosomonas* and nitrite to nitrate by *Nitrobacter*. These bacteria require aerobic conditions.

Nitrogen fixation

Atmospheric nitrogen can be converted directly into ammonia by nitrogen-fixing bacteria. Free living nitrogen-fixing bacteria include *Azotobacter*. This species of bacteria reduces gaseous nitrogen to ammonia, which they use to manufacture amino acids. This accounts for most of the nitrogen fixation. There are also symbiotic nitrogen-fixing bacteria, *Rhizobium*, found in the root nodules of legumes (peas, beans and clover).

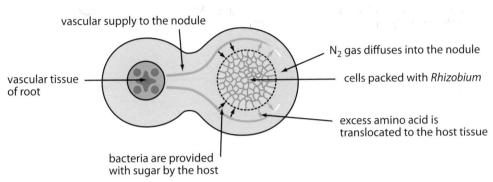

vascular supply to the nodule

vascular tissue of root

N₂ gas diffuses into the nodule

cells packed with *Rhizobium*

excess amino acid is translocated to the host tissue

bacteria are provided with sugar by the host

▲ *Cross section of root nodule of legume*

Atmospheric nitrogen is reduced to ammonia by *Rhizobium*, using the enzyme nitrogenase. Ammonia is combined with organic acid to make amino acids. The nodules are a pink/red colour due to the presence of haemoglobin that is formed in the nodule by the plant cells. Nitrogenase enzyme is inhibited by oxygen. The haemoglobin acts to protect the enzyme from oxygen, and facilitates nitrogen fixation.

The nodules and the bacteria they contain enable leguminous plants to grow successfully even when soil nitrates are scarce. On the death of the plant, soil fertility is further improved because the nodules break down and bacteria and ammonium compounds are released into the soil.

Denitrification

Nitrogen is lost from ecosystems by denitrification. This is a particular problem in waterlogged soils with anaerobic conditions where anaerobic bacteria, such as *Pseudomonas*, can reduce nitrates and ammonium ions back to nitrogen.

Human activities can improve the circulation of nitrogen:

- By fixing atmospheric nitrogen artificially using chemical processes that convert it to fertilisers.
- Large amounts of animal waste from stock rearing are used as manure.
- Sewage disposal boosts organic nitrogen supplies.
- Micro-organisms can be used for making compost and silage.
- Farming practices such as:
  - Planting fields of clover to encourage nitrogen fixation.
  - Draining land and reducing anaerobic conditions.
  - Ploughing fields in order to improve aeration of the soil.

▼ **Study point**

Draining land and ploughing fields ensures that anaerobic bacteria cannot compete with aerobic bacteria thus preventing denitrification.

▼ **Study point**

The relationship of *Rhizobium* bacteria and the roots of leguminous plants is an example of mutualism.

 Link The effect of using nitrogen-containing fertilisers on the environment is studied on page 180

12

Knowledge check

Match the terms 1–5 with the statements A–E.

1. Nitrification
2. *Rhizobium*.
3. Ammonification.
4. Nitrogen fixation.
5. Denitrification.

A. The conversion of nitrates back to nitrogen.
B. The decomposition of dead organisms.
C. The conversion of atmospheric nitrogen into nitrogen compounds.
D. A bacterium found in the root nodules of clover.
E. The conversion of ammonium ions to nitrate ions.

Controlling population size

1   The diagram shows the growth curve for a population of a simple organism such as yeast.

(a)   Name the phases of growth W, X, Y and Z. (2)

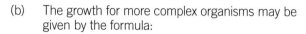

Y = stationary phase

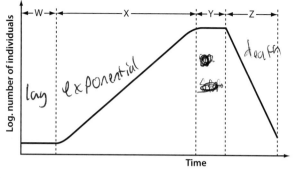

lag   exponential   death

(b)   The growth for more complex organisms may be given by the formula:

   Population growth = (births + immigrations) minus (deaths + emigrations)

(i)   Indicate on the solid line the phase where (deaths + emigrations) exceeds (births + immigrations). (1)

(ii)   Explain the term 'carrying capacity'. (2)

(iii)   State two examples of density-dependent factors that can affect the carrying capacity of an ecosystem. (2)

(iv)   State one example of a density-independent factor. (1)

(v)   How would the dashed line be extended to show what is likely to happen to a population the size of which substantially exceeds the carrying capacity? (1)

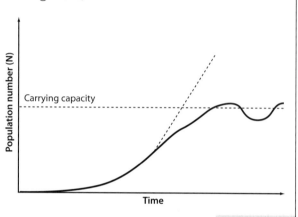

WJEC BY4 JUNE 2011

2 (a)   Two species of a single celled organism called *Paramecium*, *P. aurelia* and *P. caudatum*, were grown together in a single culture of the bacterium *Bacillus pyocyaneus*, on which they both feed. Their population densities were measured every two days and the results are shown in the graph.

(i)   For *P. aurelia* on which day of the experiment did the population growth enter the stationary phase? (1)

(ii)   On which days of the experiment is the population growth of *P. caudatum* in the death phase? (1)

(b)   The experiment shows both interspecific and intraspecific competition.

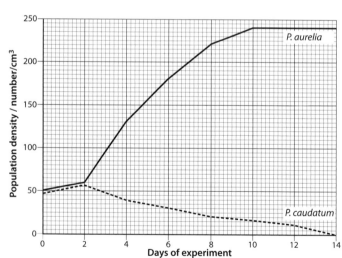

(i)   Which type of competition is most likely to have caused the population of *P. caudatum* to decrease after day 2? (1)

(ii)   What was the carrying capacity for *P. aurelia* in this experiment? (1)

(iii)   How might the carrying capacity have been increased in this experiment? (1)

(iv)   Suggest with an explanation, what would happen to the numbers of *P. caudatum* if *P. aurelia* became infected with a parasitic micro-organism at day 8. (2)

WJEC BY4 JAN 2011

3 The following shows a simplified diagram of the nitrogen cycle.

(a) Name the process at A. (1)

(b) Name two bacteria involved in process B. (2)

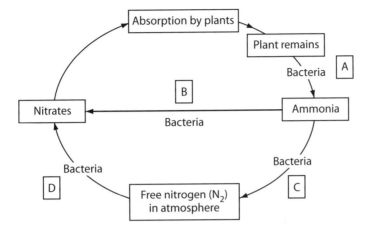

(c) Name the process C and state the condition in which this is most likely to occur. (2)

(d) Most nitrogen-fixing bacteria form symbiotic associations with leguminous plants, where they are provided with nutrients by the plant and protected from oxygen. Oxygen inhibits the enzyme, nitrogenase, required for nitrogen fixation.

Azotobacter are free living in the soil and have the ability to fix atmospheric nitrogen by converting it to ammonia. Like other nitrogenases, *Azotobacter* nitrogenase is oxygen-sensitive, but it is believed that the extremely high respiration rate of *Azotobacter* protects the nitrogenase.

(i) Name the bacteria that form the symbiotic relationship with leguminous plants. (1)

(ii) A type of haemoglobin is present in root nodules. How does this limit the exposure to oxygen of bacteria in the root nodule? (1)

(e) Using your knowledge of respiration, suggest how the high metabolic rate of *Azotobacter* would protect nitrogenase from oxygen. (2)

WJEC BY4 JUNE 2010

---

4 Describe the nitrogen cycle, include the form that nitrogen takes in each part of the cycle, and the roles of the bacteria giving their specific names wherever possible. (10)

WJEC BY4 JUNE 2011

---

5 Fill in the missing words with appropriate scientific terms. (7)

Proteins in dead organisms are decayed by _____ into _____ . The bacterium called _____ converts these into _____ and finally the bacterium _____ converts the waste products of these bacteria into nitrate ions.

Bacteria called _____ which live in the root nodules of legumes can fix atmospheric nitrogen.

The bacterium _____ found free living in the soil, can also fix nitrogen.

WJEC BY4 JAN 2012

BY4

Homeostasis and kidney function

Homeostasis is the term that describes the various mechanisms by which the body achieves a constant internal environment. These mechanisms include thermoregulation, control of blood sugar levels and the osmoregulatory function of the kidney. The complex chemical reactions that take place in all living cells produce waste products which must be eliminated from the body by the process of excretion. In mammals the main organ of excretion is the kidney, which removes the waste product, urea. The kidney also regulates the balance of water and dissolved solutes in the blood. Organisms living in different environments, particularly those living in the desert, have adapted in order to conserve water.

Topic contents

By the end of this topic you should be able to:

- Explain the principles of homeostasis in terms of the stages involved in a feedback loop.
- Describe the structure of the kidney.
- Describe and explain the production of urine with reference to the processes of ultrafiltration and selective reabsorption.
- Explain the role of the loop of Henle and the counter-current multiplier mechanism in the reabsorption of water.
- Describe how osmoreceptors in the hypothalamus of the brain monitor the water potential of the blood.
- Explain the role of the hormone ADH in osmoregulation.
- Explain why fish, birds, insects and mammals produce different excretory products.
- Explain how desert-living mammals have adapted to conserve water.

Homeostasis and kidney function

The maintenance of a constant environment is called homeostasis. The internal environment is made up of tissue fluids that bathe cells, supplying nutrients and removing wastes. Maintaining these fluids at an optimum level protects these cells from changes in the external environment. In other words, it allows cells to function normally despite external changes. Nevertheless, changes in pH, temperature and water potential still take place. However, these changes fluctuate around a set point. Homeostasis is the ability to return to that set point.

▼ *Set point*

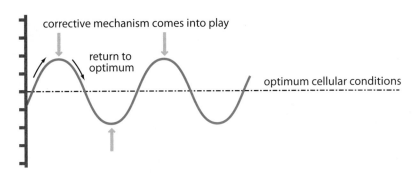

The control of any self-regulating system involves a series of stages:

- The set point, which is the desired level, or norm, at which the system operates.

- A receptor, which detects any deviation from the set point.

- The receptor sends instructions to a co-ordinator or controller.

- The co-ordinator communicates with one or more effectors which carry out the corrective procedures.

- Once the correction is made and the factor returned to normal, information is fed back to the detector which then 'switches off'.

- In most biological control systems the co-ordinator is no longer alerted to the deviation from the normal. This is an example of a **negative feedback**.

The kidney

The kidney performs two main functions:

- Removal of nitrogenous metabolic waste from the body.

- Osmoregulation, the mechanism by which the balance of water and dissolved solutes is regulated.

Production of urea

Urea is a poisonous chemical made by the liver. If there is too much protein in the diet any excess has to be broken down. Amino acids, which make up protein, are **deaminated** in the liver. The reaction produces ammonia, which is quickly converted to urea. Urea is released into the blood, and travels around the body until it is removed by the kidneys.

YOU SHOULD KNOW ›››

››› that homeostasis uses a negative feedback mechanism

Key Term

Negative feedback = occurs when the feedback causes the corrective measures to be turned off returning a system to its normal level.

FEEDBACK LOOP
negative feedback if it turns system off

OUPUT system returned to set point	INPUT change to the system
EFFECTORS bring about changes to the system in order to return it to the set point	**RECEPTOR** measures level of a factor
	CONTROL UNIT operational information is stored here and used to co-ordinate effectors

▲ *Stages in a typical control system*

Key Term

Deamination = the breakdown of excess amino acids in the liver, by the removal of the amine group. Urea is produced as the final product.

Structure of the kidney

Humans have two kidneys and these are the main organs that filter waste products from the blood.

Each kidney receives blood from a renal artery and returns blood to the general circulation via the renal vein. A narrow tube, the ureter, carries urine from the kidney to the bladder. The kidney is covered by a tough capsule. There are three main areas in a kidney: the cortex, the medulla and the region where the ureter joins the pelvis.

A microscope section through a kidney shows it to be made up of thousands of minute tubes called nephrons or uriniferous tubules.

Blood vessels are in close association with the nephrons. Blood supply to the nephron begins as an afferent arteriole serving the glomerulus. From the glomerulus the blood is carried by the efferent arteriole to two other capillary structures:

- A capillary network serving the proximal and distal convoluted tubules.
- A capillary network running beside the loop of Henle and known as the vasa recta.

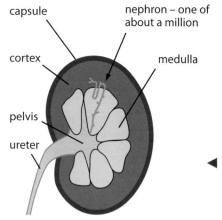

◄ *Kidney*

► *Nephron*

▼ *Photomicrograph through cortex showing renal capsule*

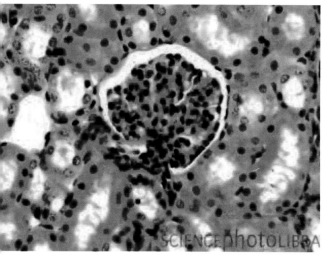

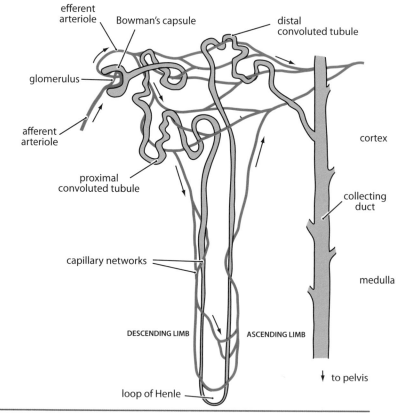

▼ **Study point**

Unlike carbohydrates and fats, protein cannot be stored.

Examiner tip

In exam questions you would be expected to interpret the histology of the kidney as seen in sections using the light microscope.

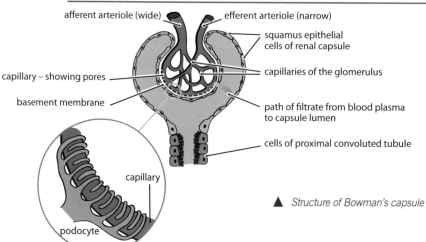

▲ *Structure of Bowman's capsule*

Ultrafiltration

Ultrafiltration is filtration under pressure that separates small soluble molecules from the blood plasma. It is the process by which small molecules such as water, glucose, urea and salts, are filtered from the knot of capillaries, the glomerulus, into the Bowman's capsule.

The blood entering the glomerulus is separated from the space inside the Bowman's capsule by two cell layers and a basement membrane.

▼ *Ultrastructure of wall of glomerular capillary and renal capsule*

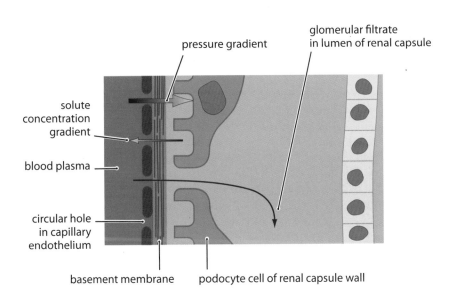

How Science Works

Using the electron microscope enabled scientists to work out the process of ultrafiltration.

▼ **Study point**

High blood pressure is maintained in the glomerulus by the contraction of the heart, the afferent arteriole having a wider diameter than the efferent arteriole and the large surface area of the capillaries of the glomerulus.

▼ **Study point**

The sieve action allows smaller-sized molecules to pass through but retains in the capillaries the blood proteins and cells.

The rate at which fluid passes from the blood in the glomerular capillaries into the Bowman's capsule is called the glomerular filtration rate. This rate is rapid and is determined by the difference in water potential between the two areas. The net effect of higher pressure in the capillary and lower solute concentration in the Bowman's capsule is that fluid moves out of the capillary and into the lumen of the capsule.

It is necessary to study the structure of the glomerulus and capsule to understand how ultrafiltration takes place.

- The basement membrane of the capillary forms the selective barrier between the blood and the nephron and acts as a molecular sieve.
  - The first cell layer is the wall of the capillary. This single layer of cells contains many small gaps.
  - The basement membrane between the two cell layers acts as a molecular filter.
  - The second cell layer makes up the wall of the Bowman's capsule. The epithelial cells in this layer are called podocytes.
- Most of the pressure forcing molecules through the filter comes from the hydrostatic pressure of the blood in the glomerular capillaries. This pressure is amplified by the pressure in the capsule produced by the narrow efferent vessels and also by the water potential in the blood produced by the colloidal plasma proteins. The glomerular pressure can be altered by changes in the diameter of the afferent and efferent arterioles entering and leaving the glomerulus.

Examiner tip

You are expected to interpret the ultrastructure of the kidney showing the arrangement of the pores in the Bowman's capsule.

▼ Study point

Materials in the blood include blood cells, plasma proteins, glucose, salts, water, and urea. The blood cells and plasma proteins remain in the blood. All the glucose is reabsorbed into the blood. Most of the water and salts are also reabsorbed into the blood, leaving urine, which is made up of urea with some water and salts, which passes to the bladder.

▼ Study point

The vasa recta, the capillaries surrounding the loops in the medulla have a dual role to deliver nutrients to the cells of the medulla and to carry water reabsorbed from the kidney.

Selective reabsorption

Selective reabsorption is the process by which useful products such as glucose and salts are reabsorbed back into the blood as the filtrate flows along the nephron.

- All the glucose and most of the water and salt (sodium and chloride ions) are reabsorbed in the proximal convoluted tubule. The cells in the wall of the tubule are adapted by having:
  - Microvilli providing a large surface area for absorption.
  - Numerous mitochondria providing ATP for the active transport of glucose and salts. Water is reabsorbed passively by osmosis following the transport of salt.
- Small amounts of water and salt are reabsorbed in the distal tubule.
- Most of the remaining water is reabsorbed in the collecting duct by a mechanism which involves the loop of Henle.

▼ *Cells from the wall of the proximal convoluted tubule*

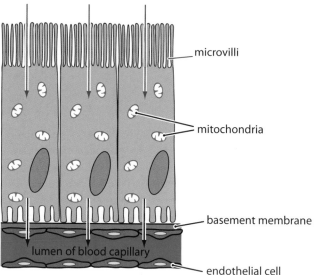

reabsorption by active transport and diffusion

microvilli

mitochondria

basement membrane

lumen of blood capillary

endothelial cell

Reabsorption of water and the role of the loop of Henle and the collecting duct

The numerous loops of Henle collectively concentrate salts in the tissue fluid of the medulla of the kidney. The high concentration of salt then causes an osmotic flow of water out of the collecting ducts thereby concentrating the urine and making it hypertonic to the blood.

The first part of the loop of Henle is called the descending limb and the second part, the ascending limb. To explain how it works it is best to begin at the ascending limb. Here the walls are impermeable to water. The cells in the walls actively transport sodium and chloride ions out of the fluid in the tubule and into the tissue fluid between the two limbs. This produces an area of low water potential.

The walls of the descending limb are permeable to water, and also to sodium and chloride ions. As fluid flows down the tubule, water passes out, by osmosis, into the region of low water potential. At the same time sodium and chloride ions diffuse into the descending limb. As the fluid flows down the descending limb it contains progressively less water and so the solution is more concentrated at the bottom of the hairpin.

Also, as sodium and chloride ions diffuse across at each level, the solution is even more concentrated when it reaches the bottom of the loop. This concentrated fluid now turns the corner and begins to flow up the ascending limb. Having two limbs of the loop running side by side, with the fluid flowing down in one and up in the other, enables the maximum concentration to be built up both inside and outside the tube at the apex of the loop. This mechanism is called the counter-current multiplier.

The fluid flowing up the ascending limb becomes more dilute as it loses sodium and chloride ions and so has a higher water potential. When the fluid reaches the collecting duct it runs back down into the medulla passing through the region of low water potential. Water therefore passes out of the collecting duct by osmosis towards this region. The water passes into the blood capillaries (vasa recta) surrounding the loop of Henle and into the general circulation.

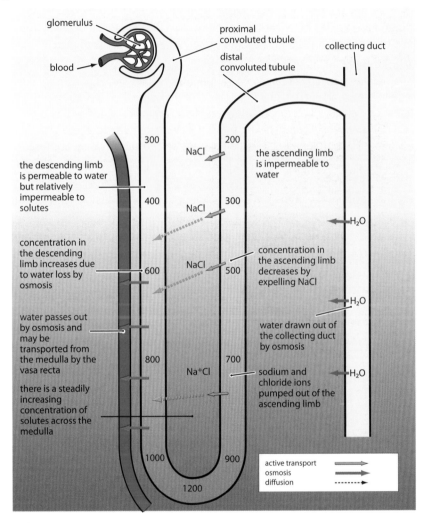

▲ *Counter-current multiplier*

Osmoregulation

Mammals have to maintain a balance between water gain and water loss. Humans gain most of their water from drinking and from food. Most of the water is lost as urine. Other losses are due to:

- Sweating
- Keeping exchange surfaces moist
- Loss in faeces.

 Key Term

Osmoregulation = the homeostatic control of body water.

▼ **Study point**

The counter-current multiplier mechanism is a difficult concept.

The end result is a low water potential at the apex of the loop. Collectively the large number of loops create a region of low water potential in the medulla and, as the collecting ducts carrying urine pass through the medulla, water is drawn out by osmosis resulting in more concentrated urine. It thus acts as a 'fine control' of osmoregulation.

13

Knowledge check

Match the parts of the nephron 1–4 with the statements A–D.

1. Proximal convoluted tubule.

2. Glomerulus.

3. Ascending limb of loop of Henle.

4. Collecting duct.

A. ADH acts on this region.

B. Main site of selective reabsorption.

C. Involved in ultrafiltration.

D. Sodium ions actively pumped from this region.

▼ **Study point**

If blood has a lower water potential than the norm, the release of ADH and its effect on the permeability of the walls of the collecting duct and distal convoluted tubule results in water being drawn by osmosis from these areas towards the area of low water potential in the medulla where it passes into the blood.

Osmoregulation operates on the principle of negative feedback, typical of homeostasis. There needs to be a receptor or detector that monitors the solute concentration of the blood. This is carried out by osmoreceptors located in the hypothalamus, at the base of the brain. There also needs to be an effector that carries out an action to bring the condition back to normal if it deviates too far. The co-ordinator is the posterior pituitary gland which stores ADH. The walls of the collecting ducts act as effectors.

- The permeability of the walls of the collecting duct, like the walls of the distal convoluted tubule, is subject to hormonal control. This hormonal effect, together with the hypertonic interstitial fluids built up by the loop of Henle in the medulla, determine whether hypotonic or hypertonic urine is released from the kidney.

- ADH makes the walls of the collecting duct more permeable so that water is reabsorbed and the urine has a concentration close to the concentration of the tissues near the bottom of the loop, that is, hypertonic to the general body fluids.

- Water reabsorbed is controlled by a feedback system. Negative feedback restores the normal osmotic concentration if blood is diluted or becomes more concentrated.

- A fall in water potential of the blood may be caused by one or a combination of factors – reduced water intake, sweating, intake of large amounts of salt. The concentration of sodium chloride in the blood is an indirect indication of the volume of water in the body. The hypothalamus is sensitive to the concentration of sodium chloride in the blood flowing through it. If the water content is low, a fall in water potential is detected by osmoreceptors (osmotic receptors) in the hypothalamus and results in nerve impulses passing to the posterior pituitary gland, which then releases ADH into the blood stream. This has the following effects:

- ADH increases the permeability of the distal convoluted tubule and the collecting duct to water.

- This allows more water to be reabsorbed from these tubules into the region of high solute concentration in the medulla.

- More water is reabsorbed into the blood.

- Consequently the small volume of urine eventually eliminated is relatively concentrated.

▼ *Negative feedback mechanism*

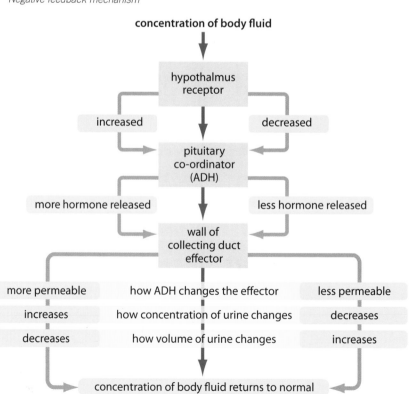

14

Knowledge check

Identify the missing word or words.

On a hot day the body needs to conserve water. Osmoreceptors in the •••• of the brain detect the solute concentration of the blood resulting in nerve impulses passing to the •••• gland which releases •••• into the blood stream. This hormone increases the permeability of the distal convoluted tubule and •••• •••• to water. The water is reabsorbed into the region of low water potential in the ••••. This results in the production of a •••• volume of more •••• urine.

Adaptations to different environments

The environment in which an animal lives plays a part in the type of nitrogenous waste produced and different animals deal with its disposal in different ways:

- Most aquatic animals, for example fish, produce ammonia which, although highly toxic, is extremely soluble in water. The ammonia diffuses out across the gills and is quickly diluted to non-toxic levels.

- Birds and insects excrete uric acid, which is almost insoluble in water and is non-toxic. There is a large energy cost to its production but very little water is needed for its excretion. This is important in conserving water and allows these organisms to live in environments where there is a shortage of water.

- Mammals excrete urea. Its production also requires energy but it is less toxic than ammonia and so tissues can tolerate it in higher concentrations for relatively short periods of time.

Desert-living mammals have adapted in order to conserve water.

The loop of Henle is concerned with water reabsorption. The longer the loop, the greater the water potential in the medulla. This enables more water to be reabsorbed, resulting in a more concentrated urine. Mammals, such as the kangaroo rat, live in the desert and have particularly long loops of Henle.

Many desert animals survive with little or no water. How do they do this? They live on '**metabolic water**'. That is, water produced from the breakdown of food during respiration in the cells. Many desert animals also remain underground during the day, living in burrows which are cool and humid, reducing water loss by evaporation. The table shows the urine concentration of mammals living in different habitats.

Key Term

Metabolic water = water produced from the oxidation of food reserves.

Examiner tip

Adaptations to conserve water may be anatomical, biochemical or behavioural.

Mammal	Habitat	Urine concentration mOsmol dm^{-3}
beaver	freshwater	520
rabbit	mesic	3100
kangaroo rat	desert	5500

▼ *Kidney structure in different environments*

Kidney structure and water conservation

There are two types of nephron, having different positions in the kidney

nephrons with short loops of Henle which only just extend into the medulla function most importantly when water supply is normal to excessive

nephrons with long loops of Henle which extend deeply into the medulla function most importantly when water supply is low

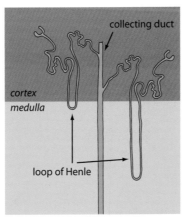

collecting duct

cortex
medulla

loop of Henle

15

Knowledge check

Match the animals 1–3 with their excretory product A–C.

1. Fish.
2. Insect.
3. Mammal.

A. Urea.
B. Ammonia.
C. Uric acid

The kidney tubule in contrasting mammals

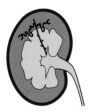 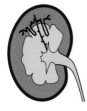 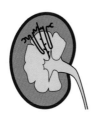 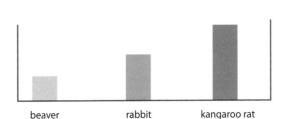

beaver
(aquatic habitat)

rabbit
(terrestrial habitat with adequate water supply)

kangaroo rat
(arid habitat with no water to drink)

beaver   rabbit   kangaroo rat

relative concentration of urine produced
(not to scale)

Homeostasis and kidney function

1 (a) Name the functional unit of the mammalian kidney shown in the diagram. (1)

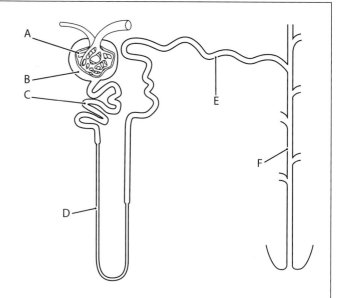

(b) (i) Name the parts labelled A to F. (3)

  (ii) State the function of part D. (1)

  (iii) How is part D adapted in the kidneys of desert mammals such as the kangaroo rat? (1)

(c) Parts E and F have restricted permeability which is subject to hormonal control.

  (i) Which hormone controls the permeability of parts E and F? (1)

  (ii) Which part of the mammal's body releases this hormone into the blood? (1)

  (iii) Use your answers to parts (i) and (ii) to identify the osmoregulatory feedback loop below.

    (I) the detector (1); (II) the effector (1).

  (iv) The diagram below is of an osmoregulatory feedback loop. It explains the mechanism for adjusting urine during osmoregulation.

    Complete the spaces G to L in the diagram.

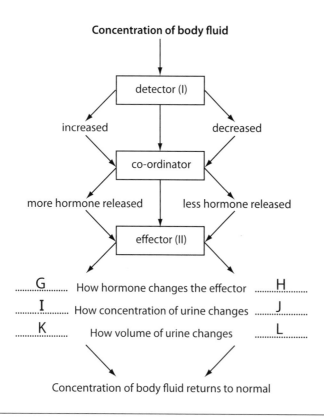

WJEC BY4 JUNE 2011

2 The diagram shows part of a kidney tubule or nephron.

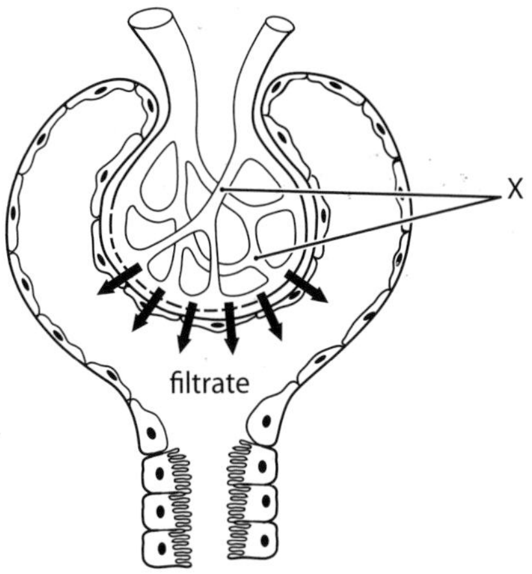

(a) (i) Name the network of capillaries labelled X. (1)

(ii) Apart from water and glucose, name two substances which will be present in the filtrate. (1)

(iii) Name the process that separates these molecules from the blood plasma. (1)

(iv) The filtration rate is the total volume of filtrate formed per minute. Explain the effect of a large loss of blood from the body on the filtration rate. (2)

(b) Much of the water in the kidney filtrate is reabsorbed from the collecting duct.

(i) Name the part of the nephron which provides the osmotic gradient for reabsorption. (1)

(ii) Selective reabsorption occurs in the proximal convoluted tubule. Describe two ways in which the cells of this tubule are adapted for reabsorption. (2)

(c) The environment in which an animal lives plays a part in the type of nitrogenous waste produced.

Animal	Main excretory product	Toxicity	Solubility
Freshwater fish		high	high
Bird		low	low
Mammal		medium	medium

(i) For the animals listed in the table, name the excretory products. (3)

(ii) Which excretory product requires the least volume of water for its excretion? (1)

(iii) Explain one further advantage of the excretory product you have named in (c) (ii). (1)

WJEC BY4 JAN 2011

3 Fill in the missing words with appropriate scientific terms. (12)

The general name given to glands which produce hormones is _____ glands. The maintenance of a constant internal environment is referred to as _____ and hormones are involved in this process. If there is a move away from the norm or set point a corrective procedure takes place which returns it to the norm. This is referred to as _____ _____ .

Osmoreceptors in the _____ of the brain constantly monitor the _____ _____ of the blood. ADH is a hormone that is produced in specialised nerve cells and it is then stored in the _____ _____.

If there is a need for the body to conserve water a nerve impulse causes the release of ADH into the _____ which transports it to the target organ. ADH acts on the cells of the _____ _____ where it attaches to _____ on the membrane of these cells. This causes protein channels to open and water passes through these channels by _____ into the _____ _____ of the medulla and then into the blood. A small volume of concentrated _____ is produced.

WJEC BY4 JUNE 2012

BY4

Co-ordination

To enable plants and animals to survive they must react to changes in their external environment. Mechanisms are in place for the detection of changes to bring about appropriate responses. Since structures that detect changes may be some distance from those that respond, organisms require a means of communication. Animals have nervous systems and hormonal mechanisms, whereas plants have only the latter. Environmental stimuli must be monitored and the information fed into the appropriate system. Both plants and animals respond to the information transmitted.

The mammalian nervous system is dual in nature. The central nervous system (CNS) co-ordinates and controls the activities of the animal. The peripheral nervous system, the nerves and ganglia, forms the connecting link between the organs and the CNS. Many body functions and actions are controlled by reflex actions which involve both parts of the nervous system.

Topic content

By the end of this topic you should be able to:

- Understand that the nervous system controls and co-ordinates actions by detecting stimuli, processing the information and initiating responses.
- Understand that the stimuli are detected by receptors and the responses are brought about by effectors.
- Describe the simple nerve net system of the coelenterate (Cniderian), *Hydra*.
- Describe the reflex arc as an involuntary response involving the basic functional units of the nervous system.
- In a reflex arc, sensory neurones carry impulses to the brain and spinal cord, and via relay neurones pass impulses through motor neurones to effectors.
- Describe the structure of a motor neurone.
- Explain the transmission of a nerve impulse in terms of how an action potential is generated.
- Describe the factors affecting the speed of conduction of the nerve impulse.
- Describe the synapse as the junction of two functional neurones.
- Explain synaptic transmission by means of the neurotransmitter, acetylcholine.
- Explain how caffeine and organophosphate affect synaptic transmission.
- Explain how flowering in plants is determined by the relative lengths of daylight and darkness.

The nervous system

The nervous system carries out the following:

- Detects changes or stimuli inside the body and from the surroundings.
- Processes the information.
- Initiates responses.

The nervous system is divided into two main parts:

- The central nervous system (CNS) comprising the brain and spinal cord.
- The peripheral nervous system, which is made up of pairs of nerves that originate from the brain or the spinal cord, These consist of sensory neurones which carry impulses from receptors to the CNS, and motor neurones which carry impulses away from the CNS to effectors.

A stimulus is a detectable change in the internal or external environment of an organism that produces a response in that organism. Receptors which range from specialised sensory cells, such as those in the skin, to the more complex sense organs such as the ear and eye, detect the information from inside the body and from the surroundings.

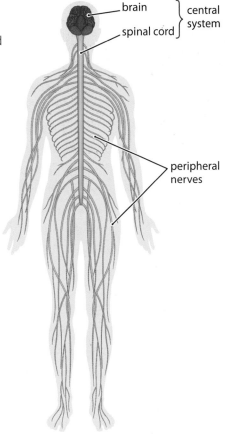

brain ⎱ central
spinal cord ⎰ system

peripheral nerves

▲ Nervous system

It is the role of the CNS to process the information and initiate a response. Effectors bring about responses. Effectors may be muscles or glands. Sensory receptors detect one form of energy and convert it into electrical energy. They are acting as transducers. The electrical impulses travel along nerves and are called nerve impulses.

▼ Main components of nervous control mechanism

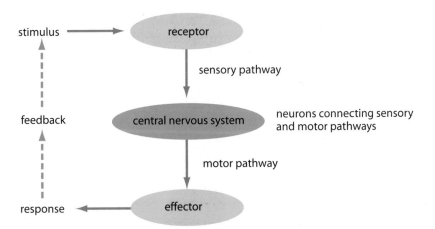

stimulus → receptor

sensory pathway

feedback

central nervous system — neurons connecting sensory and motor pathways

motor pathway

response ← effector

The simplest type of nervous response to a stimulus is a reflex arc. An example of a reflex arc is the withdrawal reflex, when you immediately withdraw your hand if, for example, you place it on a hot object.

Key Term

Reflex arc = the pathway along which impulses are carried from a receptor to an effector, without involving the brain.

Study point

Being able to respond to stimuli increases the chance of survival.

Examiner tip

Remember the sequence: stimulus, receptor, sensory neurone, relay neurone, motor neurone, effector, response.

Knowledge check

Identify the missing word or words.

The nervous system has two main divisions: the CNS comprising the •••• and •••• and the peripheral nervous system. The latter is made up of the •••• nerves that carry impulses to the CNS and the •••• nerves that carry impulses away from the CNS. The spinal reflex is an •••• response that involves the spinal cord.

Examiner tip

Be prepared to label a given diagram of a reflex arc showing the direction of the nerve impulse.

▾ **Study point**

The cell bodies of sensory neurones in a reflex arc are accommodated in a swelling called a ganglion.

▼ *Nerve net*

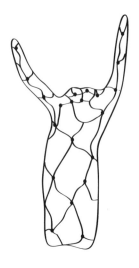

Reflex arc

- A reflex action is a rapid, involuntary response resulting from nervous impulses initiated by a stimulus. The action is involuntary in that the brain is not involved. Reflex actions are generally protective in function.

- The withdrawal reflex involves the following:
  - Stimulus – the hot surface.
  - Receptor – temperature and pain receptors in the skin.
  - Sensory neurone sends impulse to the spinal cord.
  - Relay neurone connects a sensory neurone to a motor neurone.
  - Motor neurone sends impulse to an effector, (in this case a muscle).
  - Response – arm muscles contract and the hand is removed from surface.

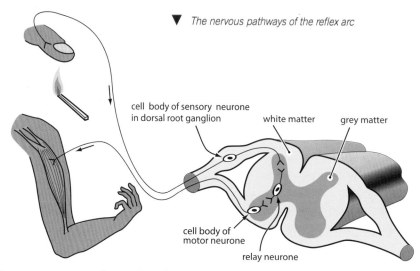

▼ *The nervous pathways of the reflex arc*

cell body of sensory neurone in dorsal root ganglion

white matter

grey matter

cell body of motor neurone

relay neurone

Nerve nets in *Hydra*

The nerve net consists of simple nerve cells with short extensions joined to each other and branching in a number of different directions. This results in a slow transmission of the nerve impulse.

Simple organisms do not possess many receptors and effectors. The sense receptors respond to a limited number of stimuli and the number of effectors is small. An example of a simple organism is the *Hydra*, which is a member of the jellyfish group (coelenterates). The *Hydra* does not have a recognisable brain or true muscles. The nerve net is a very simple system compared to mammalian nervous systems. Nerve nets connect sensory photoreceptors and touch-sensitive nerve cells located in the body wall and tentacles.

This enables *Hydra* to sense its surroundings and respond to stimuli in an appropriate way. Responses may be to attack prey or avoid danger by retracting the body from a predator.

▶ *Hydra*

Neurones

Nerve cells (or neurones) are specialised cells adapted to rapidly carrying nerve impulses from one part of the body to another.

There are three types of neurones, classified according to their function:

- Sensory – which bring impulses from the sense organs or receptors into the CNS.
- Motor – these carry impulses from the CNS to the effector organs (muscles or glands).
- Connector (intermediate or relay) – these receive impulses from sensory neurones or other intermediate neurones and relay them to motor neurones or other intermediate neurones.

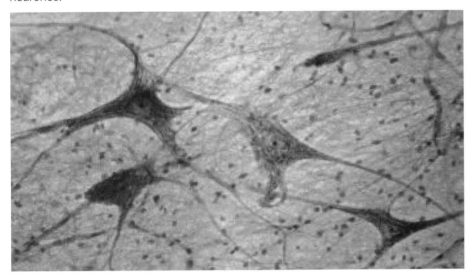

▲ *Photomicrograph of neurones*

Each cell consists of:

- A cell body containing a nucleus and granular cytoplasm containing many ribosomes. These ribosomes are grouped together forming Nissl granules which are concerned with the formation of neurotransmitter substances.

- Many thin extensions carry impulses towards the cell body. The short extensions are called dendrites. These receive impulses from other nerve cells and carry the information towards the cell body. Some neurones also have a long membrane-covered cytoplasmic extension, the axon, which transmits impulses from the cell body.

- At its end, an axon divides into branches which form synapses with other neurones.

- Peripheral neurones are surrounded by and supported by Schwann cells. In myelinated neurones, found only in vertebrate nervous systems, these grow around the axons of the nerve cells to form a multi-layered lipid myelin sheath. This acts as an electrical insulator and speeds up the transmission of impulses.

- The myelin sheath has thin areas at intervals, nodes of Ranvier, which are important in impulse transmission.

The structure of a myelinated motor neurone is shown below.

▼ *Mammalian motor neurone*

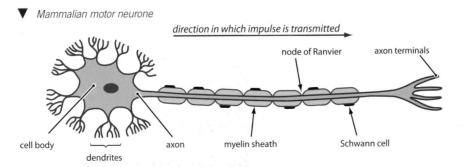

direction in which impulse is transmitted

node of Ranvier   axon terminals

cell body   axon   myelin sheath   Schwann cell

dendrites

‹ Link › Neurotransmitters are involved with synapses and are studied on page 73.

Examiner tip

You are required to know the structure of a motor neurone only.

17

Knowledge check

Identify the missing word or words.

Neurones which bring impulses from receptors into the CNS are called ···· neurones, whereas those that carry impulses from the CNS to the ···· are called ···· neurones.

A neurone consists of a ···· ···· containing a nucleus and a long extension called the ···· . In vertebrates the extension has a fatty layer called a ···· ···· . This acts as an ···· and speeds up the transmission of impulses.

Key Term

Resting potential = the potential difference between the inside and the outside of a membrane when a nerve impulse is not being conducted

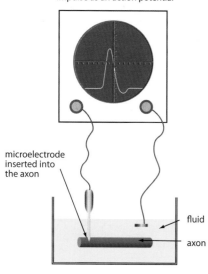

▲ *Oscilloscope*

Examiner tip

Refer to sodium ions or potassium ions rather than merely sodium or potassium.

▼ Study point

Roughly three sodium ions are pumped out for every two potassium ions that are pumped in.

▼ Study point

Two different methods of transporting ions operate. Ions transported by active transport use sodium–potassium pumps; ions transported through channels use the process of diffusion.

The nerve impulse

The change in potential associated with a typical nerve impulse is very small (50 millivolts). Nevertheless, nerve impulses can be recorded and measured using an apparatus which is sensitive to small electrical changes. Impulses can be picked up from the nerve through a pair of microelectrodes and fed into a cathode ray oscilloscope. This can measure the magnitude and speed of transmission of impulses and analyse the pattern of impulses generated in different parts of the nervous system.

Neurones transmit electrical impulses along the cell surface membrane surrounding the axon. Experiments involving inserting microelectrodes into axons and measuring the changes in electrical potential have shown that in a resting axon, the inside of the membrane has a negative electrical charge compared to the outside.

Resting potential

Resting potentials are typically minus values, the minus indicating the inside is negative with respect to the outside. The membrane is said to be polarised. How does this happen?

- Sodium and potassium ions are transported across the membrane against a concentration gradient by active transport.
- This involves sodium–potassium exchange pumps (these are trans-membrane proteins), which maintain the concentration and an uneven distribution of sodium ions and potassium ions across the membrane.
- Sodium ions are transported out of the axon by the sodium–potassium pumps.
- Potassium ions are transported into the axon by the sodium–potassium pumps.
- However, the Na^+ ions are passed out faster than the K^+ ions are brought in.
- Most of the channels that allow the potassium ions to diffuse out are open, whilst most of the channels that allow the sodium ions to move through are closed.
- As a result, the axon membrane is 100 times more permeable to potassium ions, which therefore diffuse out faster than the sodium ions diffuse back in.
- The net result is that the outside of the membrane is positive compared to the inside.

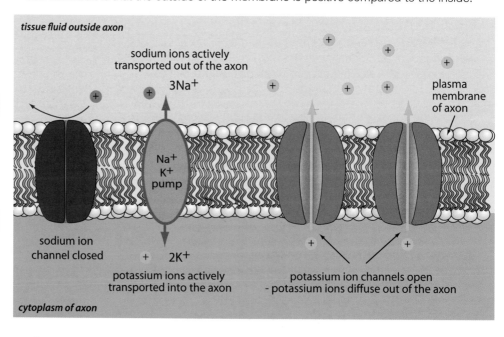

▲ *Distribution of ions at resting potential*

The action potential

When a stimulus is received by a receptor or nerve ending, a reversal of the charges on the axon membrane takes place. As a result, the negative charge of –70mV inside the membrane becomes a positive charge of +40mV. This is known as the **action potential** and lasts about three milliseconds. In this condition the membrane is said to be depolarised.

The sequence of events is described as follows:

- The energy of the stimulus causes some of the sodium channels to open. This sudden increase in the permeability of the membrane to Na$^+$ results in an influx of Na$^+$ which **depolarises** the membrane.

- Once the action potential of +40mV is established, the sodium ion channels close, preventing any further influx of sodium ions.

- The potassium channels open and potassium ions diffuse out again and repolarise the membrane. There is a temporary overshoot of K$^+$ leaving as the K$^+$/Na$^+$ pump restores the ionic balance. This is called the refractory period during which another action potential cannot be generated. This time delay ensures a unidirectional impulse and limits frequency.

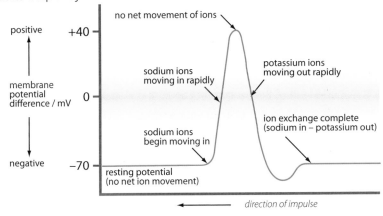

▲ Action potential

How the action potential travels along an axon

The action potential causes a small electric current across the membrane and as a portion of the membrane is depolarised, depolarisation of the next portion is initiated. There is a series of local currents propagated along the axon. The sodium pump is active all the time and behind the transmission; this pump restores the resting potential. Once the resting potential is restored, another impulse can be transmitted. As the impulse progresses, the out-flux of K$^+$ causes the neurone to be repolarised behind the impulse.

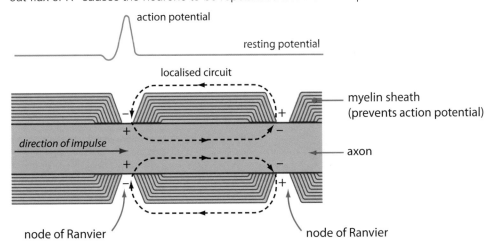

▲ Passage of action potential along myelinated nerve

Key Terms

Action potential = a change that occurs in the electrical charge across the membrane of an axon when it is stimulated and a nerve impulse passes.

Depolarisation = a temporary reversal of charge on the membrane of a neurone that takes place when a nerve impulse is transmitted.

▼ Study point

Nerve impulses are due to changes in the permeability of nerve cell membrane to K$^+$ ions and Na$^+$ ions, which leads to changes in the potential difference across the membrane and the formation of action potential.

▼ Study point

When the resting potential is re-established, the axon membrane is said to be repolarised.

How Science Works

Measurements of electrical charges associated with typical nerve impulses led scientists to work out that when a nerve impulse is initiated the resting potential changes.

▼ Study point

In myelinated nerve fibres the speed of transmission is up to 100 ms^{-1}, whereas in non-myelinated nerve fibres it is about 0.5 ms^{-1}.

Key Term

Saltatory conduction = transmission of a nerve impulse along a myelinated axon in which the action potential jumps from one node of Ranvier to another.

Properties of nerves and impulses

The 'all or nothing principle': The size of the impulse is independent of the size of the stimulus.

If the intensity of a stimulus is below a certain threshold intensity, no action potential is initiated. But, if the intensity of the stimulus exceeds the threshold value, an action potential *is* initiated. Any further increase in the intensity of the stimulus does not give a greater action potential. Instead, the frequency of action potentials changes. A strong stimulus produces a greater frequency of action potentials as the intensity of stimulation increases. A weak stimulus generates fewer action potentials.

The all or nothing nature of the action potential acts as a filter, preventing minor stimuli from setting up nerve impulses, thus preventing the brain from being overloaded with information.

▼ *Effect of stimulus intensity on impulse frequency*

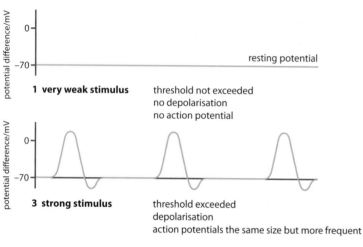

1 very weak stimulus   threshold not exceeded
no depolarisation
no action potential

3 strong stimulus   threshold exceeded
depolarisation
action potentials the same size but more frequent

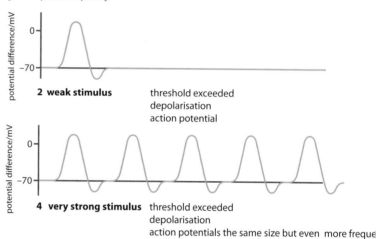

2 weak stimulus   threshold exceeded
depolarisation
action potential

4 very strong stimulus   threshold exceeded
depolarisation
action potentials the same size but even more freque

Factors affecting the speed of conduction of the nerve impulse

▼ Study point

Myelinated axons use less ATP to transmit a nerve impulse than a non-myelinated axon of the same diameter because active transport of sodium ions occurs only at the nodes rather than the whole length of the axon.

Two factors are important in determining the speed of conduction of the nerve impulse:

- Myelination speeds up the rate of transmission by insulating the axon. Depolarisation and action potentials cannot occur in the myelinated parts of the axon, except at the nodes of Ranvier. The result is that the impulse jumps from one node to the next, speeding the overall passage along the axon. This is called **saltatory conduction**.

- The diameter of the axon – the greater the diameter of the axon, the greater the velocity of transmission. Giant axons are found in the squid and are thought to be associated with rapid escape responses.

▼ *Comparison of impulse conduction*

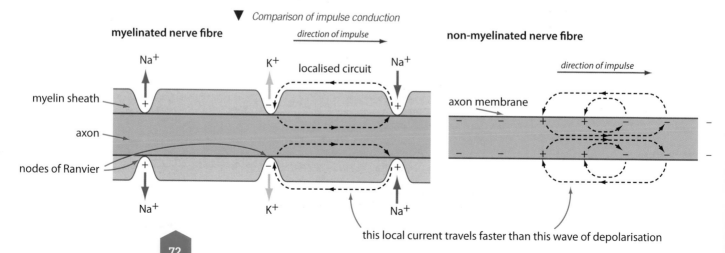

Synapse

Neurones are not in direct contact with each other but are separated by tiny gaps known as synapses. The main role of the synapse is to convey action potentials between neurones in one direction only.

Structure of a synapse

Most junctions between neurones take the form of chemical synapses. Branches of axons lie close to dendrites of other neurones but do not touch, leaving a gap of about 20nm between them. When impulses are transmitted a neurotransmitter diffuses across the gap from the axon membrane (pre-synaptic membrane), to stimulate the post-synaptic membrane.

▼ *A synapse*

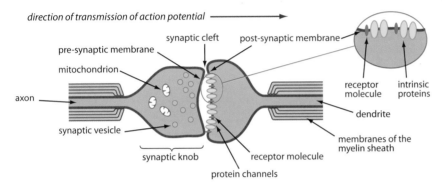

Synaptic transmission

- The arrival of the impulses at the synaptic knob alters its permeability allowing calcium ions to enter.

- The influx of calcium ions causes the synaptic vesicle to fuse with the pre-synaptic membrane so releasing the neurotransmitter, acetylcholine, into the synaptic cleft.

- When the transmitter diffuses across the synaptic cleft, it attaches to a receptor site on the post-synaptic membrane, depolarising it and so initiating an impulse in the next neurone.

▼ *How the acetylcholine receptor works*

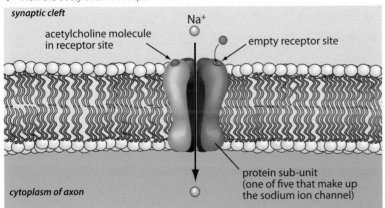

- The receptor spans the membrane and is made up of protein sub-units containing two receptor sites. When acetylcholine binds with both of these receptor sites the proteins change shape, opening the channel between the units. This allows sodium ions to diffuse from the cleft through the channel and into the post-synaptic neurone. If the membrane becomes sufficiently depolarised, an action potential is initiated in the axon of the post-synaptic neurone.

YOU SHOULD KNOW ›››

››› the structure of a synapse

››› the role of the membrane and acetylcholine in synaptic transmission of nerve impulses

››› the function of synapses

››› the effect of organophosphates and psychoactive drugs (in brief) on synapses

Examiner tip

This topic is synoptic in that it brings together several topics already encountered, such as membranes, diffusion, enzyme action, mitochondria.

18

Knowledge check

Place the statements 1–7 in the correct order.

1. Acetylcholine is released into the synaptic cleft.

2. Sodium ions diffuse into the post-synaptic neurone.

3. The synaptic vesicle fuses with the pre-synaptic membrane.

4. Calcium ions enter the pre-synaptic membrane.

5. An action pot ential is initiated.

6. Acetylcholine attaches to a receptor site on the post-synaptic membrane.

7. Acetylcholine diffuses across the synaptic cleft.

Key Term

Neuromuscular junction = a synapse that occurs between a neurone and a muscle.

• Acetylcholine, when released, is quickly destroyed by enzymes in the synaptic cleft, so its effect is limited and the merging of impulses is prevented. If insufficient acetylcholine is released, the post-synaptic membrane will not be stimulated. The enzyme which destroys acetylcholine is called cholinesterase. The resulting choline and ethanoic acid diffuse back across the synaptic cleft to re-form acetylcholine. ATP is required to re-form transmitter molecules and store them in vesicles.

Function of synapses

The function of the synapse is to convey action potentials between neurones.

• Transmit information between neurones.

• Pass impulses in one direction only.

• Act as junctions – since synaptic vesicles are present only in the knob of the pre-synaptic neurone, impulses can only pass across a synapse in one direction.

• Filter out low level stimuli. That is, remove 'background noise' from the nervous system.

• To protect the response system from overstimulation.

Effects of drugs

Amplification at the synapse may be due to chemicals mimicking the action of natural transmitters. That is, they have the same shape and affect the post-synaptic neurone in the same way that the transmitter would. They may prevent the breakdown of the transmitter, for example, by inhibiting the enzyme that normally does this.

A psychoactive drug is a chemical substance that acts primarily on the central nervous system where it alters brain function resulting in temporary changes in perception, mood, consciousness and behaviour. Most of these drugs were originally developed to be used therapeutically as medication. Because psychoactive substances bring about subjective changes in consciousness and mood which the user may find pleasant (e.g. euphoria) or advantageous (e.g. increased alertness), many psychoactive substances are abused, that is used outside of the guidance of a medical professional and for reasons other than their original purpose. With sustained use physical dependence may develop making the cycle of abuse even more difficult to interrupt. Examples of psychoactive drugs include tobacco, cannabis, amphetamines, ecstasy, cocaine, heroin.

Most drugs that affect the nervous system influence the transmission of nerve impulses across synapses. These drugs can be classified into two types:

• Excitory drugs, which stimulate the nervous system by creating more action potentials in post-synaptic membranes.

• Inhibitory drugs, which inhibit the nervous system by creating fewer action potentials in post-synaptic membranes.

• If a drug is taken over a period of time then the synapse may be modified to adjust to its use. For example, if the drug blocks particular receptors at synapses, then new receptors may be made to make up for the ones that are no longer in use. This means that more drug has to be taken to have the same effect. This is known as tolerance to the drug. An increasing tolerance indicates an increase in dependency on the drug. Dependency occurs when, as a result of changes to the CNS, the individual can no longer manage without the drug.

• Organophosphorus insecticides block the enzyme that breaks down the transmitter substance once the molecules are attached to the receptor proteins of the post-synaptic membrane. This prolongs the effect of the neurotransmitters. With organophosphorus molecules acing as a cholinesterase inhibitor, acetylcholine remains in the synaptic cleft and causes repeated firing of the post-synaptic neurone. If the inhibitor is acting at a **neuromuscular junction**, repeated contractions of the muscle occur. That is, the nervous system becomes overactive and muscles contract uncontrollably.

▼ Study point

The specification refers to 'the effect of organophosphates and psychoactive drugs on synaptic transmission'.

As it does not refer to any specific drug, information will be supplied in the question. You will then be expected to apply your knowledge of how synapses work. You are not expected to have any detailed knowledge of named drugs. The text supplied is for information only.

Examiner tip
Several questions referring to caffeine have appeared in exam papers.

Caffeine increases the metabolic rate in pre-synaptic cells. That is, there is increased production of ATP which stimulates neurotransmitter synthesis.

Examiner tip
You should have knowledge of how organophosphates act.

Photoperiodism

Plants do not have a nervous system. Instead growth is co-ordinated by plant growth substances. Their responses are slow because co-ordination is achieved by hormones. One response to light in plants is called **photoperiodism**. This is the response of a plant to relative lengths of daylight and darkness. Flowering is influenced by day length.

Phytochrome

The photoreceptor responsible for absorbing light has been identified as phytochrome, a blue-green pigment found in very minute quantities in plants. Phytochrome exists in two forms that are inter-convertible:

red light	far-red light
phytochrome 660 (Pr) ⟷	phytochrome 730 (Pfr)

Sunlight contains more light of wavelength 660 nm (red light) than 730 nm, therefore during daylight Pr is converted to Pfr, which accumulates.

On absorbing light of a particular wavelength, each form of phytochrome is converted to the other form. Pfr is unstable and, during the hours of darkness, slowly reverts back to Pr, which accumulates.

The plant measures day length or length of darkness by the amount of phytochrome existing in each of the two forms. In daylight, Pfr is the main form.

The photoperiodic stimulus is detected by the leaves of a plant. This can be demonstrated using a single plant and exposing one leaf to light whilst covering up the remainder of the leaves. The stimulus must be transmitted through the plant to the buds, which then develop flowers. Flowering in plants is thought to be initiated by the hormone 'florigen'.

▼ *Phytochrome and flowering*

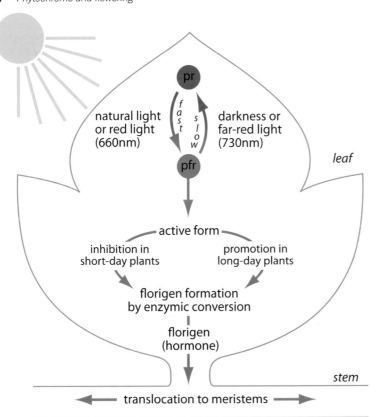

Key Term

Photoperiodism = is the term used to describe the influence of relative periods of light and darkness on flowering.

▼ Study point

Historically, plants are categorised as short-day or long-day. This is unfortunate as it is the length of the dark period that is crucial.

▼ Study point

Plant hormones are also referred to as plant growth regulators.

How Science Works

The hormone for the activation of flowering is called florigen, but it has never been isolated.

19

Knowledge check

Identify the missing word or words.

Plants flower in response to •••• •••••. This response is known as ••••.

The photoreceptor responsible for absorbing light has been identified as the pigment, ••••. The stimulus is detected by the •••• of the plant.

Photoperiodism

Flowering plants can be divided into three groups according to their photoperiodic requirements prior to the production of flowers:

- Day neutral plants – flowering does not seem to be affected by the day length, e.g. tomato, cotton, cucumber.

- Long-day plants – flowering is induced by exposure to dark periods (number of hours) shorter than a critical length, e.g. cabbage, petunia.

- Short-day plants – flowering is induced by exposure to dark periods longer than a critical length, e.g. chrysanthemum, tobacco, poinsettia.

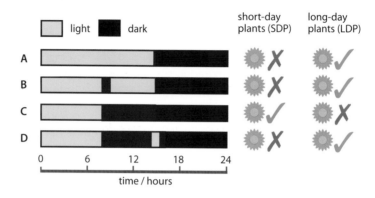

▲ *Comparison of photoperiodism in short- and long-day plants*

In short-day plants flowering is inhibited by exposure to red light, and exposure to far-red light will bring about flowering. It seems that these plants will flower only if the level of Pfr is low enough, but the situation in the long-day plants is reversed and flowering is triggered by high levels of Pfr. The length of the photoperiod is less critical than the length of the dark period and if the photoperiod is interrupted with a short period of darkness, flowering still follows.

If the dark period is interrupted by as little as one minute's exposure to light, flowering is prevented. Red light is most effective in this respect yet the effect of red light treatment can be overcome if the plant is immediately exposed to infrared light.

The practical applications of photoperiodism are that it enables:

- Plant breeders to cross-pollinate flowers which would not normally flower at the same time.

- Horticulturists to delay flowering for specific occasions such as Easter or Christmas.

▶ Poinsettia – *a short day plant*

Co-ordination

1   The simplified diagram shows part of an axon
     of a motor neurone.

   (a)   Name the regions labelled X and Y in the
         diagram. (2)

   (b)   Name the main chemical present in the region
         labelled X. (1)

   (c)   State the effect of this chemical on the part of
         the axon it covers. (1)

   (d)   Describe the effect of the distribution of this
         chemical on the transmission of impulses along
         the neurone. (2) *Speeds rate of transmission of impulses*

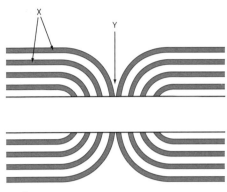

WJEC HB4 JUNE 2010

2 (a)   Synapses are found in both the nervous system of vertebrates and in the nerve nets of invertebrates.
        State three functions of a synapse. (3)

   (b)   State two differences between the structure or functioning of the neurones in a vertebrate and in the
         nerve net found in organisms such as *Hydra* and jellyfish. (2)

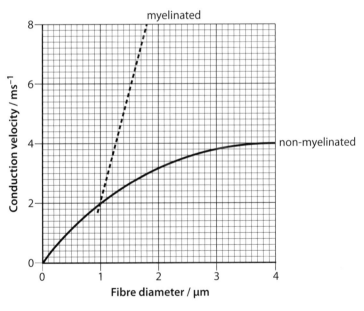

   (c)   The graph shows the relationship between fibre diameter and the conduction velocity in myelinated and
         non-myelinated neurones in the cat.

     (i) Using the information on the graph, describe the relationship between fibre diameter and speed of
         conduction in myelinated and non-myelinated neurones. (3)

     (ii) Suggest why myelinated fibres are never less than 1.0 μm in diameter. (1)

     (iii) Suggest three ways in which organisms have become adapted to speed up the rate of conduction of the
         nerve impulse. (3)

WJEC BY4 JAN 2010

3 (a) What is a reflex action? (2)

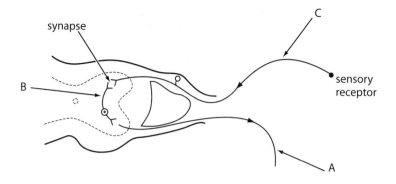

(b) The diagram shows the neurones in a reflex arc.

Name the types of neurone labelled, A, B and C. (1)

(c) The diagram below represents a neurone. Label the structures X, Y and Z. (3)

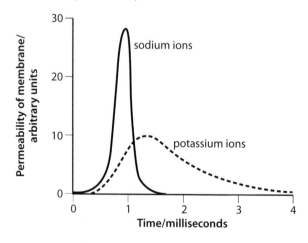

(d) The graph below shows the changes in permeability of an axon membrane to sodium and potassium ions, during an action potential in a neurone.

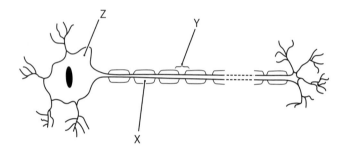

(i) Explain why at the start of an action potential, the potential difference across the membrane rapidly changes from negative to positive. (2)

(ii) Suggest why, during periods of intense nervous activity, the metabolic rate of a nerve cell increases. (1)

(iii) Suggest what would be the effect of lowering the external concentration of sodium ions on the action potential. Explain your answer. (2)

WJEC BY4 JAN 2011   WJEC HB4 JUNE 2010

4 The diagram shows the structural components of the axon membrane that are responsible for an action potential.

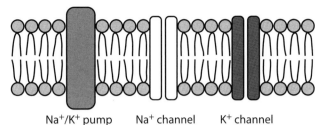

Na^+/K^+ pump Na^+ channel K^+ channel

(a) From which type of biological molecules are the following made?

(i) Pumps and channels. (1)

(ii) The bilayer. (1)

(b) With reference to the diagram, describe how the following events are brought about.

(i) Resting potential. (2)

(ii) Depolarisation. (2)

WJEC BY4 JUNE 2011

5 Pacinian corpuscles are receptors found in the skin and consist of a single sensory neurone surrounded by connective tissue. The receptors respond to changes in pressure.

The Pacinian corpuscle was stimulated and the electrical activity across the membrane of the sensory neurone was recorded using a microelectrode as shown in the diagram.

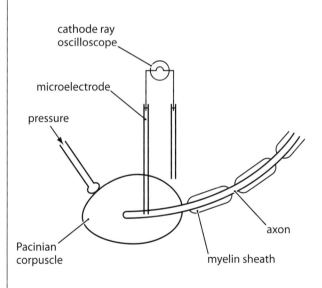

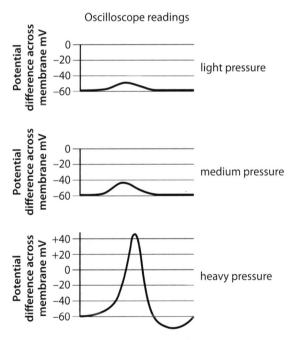

(a)(i) Explain the change in potential difference shown by the microelectrode after light pressure was applied. (3)

(ii) Explain the change in potential difference across the membrane shown by the microelectrode when heavy pressure was applied. (6)

(b) Many chemical substances affect the transmission of the nerve impulse across the synapse.

(i) Suggest two ways by which excitory drugs could change activity at the synapse. (2)

(ii) Suggest two ways by which chemicals could inhibit activity at the synapse. (2)

WJEC BY4 JUNE 2012

Overview: BY5
Environment, Genetics and Evolution

The genetic code and cell function p81

- DNA is able to make copies of itself by semi-conservative replication.
- DNA acts as a template to produce mRNA which carries the coded information from DNA in the nucleus to the ribosomes where polypeptides are synthesised.
- During meiosis there are two divisions, and exchange of chromosome material results in variation as a result of random segregation and crossing over.
- Meiosis results in the formation of haploid gametes each being genetically different.

Sexual reproduction p94

- During sexual reproduction haploid gametes fuse to produce a diploid zygote.
- In humans, testes produce spermatozoa and the ovaries produce ova.
- Spermatogenesis is the production of sperm, and oogenesis is the production of the secondary oocyte.
- Following the release of sperm into the female tract, fertilisation occurs only after the process of capacitation.
- In flowering plants, there are two main methods of pollination, insects and wind.
- Cross-pollination results in far greater genetic variation in a population than self-pollination.
- Double fertilisation is unique to flowering plants.
- The resulting seed is enclosed within an ovary and contains the zygote, which develops into the embryo plant, together with the food store, the endosperm.

Inheritance p112

- A monohybrid cross is the study of the inheritance of one gene; a dihybrid cross involves the inheritance of two separate genes.
- During meiosis only one of a pair of alleles enters a gamete.
- In dihybrid inheritance either of a pair of alleles may combine randomly with either of another pair.
- Co-dominance is where the heterozygote individual has a phenotype intermediate between the two homozygous parents.
- Genes present on the same chromosome are said to be linked and are inherited together.
- Genes carried on the same sex chromosome are said to be sex-linked.

Variation and evolution p127

- Variation is the result of both genetic change and environmental factors.
- A mutation is an unpredictable change in the genetic material of an organism.
- A gene mutation results from a change in the base sequence of DNA.
- A chromosome mutation results from a change in the chromosome structure or change in the number of whole sets of chromosomes or individual chromosomes.
- The theory of natural selection proposes that those organisms that are best adapted for survival reproduce to pass on their alleles for beneficial characteristics to the next generation.
- A population of organisms reproducing sexually contains a large amount of genetic variation called the gene pool.
- The separation of two populations as a result of isolation may result in the formation of a new species.
- There are two main forms of isolation mechanisms, geographical and reproductive.

Applications of reproduction and genetics p139

- Cloning can be used to produce large numbers of genetically identical organisms in a fairly short period of time.
- Micropropagation provides a rapid method of obtaining large numbers of genetically identical plants.
- Artificial clones can be formed in animals by separating embryos at an early stage.
- The technique of growing cells in a laboratory is called tissue culture.
- Central to tissue engineering is the use of stem cells.
- Therapeutic stem cell cloning has enormous medical potential. Stem cell research raises ethical issues.
- The Human Genome Project has determined the order of bases in the Human Genome together with their identification, sequencing and mapping.
- Genetic engineering involves the extraction of a gene or genes from one organism and their transfer into a host organism.
- Recombinant DNA technology involves the introduction of DNA from various organisms into bacterial cells, which will then produce a desired product.
- A transgenic or genetically modified organism has its genotype altered, producing a new strain of organism. This has tremendous potential in agriculture and health.
- Gene therapy treats a genetic disease by replacing defective genes in the patient's body with replicated non-defective genes.
- The polymerase chain reaction can produce large quantities of identical DNA from a small sample.
- A person's DNA profile or 'genetic fingerprint' is unique and can be used to provide forensic evidence and also determine parents in paternity cases.

Energy and ecosystems p160

- An ecosystem is a natural unit of living components in a given area as well as the non-living factors with which they interact.
- The study of the flow of energy through the ecosystem is known as ecological energetics.
- Energy passing from one trophic level to the next results in energy lost due to respiration and excretion.
- Energy pyramids are an accurate method of representing feeding relationships.
- Succession is the change in the structure and species composition of a community over time.

Effects of human activities p168

- Human activity has a great influence on the environment.
- There is an increased tendency for organisms to become resistant to pesticides as a result of overuse.
- Artificial selection is the process of cross-breeding plants and animals with useful characteristics.
- Human activity is the main cause of species extinction.
- Species conservation ensures the preservation of existing gene pools.
- Conflicts exist between farming and conservation.
- Deforestation means the loss of important habitats, soil erosion and a change in the balance of atmospheric gases such as carbon dioxide.
- A dramatic increase in the intensity and efficiency of commercial fishing methods has resulted in over-fishing in many areas of the world.
- Increasing levels of carbon dioxide are the cause of the greenhouse effect and possibly global warming.
- The use of biofuels is theoretically a method of reducing greenhouse gas emissions but their adoption may result in a reduction in habitats for animals and plants.
- Fertilisers contribute to water pollution resulting in eutrophication.

BY5

The genetic code and cell function

In a eukaryotic cell DNA molecules are linear in the form of a helix. The DNA is held in position by proteins to form chromosomes. DNA is the hereditary material that is responsible for passing genetic information from cell to cell and generation to generation. It acts as a store of genetic information which must be replicated or copied in each generation. DNA also acts as a template which determines the characteristics of an organism through protein synthesis. Each chromosome is composed of thousands of short sections called genes, each of which contains the coded information needed to make a particular protein. For this reason the information is known as the genetic code.

Chromosomes must make copies of themselves so that when cells divide, each daughter cell receives an exact copy of the genetic information. This is called replication and takes place in a cell during the interphase stage of cell division.

There are two types of cell division, mitosis and meiosis. At AS you studied the process of mitosis, which describes how cells increase in number. In this unit you will study the process of meiosis, which takes place during sexual reproduction and results in the production of gametes possessing half the normal chromosome number.

By the end of this topic you should be able to:

- Explain how DNA is able to make copies of itself by semi-conservative replication.
- Describe what is meant by a 'triplet code'.
- Describe how DNA is able to make messenger RNA by a process called transcription.
- Describe how messenger RNA carries the coded information from DNA in the nucleus to the ribosomes in the cytoplasm where polypeptides are synthesised by the process called translation.
- Describe how transfer RNA carries specific amino acids to the ribosomes for use in translation.
- Describe the process of meiosis as the formation of haploid gametes from diploid cells in the testis or ovary.
- Explain the importance that gametes are haploid so that at fertilisation a diploid zygote is formed.
- Describe meiosis as consisting of two divisions where genetic material is exchanged by the process of crossing over resulting in variation.

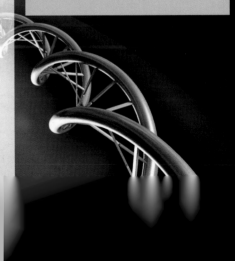

YOU SHOULD KNOW ›››

››› details of the Meselsohn–Stahl experiment

››› why the process of DNA replication is called semi-conservative

Examiner tip

Consider reviewing DNA structure from BY1.

Examiner tip

The bacteria were washed before transfer to prevent contamination, so ^{15}N is not incorporated into the new strand.

Replication

Chromosomes must make copies of themselves so that when cells divide, each daughter cell receives an exact copy of the genetic information. This copying of DNA is called replication and takes place in a cell during interphase.

When Watson and Crick proposed their theory for the structure of DNA in 1953 they also suggested a copying process for the genetic material. They called this the semi-conservative hypothesis. The next step was for scientists to carry out experiments to show whether DNA remained intact or did indeed separate during replication. If the former, then of the molecules present at the end of the experiment each molecule would be made of entirely new material, while the other would consist of entirely original material. If the semi-conservative theory were true then each of the new molecules would have one strand of original material and one strand of new material.

Experiments were carried out to confirm the hypothesis. The experiments involved the use of an ultra-centrifuge. This rotates centrifuge tubes containing liquid suspensions at very high speeds, which results in the denser particles separating out at a lower point in the tube than the lighter particles.

1. Two scientists, Meselsohn and Stahl carried out an experiment in which they cultured the bacterium, *Escherichia coli*, for several generations on a medium containing amino acids made with the heavy isotope of nitrogen ^{15}N. The bacteria incorporated the ^{15}N into their nucleotides and then into their DNA so that all the DNA contained ^{15}N. They extracted the bacterial DNA and centrifuged it. The DNA settled at a low point in the tube.

2. The ^{15}N bacteria were washed, then transferred to a medium containing the normal, lighter form of nitrogen, ^{14}N, and were allowed to divide once more.

3. When extracts of DNA from this first generation culture were centrifuged, it was shown to have a mid-point density, since half the strand was made up of the original strand of ^{15}N DNA and the other half was made up of the new strand containing ^{14}N.

4. When extracts were taken from the second generation grown in ^{14}N, the DNA settled at mid points and high points in the tube. This was conclusive evidence for the semi-conservative hypothesis.

Details of the experiments and the results are summarised below.

YOU SHOULD KNOW ›››

››› that DNA bases contain nitrogen; nitrogen has a light form ¹⁴N and a heavy form ¹⁵N; bacteria use the nitrogen provided to make DNA

bacteria grown in ¹⁴N medium

bacteria grown in ¹⁵N medium for many generations

bacteria, washed and transferred to ¹⁴N medium and samples removed at intervals

after one generation

after two generations

after three generations

DNA extracted and suspension centrifuged

point where light DNA settles

centrifuging DNA from bacteria grown only ¹⁵N

one generation only ¹⁴N

second generation only ¹⁴N

third generation only ¹⁴N

control – both strands light

DNA contains all heavy ¹⁵N

intermediate DNA half heavy ¹⁵N and half light ¹⁴N

half of DNA is intermediate and half light

one quarter intermediate DNA three quarters light

▲ *Meselsohn–Stahl experiment*

**Key Term**

Template = the blueprint from which a copy is made.

▼ **Study point**

To understand the purpose of this experiment you should know that DNA bases contain nitrogen; nitrogen has a light form ¹⁴N and a heavy form ¹⁵N; bacteria use the nitrogen provided to make DNA.

How Science Works

These experiments by Meselsohn and Stahl show how experimental evidence supports a proposed theory.

It is now accepted that replication occurs as follows:

- The hydrogen bonds holding the base pairs together break and the two halves of the molecule separate.

- DNA unwinds and as the strands separate, DNA polymerase catalyses the addition of free nucleotides to the exposed bases.

- Each chain acts as a **template** so that free nucleotides can be joined to their complementary bases by the enzyme, DNA polymerase.

- The result is two DNA molecules, each made up of one newly synthesised chain and one chain conserved from the original molecule.

This is called the semi-conservative hypothesis.

▼ **Study point**

DNA has two major functions in the cell: replication, in dividing cells; carrying information for protein synthesis in all cells.

YOU SHOULD KNOW ›››

››› why the code is a triplet code

››› how genes code for amino acids

Key Term

Gene = length of DNA on a chromosome normally coding for a particular polypeptide.

1

Knowledge check

Link the appropriate terms 1–4 with the phrases A–D.

1. Non-overlapping.
2. Universal.
3. Stop code.
4. Degenerate.

A. More than one triplet codes for each amino acid.
B. The same in all living organisms.
C. Each triplet is read separately.
D. Act as terminating signals.

amino acid	abbreviation
alanine	ala
arginine	arg
asparagine	asn
aspartic acid	asp
cysteine	cys
glutamine	gln
glutamic acid	glu
glycine	gly
histidine	his
isoleucine	ile
leucine	leu
lysine	lys
methionine	met
phenylalanine	phe
proline	pro
serine	ser
threonine	thr
tryptophan	trp
tyrosine	tyr
valine	val

The genetic code

DNA acts as a store of genetic information. Chromosomes are divided up into thousands of shorter sections called **genes**. This information is called the genetic code. The codes carried by DNA determine what reactions can take place in an organism. Genes control the formation of enzymes which are proteins. By determining which enzymes are produced, the DNA can determine the characteristics of an organism.

Why is the code a triplet code?

- Each amino acid must have its own code of bases on the DNA.
- There are four different bases in DNA (adenine, guanine, cytosine and thymine) but there are over twenty different amino acids.
- If one base coded for one amino acid, it would be possible to make only four amino acids. That is A, T, G and C for each amino acid.
- If two bases coded for one amino acid it would be possible to produce 16 different codes to make 16 amino acids, which are too few possibilities:
Having three bases for each amino acid would give a permutation of 64 codes, more than enough to make 20 amino acids.

	A	T	G	C
A	AA	TA	GA	CA
T	AT	TT	GT	CT
G	AG	TG	GG	CG
C	AC	TC	GC	CC

Characteristics of the code

- As the code has three bases it is called the triplet code.
- The code is known as a 'degenerate code' as most amino acids have more than one triplet code.
- Three triplet codes do not code for amino acids at all. These are called 'stop' codes and mark the end of the reading of the code. In fact they are rather like a full stop at the end of a sentence.
- It is the sequence of bases in the DNA chain that codes for the sequence of amino acids in a polypeptide.
- The portion of DNA which codes for a whole polypeptide is called a **gene**. (This is the basis of the one gene – one polypeptide hypothesis.)
- Each amino acid is coded for by three bases (the triplet code) called a codon.
- All the codons are universal, that is, they are exactly the same for all living organisms.
- The code is non-overlapping in that each triplet is read separately.

▼ *Table of mRNA codons and the amino acids for which they code.*

		2nd base				
		U	**C**	**A**	**G**	
1st base	**U**	UUU UUC } Phe UUA UUG } Leu	UCU UCC UCA UCG } Ser	UAU UAC } Tyr UAA Stop UAG Stop	UGU UGC } Cys UGA Stop UGG Trp	U C A G
	C	CUU CUC CUA CUG } Leu	CCU CCC CCA CCG } Pro	CAU CAC } His CAA CAG } Gln	CGU CGC CGA CGG } Arg	U C A G
	A	AUU AUC AUA } Ile AUG Met	ACU ACC ACA ACG } Thr	AAU AAC } Asn AAA AAG } Lys	AGU AGC } Ser AGA AGG } Arg	U C A G
	G	GUU GUC GUA GUG } Val	GCU GCC GCA GCG } Ala	GAU GAC } Asp GAA GAG } Glu	GGU GGC GGA GGG } Gly	U C A G

(3rd base)

Protein synthesis

The basic process of protein synthesis occurs as follows:

- DNA acts as a template providing the instructions in the form of a long sequence of nucleotides.
- A complementary section of part of this sequence is made into mRNA by a process called transcription.
- The mRNA acts as a template to which complementary tRNA molecules attach and the amino acids they carry are linked to form a polypeptide by a process called translation.

Transcription

DNA does not leave the nucleus but acts as a template for the production of mRNA, which carries the instructions needed for protein synthesis from the nucleus to the cytoplasm. The function of the ribosomes situated in the cytoplasm is to provide a suitable surface for the attachment of mRNA and the assembly of protein.

Transcription is the process whereby part of the DNA, the gene, acts as a template for the production of mRNA. The process occurs as follows:

- The enzyme, DNA helicase, acts on a specific region of the DNA molecule, called the cistron, to break the hydrogen bonds between the bases. This causes the two strands to separate and expose the nucleotide bases in that region.
- The enzyme RNA polymerase links to the template strand of DNA at the beginning of the sequence to be copied. The double-stranded DNA first unwinds and then unzips in the relevant region.
- Transcription occurs when free RNA nucleotides align themselves opposite the template strand.
- Because of the complementary relationship between the bases in DNA and the free nucleotides, cytosine in the DNA attracts a guanine, guanine a cytosine, thymine an adenine, and adenine a uracil.
- RNA polymerase moves along the DNA forming bonds that add nucleotides one at a time to the RNA. This results in the synthesis of a molecule of mRNA alongside the unzipped portion of DNA. Behind the RNA polymerase the DNA strands rejoin to reform the double helix.
- The RNA polymerase separates when it reaches a 'stop' code. Then the production of mRNA is complete.
- The mRNA carries the DNA code out of the nucleus through a nuclear pore to the cytoplasm and attaches itself to a ribosome consisting of ribosomal RNA and protein.

▶ *Transcription*

YOU SHOULD KNOW ›››

››› how mRNA is produced from DNA in the nucleus by the process of transcription

››› the role of tRNA in the attachment of specific amino acids and their transport to the ribosome

››› the roles of mRNA and tRNA in translating the code at the ribosome

▼ **Study point**

In RNA there is no thymine. It is replaced by uracil which pairs with adenine.

▼ **Study point**

Consider reviewing previous work from BY1 regarding the three different types of RNA: messenger RNA, ribosomal RNA and transfer RNA.

▼ **Study point**

Each amino acid is coded for by a DNA codon. The mRNA molecule carries complementary RNA codons.

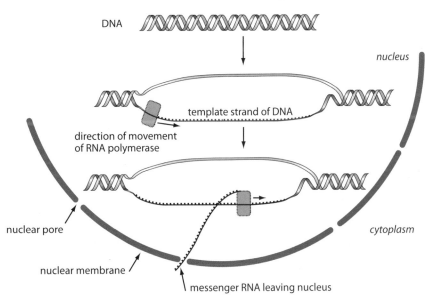

DNA

nucleus

template strand of DNA

direction of movement of RNA polymerase

nuclear pore

cytoplasm

nuclear membrane

messenger RNA leaving nucleus

Translation

This stage involves translating the codons on the mRNA into a sequence of amino acids known as a polypeptide. This process takes place on a ribosome and involves tRNA.

Each ribosome is made up of two sub-units, with a larger sub-unit having two sites for the attachment of tRNA molecules. This means that two tRNA molecules are associated with a ribosome at any one time. The ribosome acts as a framework moving along the mRNA, reading the code, holding the codon–anticodon complex together until two amino acids join. The ribosome moves along adding one amino acid at a time until the polypeptide chain is assembled.

The process of translation occurs as follows:

- A ribosome becomes attached to the starting codon at one end of the mRNA molecule.

- The first tRNA with the anticodon complementary to the first codon on the mRNA attaches itself to the ribosome. Then a second tRNA with an anticodon complementary to the second codon on the mRNA attaches to the other attachment site. The two amino acids are sufficiently close for a peptide bond to form between them. The first tRNA leaves the ribosome, leaving an attachment site vacant. The ribosome now moves one codon along the mRNA strand.

- One site binds tRNA with the growing polypeptide; the other site is for tRNA carrying the next amino acid in the sequence.

- Translation by ribosomes allows the assembly of amino acids into polypeptides according to the original DNA code. A ribosomal enzyme catalyses peptide bond formation between an amino acid on one tRNA and the growing polypeptide on the other tRNA.

- A ribosome passes along mRNA, one codon at a time, the tRNA with the appropriate anticodon fills the vacant slot and the amino acid forms a peptide bond with the last member of the chain until a stop codon is reached.

- Each time one ribosome moves along the mRNA a molecule of polypeptide is produced.

- Usually a number of ribosomes can be found on a single mRNA, each reading from the coded information at the same time. This is called a polysome system and so many molecules of a polypeptide are formed.

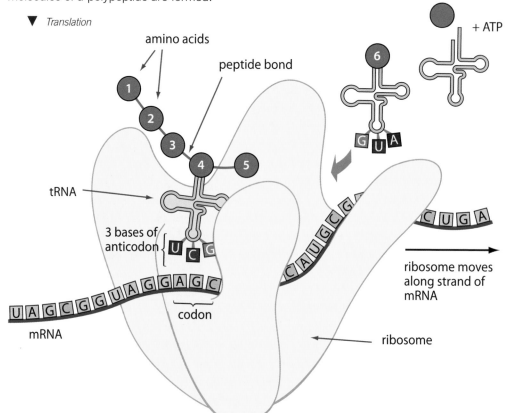

▼ *Translation*

tRNA and amino acid activation

The sequence of bases on the tRNA, or anticodon, determines which amino acid it carries. If, for example, the sequence of the anticodon is CCC then the amino acid glycine will attach to the other end of the tRNA molecule. (See table of mRNA codons and the amino acids for which they code on page 84.) This anticodon will combine with codon GGG on the mRNA molecule. The mRNA codon therefore translates into the amino acid glycine.

Once the tRNA is released from its specific amino acid, it is free to collect another amino acid from the amino acid pool in the cell. Energy from ATP is required for the specific amino acid to attach itself to the tRNA. This process is referred to as activation.

③

Knowledge check

Link the appropriate molecules 1–4 with the phrases A–D.

1. mRNA.
2. tRNA.
3. DNA.
4. ATP.

A. Transcribed but not translated.
B. Carries an amino acid to the ribosome.
C. Moves through the nuclear pore to the cytoplasm.
D. Involved in the activation of tRNA.

▼ *tRNA*

this end can attach to a specific amino acid – each type of tRNA transports its own type of amino acid

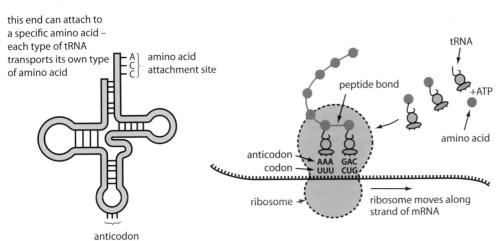

amino acid attachment site

anticodon

peptide bond

tRNA

+ATP

amino acid

anticodon
codon

ribosome

ribosome moves along strand of mRNA

◆ **Link** ▶ Consider reviewing your BY1 notes on 'Levels of protein structure' and the involvement of the Golgi body.

Polypeptides are modified into proteins

A gene determines the polypeptide made by the cell. Subsequently the polypeptide has to be modified into a protein. Proteins carry out a range of biological activities and include enzymes, antibodies, hormones, carrier and transport proteins as well as structural proteins. Occasionally the polypeptide primary structure of a protein acts as a functional protein but usually the polypeptide needs to be converted to secondary, tertiary or quaternary structures.

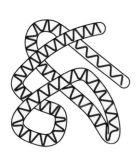

▲ *Tertiary structure*

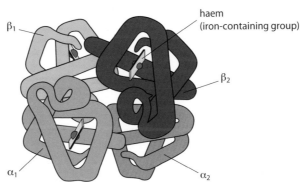

β_1

haem (iron-containing group)

β_2

α_1

α_2

▲ *Structure of haemoglobin*

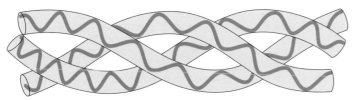

3 polypeptide strands tightly wound around one another

◀ *Structure of fibrous protein e.g. collagen*

YOU SHOULD KNOW ›››

››› the role of meiosis in sexual reproduction

››› the stages in meiosis

››› how meiosis creates genetic variation

Key Terms

Haploid = half the chromosome number.

Homologous = a pair of chromosomes, one maternal and one paternal, that have the same gene loci and therefore determine the same features.

Chromatid = one of the two copies of a chromosome that are joined together by a single centromere prior to cell division.

‹Link› Consider reviewing chromosome structure and mitosis from BY1.

‹Link› For details of crossing over see page 91.

4

Knowledge check

Link the appropriate terms 1–4 with the statements A–D.

1. Haploid.

2. Gamete.

3. Zygote.

4. Meiosis

A. Sex cell.

B. Containing a single set of chromosomes.

C. The result of the fusion of a sperm and an egg.

D. Takes place in reproductive organs.

Meiosis

Meiosis takes place in the reproductive organs of both plants and animals. It results in the formation of **haploid** gametes. In order to maintain a constant number of chromosomes from one generation to the next the number of chromosomes must be halved. In contrast to mitosis, meiosis produces cells that are not genetically identical. In fact, meiosis plays an important role in bringing about genetic variation in living organisms.

The fertilised egg or zygote divides by mitosis to form an embryo.

Meiosis involves two divisions and each diploid cell divides to produce four haploid gametes. Meiosis also results in genetic variation among the offspring. This is brought about in two ways:

• Independent assortment of **homologous** chromosomes.

• Crossing over between the **chromatids** of homologous chromosomes.

These two processes will be dealt with in more detail later in this section.

The diagram below shows that meiosis involves two divisions of the cell. The first division is sometimes called a reduction division since the chromosome number is halved. Crossing over also takes place during the first division. The second division is identical to mitosis.

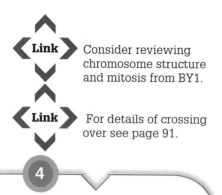

▲ *Typical animal cell life cycle*

▼ *Summary of meiosis*

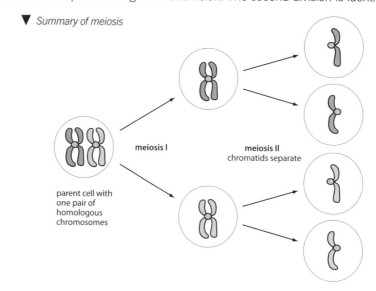

During meiosis I homologous chromosomes pair up and their chromatids wrap around each other, and equivalent portions of these chromatids may be exchanged in a process called crossing over. By the end of this stage the homologous pair separate with one chromosome of each pair going into one of the two daughter cells. This results in two daughter nuclei containing half the number of chromosomes of the parent nucleus.

During meiosis II chromatids move apart and the two new haploid nuclei divide again in a division identical to that of mitosis. The net result is that four haploid nuclei are formed from the parent nucleus each containing half the number of chromosomes.

When the cell is not dividing, it is said to be in interphase. During this phase the DNA content of the cell is doubled and new cell organelles are also formed.

Meiosis I

Prophase I

The chromosomes become shorter and thicker and can be seen as two chromatids. In cells where centrioles are present, i.e. animals and lower plants, the centrioles move to the poles of the cells and microtubules begin to radiate from them, forming asters. This results in the formation of the spindle. This stage differs from that of mitosis as homologous chromosomes associate in pairs and each pair is called a bivalent. Each bivalent consists of four strands, made up of two chromosomes, each comprising two chromatids. These chromatids wrap around each other and then partially repel each other but remain joined at certain points called chiasmata. At these points chromatids may break and recombine with a different but equivalent chromatid. This exchange of pieces of chromosomes is called crossing over.

By the end of prophase, the nuclear envelope has disintegrated and the nucleolus has disappeared.

Metaphase I

At this stage, when the pairs of homologous chromosomes align themselves on the equator of the spindle, the maternal and paternal chromosomes are arranged randomly. This random distribution and consequent independent assortment of chromosomes produces new genetic combinations.

Anaphase I

The chromosomes in each bivalent separate and one of each pair is pulled to one pole, its sister chromosome to the opposite pole. Thus each pole receives only one of each homologous pair of chromosomes and, because of their random arrangement at metaphase, these will be a random mixture of maternal and paternal chromosomes. The chromosomes reach the opposite poles and the nuclear envelope re-forms around each group of haploid chromosomes.

Telophase I

Usually the chromosomes stay in their condensed form and meiosis II follows on immediately. In animal cells cytokinesis occurs, that is, the division of the cytoplasm to give two haploid cells. Many plant cells go straight into meiosis II with no re-formation of the spindle.

Meiosis II

- Prophase II

  The new spindle develops at right angles to the old spindle.

- Metaphase II

  The chromosomes line up separately on the equator of the spindle, with each chromosome attached to a spindle fibre by its centromere.

- Anaphase II

  The centromeres divide and the chromatids are pulled to opposite poles.

- Telophase II

  On reaching the poles the chromatids lengthen and are indistinct. The spindle disappears and the nuclear membrane reforms. Cytokinesis takes place.

Examiner tip
The names of the subdivisions of prophase I are not required.

Examiner tip
Be prepared to describe the difference between prophase of mitosis and prophase I of meiosis.

Examiner tip
Expect to identify stages in given diagrams in the exam, in particular, requiring you to distinguish between stages in meiosis I and II.

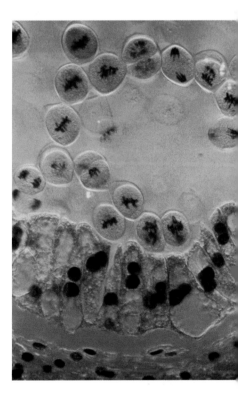

▲ *Anther cells undergoing meiosis*

 **Link** Diagrams of meiosis on page 90.

Key Term

Genotype = the genetic make-up of an organism.

▼ *Meiosis I*

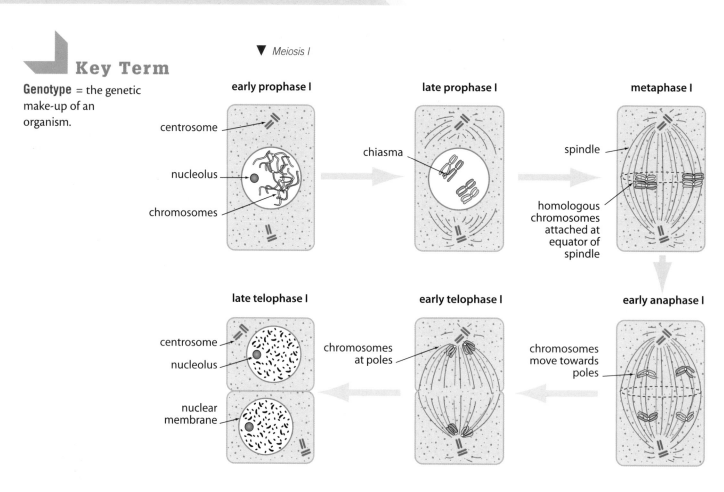

Meiosis I is followed by meiosis II, which is identical to mitosis.

▼ Study point

The result of these two meiotic divisions is that there are four haploid daughter cells and the genetic make-up of each cell is different.

▼ Study point

Mathematically, there are 2^3 possible combinations from three pairs of chromosomes. Humans have 23 pairs of chromosomes and the possible combinations are 2^{23} or over 8 million!

The significance of meiosis

Meiosis is the reduction division that occurs during gamete formation in sexually reproducing organisms. In this division the diploid number of chromosomes (2n) is reduced to the haploid (n). Thus, when two gametes join together at fertilisation, the zygote that is formed has two complete sets of chromosomes returning to the diploid condition. However, meiosis does more than halve the number of chromosomes into a cell; it also introduces genetic variation into the gametes and therefore the zygotes that are produced. When these genetically different gametes fuse, randomly, at fertilisation, more variation is produced amongst the offspring.

In the long term, if a species is to survive in a constantly changing environment and to colonise new environments, sources of variation are essential.

There are thus three ways of creating variety:

1. Each of the chromosomes making up a homologous pair carries different genetic material. During sexual reproduction the **genotype** of one parent is mixed with that of the other when haploid gametes fuse.

2. The different pairs of homologous chromosomes arrange themselves on the spindle during metaphase I of meiosis. When, they subsequently separate, they do so entirely independently of each other, so that the daughter cells contain different combinations of maternal and paternal chromosomes.

This may be explained in more detail. Consider an organism with three pairs of chromosomes represented by three different shapes as in the diagram below. During meiosis one of each shape will pass randomly to the gamete.

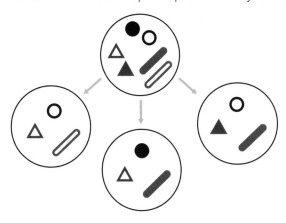

▲ *Independent assortment*

Three different combinations are shown in the diagram. Can you draw the remaining five possible combinations?

As a result of meiosis, gametes will be genetically different. When haploid gametes fuse during fertilisation their random fusion will produce variety in the offspring. Additionally as the gametes come from different parents this introduces even greater variety.

3. Crossing over during chiasmata formation during prophase 1 of meiosis.

    Equivalent parts of homologous chromosomes may be exchanged, thus producing new combinations and the separation of linked genes. This process is called recombination.This single cross-over occurring during meiosis I results in four haploid gametes having a different genetic composition.

▼ *Single cross over*

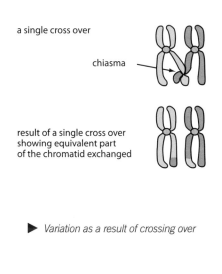

a single cross over

chiasma

result of a single cross over
showing equivalent part
of the chromatid exchanged

▶ *Variation as a result of crossing over*

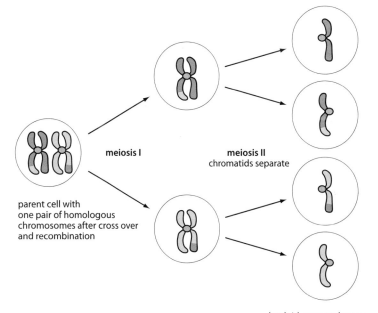

meiosis I

meiosis II
chromatids separate

parent cell with
one pair of homologous
chromosomes after cross over
and recombination

haploid gametes have a
different genetic composition

▼ Study point

In a homologous pair both alleles may be dominant, or one recessive and the other dominant, or both may be recessive. It is the different forms of the same genes that are exchanged during crossing over.

The genetic code and cell function

1 The diagram represents stages of protein synthesis.

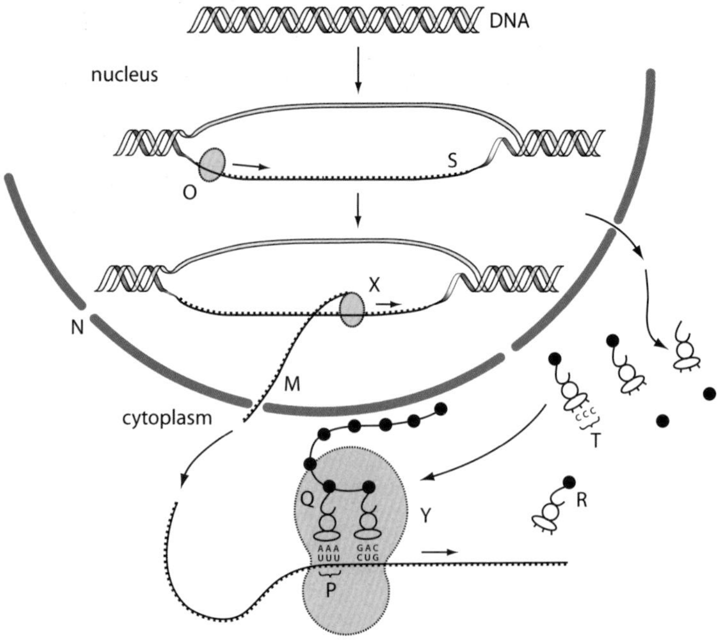

(a)(i) Give the name of the processes taking place at X and Y. (2)

    (ii) Using the letters M–S from the diagram indicate the following structures in the table. (8)

Structure	Letter
Messenger RNA	
Nuclear pore	
RNA polymerase	
Codon	
Ribosome	
Transfer RNA	
Template/ sense strand of DNA	
Anticodon	

(b) Transfer RNA (tRNA) molecules are very specific and will only carry one type of amino acid depending on three unpaired nitrogenous bases on the molecule (the anticodon).
The table shows the type of tRNA molecules which combine with certain amino acids.

Amino acid	Anticodon
glycine	CCU
cysteine	ACA
arginine	GCA
alanine	CGU

Using the information provided, state the nucleotide sequence on the DNA molecule which codes for the following polypeptide. (2)

Glycine – cysteine – arginine – alanine

WJEC BY5 JUNE 2011

2 Part of a particular sequence of bases on a DNA molecule is as follows:
    TTATCTTTCGGGATG

(a) State the sequence of nitrogenous bases on the mRNA which is obtained by using this DNA molecule as a template. (1)

(b) A sequence of nitrogenous bases on another section of mRNA is shown below.

    UACAGAGCAUCGUUA

Using the table on the right, determine the order the amino acids would be incorporated into the polypeptide constructed from this mRNA sequence. You may assume that the sequence is read from the left-hand end. (1)

(c) Suggest how the cell ensures that the code is read in the correct direction. (1)

(d) Proflavin is a chemical which alters the base sequence of DNA. What is the name given to such a change? (1)

(e) If proflavin caused the deletion of the first adenine (A) in the DNA sequence which codes for the above mRNA, what consequences would this have on the subsequent translation of the sequence? (1)

mRNA codons	Amino acid
AAU	Asparagine
ACA	Threonine
AGA	Arginine
AUA	Isoleucine
CAU	Histidine
CGG	Arginine
CGU	Arginine
CCC	Proline
CCG	Proline
CUU	Leucine
GAU	Aspartic acid
GAA	Glutamic acid
GAG	Glutamic acid
GCA	Alanine
GGA	Glycine
UAU	Tyrosine
UGC	Cysteine
UCG	Serine
UUG	Leucine
UCU	Serine
UGG	Tryptophan
UUA	Leucine
UAC	Tyrosine

WJEC BY5 JUNE 2010

3 The diagram shows four stages in the division of a cell.

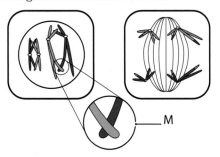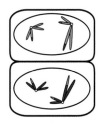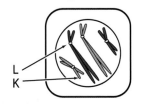

(a)(i) Name the features labelled K, L and M. (3)

(ii) Name the type of cell division shown. (1)

(b) State two sources of variation. (2)

(c)(i) Explain how variation occurs as a result of gene mutation. (2)

(ii) State two causes of mutation. (2)

(iii) Explain why variations caused by mutation can be important to the survival of a species. (2)

WJEC B2 JAN 1997

4 (a) The drawing shows one pair of homologous chromosomes during anaphase of meiosis.

(i) What evidence is shown in the diagram that the cell division taking place is meiosis? (1)

(ii) Does the diagram suggest anaphase I or anaphase II of meiosis? Give a reason for your answer. (1)

(iii) Complete the outlines of the cells below to show the appearance of the chromososmes in the four possible gametes that would arise from this pair of chromosomes. (2)

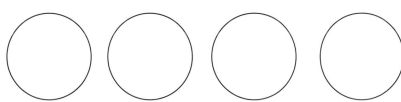

(b) During prophase of meiosis homologous chromosomes undergo crossing over. Suggest one advantage to the species resulting from this process. (1)

WJEC B2 JAN 2001

5 (a) Himalayan rabbits belong to a variety in which all the individuals carry the dominant black allele. However, the fur of new-born Himalayan rabbits is entirely white. As the rabbits grow older the ears, nose, paws and tail grow black fur.

When a patch of white fur was shaved from the back of a rabbit kept in a cool environment, the fur that grew back was black. The normal body temperature of a rabbit is 33°C.

(i) The presence of the B gene in the nucleus of the rabbit cells controls the reactions which produce the black pigment. In the sequence below, insert the processes or terms which fill the gaps linking the gene to the production of pigment. (3)

Gene $\longrightarrow$ _____ $\longrightarrow$ _____ _____ $\longrightarrow$ protein synthesis $\longrightarrow$ _____ _____ $\longrightarrow$ pigment synthesis

(ii) Explain the experimental evidence for the effect of temperature on the process. (2)

(b) Suggest explanations for:

(i) All the new-born rabbits having white fur. (1)

(ii) The colour pattern in the adults. (1)

WJEC BI5 JUNE 2002

BY5

Human reproduction

In the previous section you learnt that meiosis takes place resulting in gamete formation in sexually reproducing organisms. By this process the diploid number of cells in the testes in the male and the ovaries in the female is reduced to the haploid number. The male gametes are called spermatozoa; female gametes are called eggs or ova.

Sexual reproduction is the production and fusion of male and female gametes to form a zygote, which grows and develops to form a new individual, very similar to the parents but not identical to them.

Topic contents

By the end of this topic you should be able to:

- Describe the structure and function of the male and female reproductive systems.
- Explain spermatogenesis as the production of sperm, and oogenesis as the production of the egg, and the role of mitosis and meiosis in the processes.
- Describe sexual intercourse, fertilisation and zygote development to the blastocyst stage.
- Describe ovulation and the preparation of the uterus to receive the embryo (implantation).
- Discuss possible causes of infertility, particularly affecting the Fallopian tubes.
- Describe the use of a pregnancy testing kit to test for the presence of hCG hormone in the urine of a female.
- Describe *in vitro* fertilisation as a method of treatment for infertility.

Male reproductive system

The male system consists of a pair of testes, contained in an external sac, the scrotum; the penis, which is an intromittent organ; genital ducts connecting the two; and various accessory glands which provide constituents for the semen. Each testis consists of about a thousand seminiferous tubules which produce the spermatozoa.

The seminiferous tubules also contain interstitial cells that produce the male hormone, testosterone. When sperm have been produced they collect in the vasa efferentia and then pass to the head of the epididymis where they mature. They then pass along the coiled tube to the base of the epididymis where they are stored for a short time before passing via the vas deferens to the urethra during ejaculation. Before the vas deferens joins the urethra it combines with the duct leading from the seminal vesicle to form the ejaculatory duct. The seminal vesicles produce a mucus secretion which helps the mobility of the sperm. The ejaculatory duct then passes through the prostate gland which produces an alkaline secretion that neutralises the acidity of any urine in the urethra as well as aiding sperm mobility.

▶ *Male reproductive system*

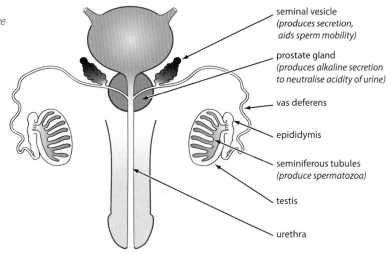

seminal vesicle
(produces secretion, aids sperm mobility)

prostate gland
(produces alkaline secretion to neutralise acidity of urine)

vas deferens

epididymis

seminiferous tubules
(produce spermatozoa)

testis

urethra

Female reproductive system

There are two ovaries each of which produces ova or eggs. They are produced in the germinal epithelium where they develop into follicles. Mature follicles migrate to the surface when their development is complete so that the ova can be shed.

Ova are passed to the Fallopian tube or oviduct which conveys them to the uterus (womb). The uterus has muscular walls and is lined internally by a mucus membrane called the endometrium. It is well supplied with blood and is part of the womb into which the embryo implants during pregnancy and which is shed during menstruation. The uterus opens into the vagina through a ring of muscle, the cervix.

▶ *Female reproductive system*

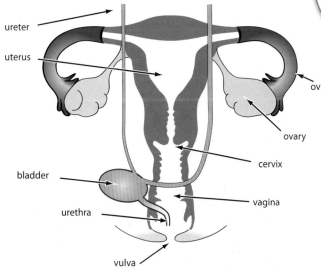

ureter

uterus

oviduct/Fallopian tubes

ovary

cervix

bladder

vagina

urethra

vulva

Gametogenesis

The production of gametes in the sex cells is known as gametogenesis.

- Spermatogenesis is the formation of sperm in the testis.
- Oogenesis is the formation of eggs or ova in the ovary.

The cells of the germinal epithelium of both the testis and the ovary undergo a sequence of mitotic and meiotic divisions to form haploid gametes. It is important that the gametes are haploid so that at fertilisation the diploid number is restored.

Spermatogenesis

The process by which spermatozoa are produced takes place within the germinal epithelium of the seminiferous tubule.

The process may be summarised as follows:

- The diploid spermatogonia divide many times by mitosis to produce primary spermatocytes.
- These then undergo meiosis and after the first meiotic division form haploid secondary spermatocytes.
- After the second meiotic division they form spermatids which differentiate into mature spermatozoa.

In the wall of the seminiferous tubule are the Sertoli cells. They secrete a fluid which nourishes the spermatids and protects them from the immune system of the male. There are also groups of interstitial cells which secrete the male sex hormone.

The spermatozoa produced are motile. The haploid nucleus is contained in the head, the middle piece is packed with mitochondria to provide ATP for movement using the tail.

▼ Seminiferous tubules

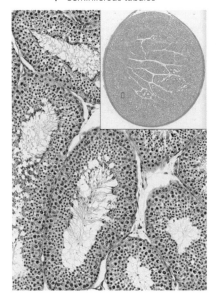

7

◄ Spermatogenesis

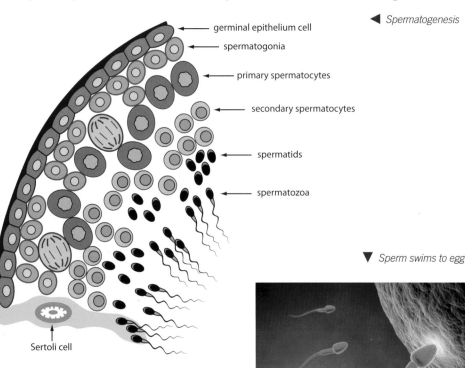

germinal epithelium cell
spermatogonia
primary spermatocytes
secondary spermatocytes
spermatids
spermatozoa

Sertoli cell

▼ Sperm swims to egg

▼ Spermatozoon

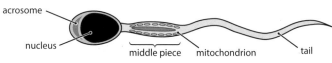

acrosome

nucleus

middle piece   mitochondrion   tail

Oogenesis

The process by which ova are produced in the ovary takes place as follows:

- Oogonia, which are formed before birth, undergo mitosis to form primary oocytes.

- The primary oocytes start to divide by meiosis but the process stops at prophase I.

- The germinal epithelium also divides to form follicle cells which surround the primary oocytes to form primary follicles.

- The primary oocytes do not mature until just before ovulation.

- At puberty, hormones stimulate the follicles to develop further. Each month several follicles start to develop but only one matures into a fully developed Graafian follicle.

- First the primary oocyte completes the first meiotic division to form the haploid secondary oocyte and a small polar body.

- The mature Graafian follicle migrates to the surface of the ovary where it bursts and the secondary oocyte is released, a process called ovulation.

- The secondary oocyte begins the secondary meiotic division but this is arrested at metaphase unless fertilisation takes place. On fertilisation this division is completed to form a large ovum and a second polar body. Once this division has taken place the nucleus of the ovum fuses with that of the sperm to form a zygote, which will then develop into an embryo.

- After ovulation the Graafian follicle becomes the *corpus luteum*. This produces hormones during pregnancy but regresses if fertilisation does not take place.

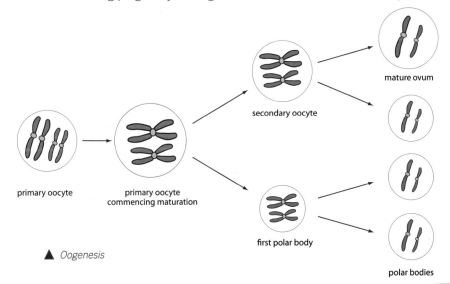

▲ *Oogenesis*

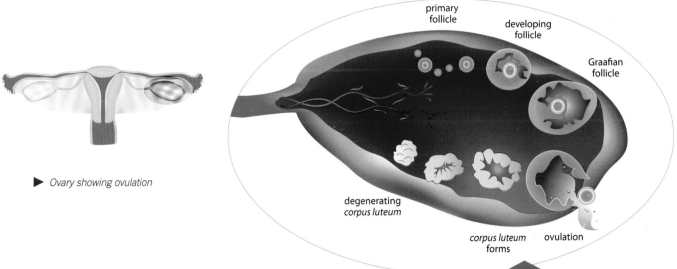

► *Ovary showing ovulation*

YOU SHOULD KNOW ›››

››› the process of fertilisation and the role of the acrosome

››› the process of implantation of the fertilised egg

››› the causes of sub-fertility

››› that pregnancy testing kits rely on a reaction between antibodies and a hormone in urine

››› the technique of IVF for aiding sub-fertility

▼ Study point

Internal fertilisation is an adaptation to life on land so that an organism becomes independent of water as the sperm is introduced directly into the female reproductive tract.

Examiner tip

Compare the transfer of the male nucleus to the ovum with the equivalent process that takes place in plant reproduction on page 107.

Sexual intercourse

So that fertilisation can take place the sperm travels in fluid called semen, from the seminiferous tubules to the oviduct of the female. Secretions from the seminal vesicles, Cowper's glands and the prostate gland, are added to the sperm to form semen. During sexual intercourse the penis is inserted into the vagina. Movements of the penis result in the ejaculation of semen into the vagina. The force of ejaculation is sufficient to propel some sperm through the cervix into the uterus, with the remainder being deposited at the top of the vagina. The sperm swim through the uterus into the oviducts by the lashing movements of their tails. However, from the several million deposited only a small number of sperm reach the site of fertilisation in the oviduct and surround the ovum.

Fertilisation and the acrosome reaction

Internal fertilisation ensures that the sperm are deposited in the female's reproductive tract. From here the sperm use their tails to swim through the cervix and up through the uterus to the oviduct. The sperm can remain viable for between 2 and 5 days. If ovulation has recently taken place, there will be a secondary oocyte in the oviduct. (The egg or ovum released from the Graafian follicle of the ovary dies within 24 hours unless fertilised.) The secondary oocyte is surrounded by the follicle cells and a clear membrane called the zona pellucida. Several hundred sperm surround the secondary oocyte but only one will penetrate it.

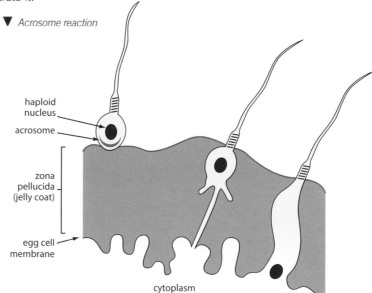

▼ *Acrosome reaction*

haploid nucleus

acrosome

zona pellucida (jelly coat)

egg cell membrane

cytoplasm

Sperm can fertilise an ovum only after a process called capacitation has taken place. This process takes several hours. It involves changes in the membrane covering the acrosome, a thin cap over the nucleus of the sperm.

When the sperm reach an oocyte, contact with the zona pellucida results in the acrosome membrane rupturing and protease enzymes are released. The enzymes digest the layers of cells surrounding the oocyte. Inversion of the acrosome results in a fine needle-like filament developing at the tip of the sperm and this pierces the already softened portion of the membrane. The whole process is called the acrosome reaction and it enables the sperm to penetrate the egg. This entry stimulates reactions of the oocyte that brings about the formation of the fertilisation membrane preventing the entry of further sperm. Entry of the sperm also stimulates the completion of the second meiotic division of the oocyte nucleus. The nuclei of the ovum and sperm are drawn together and fuse to form a diploid nucleus.

Implantation

After fertilisation, the ovum or zygote begins to divide by mitosis until a hollow ball of cells, the blastocyst, is produced. The development of the zygote continues during its passage down the Fallopian tube. After about three days the blastocyst reaches the uterus and embeds in the endometrium. This is called implantation.

Study point

You are not required to describe the development of the zygote further than the blastocyst stage.

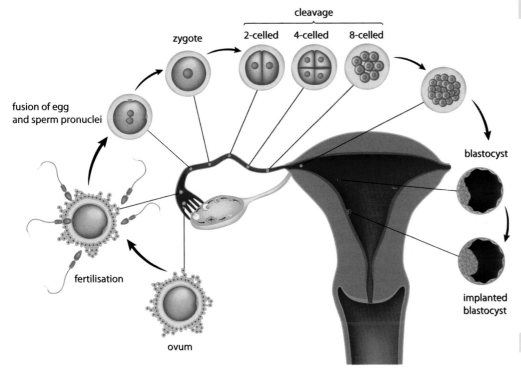

▲ *Ovulation to implantation*

The outer layer of the blastocyst is called the trophoblast. This layer develops into two membranes, the amnion and chorion, the latter of which grows a number of finger-like processes called chorionic villi. The villi increase the surface area for the absorption of nutrients from the wall of the uterus. The chorion also secretes a hormone called human chorionic gonadotropin (hCG) which prevents the degeneration of the *corpus luteum*. (This is a structure which develops from the Graafian follicle after the ovum has been released and is important in hormone production during the early stages of pregnancy.)

Detection of hCG in the urine is the basis of most pregnancy tests. The chorionic villi eventually form part of the placenta, which is attached to the foetus by the umbilical cord.

Study point

You are not required to describe the chorion and amnion membranes. They are described to introduce the hormone hCG, involved in pregnancy testing.

Sub-fertility

Sub-fertility is defined as difficulty in conceiving naturally for reasons affecting the male, female or both partners. Infertility is the complete inability to conceive a child. This is very rare.

There are two main causes of infertility:

- The failure to ovulate usually associated with absence of, or an irregular, menstrual cycle – 95% of cases are treatable with the use of a drug called clomiphene.

- A blockage of the Fallopian tubes. This prevents the passage of the ovum to the site of fertilisation in the Fallopian tubes. A blockage may be caused by infection, and treatment usually involves microsurgery.

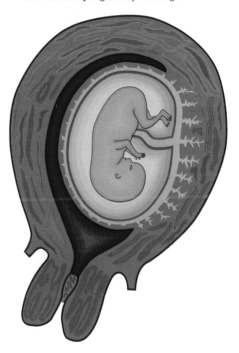

▲ *Uterus with foetus*

Pregnancy testing

Most pregnancy testing kits use **monoclonal antibodies** to test for the presence of the hormone, hCG, in urine. A monoclonal antibody is one that responds to only one foreign **antigen**. The monoclonal antibody used in the kits is specific to the hormone, hCG, which acts as an antigen.

Pregnancy testing kits involve the detection of hCG produced by the placenta during the early stages of pregnancy. The hormone is excreted in the urine and high levels act as a confirmation of pregnancy.

The test relies on the reaction between antibodies bound to coloured latex beads and hCG. It causes the hCG molecules to bind together and produce a colour change.

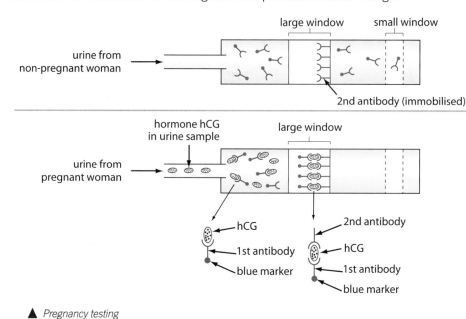

▲ Pregnancy testing

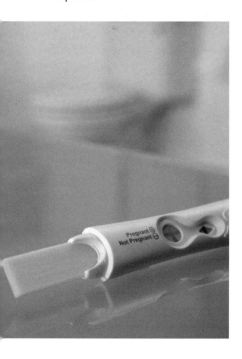

▲ Pregnancy testing kit

Link Cloning on page 140.

In vitro fertilisation (IVF)

Over the last 25 years there has been a tremendous increase in the number of couples seeking help to conceive a child. A couple are described as infertile if they have failed to conceive after 12 months. A couple seeking fertility treatment will first be assessed to try to discover the cause of the problem. Causes in the UK can be divided into three categories:

- 50% are the result of problems with the female's reproductive system.
- 35% are related to the male.
- 15% cannot be explained.

IVF is a technique which may be described as follows:

- Ovulation is stimulated using hormones at a specific dosage which aims to cause several follicles to develop at the same time.
- The oocytes are collected from the female using a tube inserted through the vagina and into the oviducts. Ultrasound is used to guide the tube.
- On the same day, the male's semen is collected and placed in liquid containing nutrients.
- Each oocyte is placed in a separate dish and about 100,000 sperm are added to each. (An alternate method involves injecting the sperm DNA into an oocyte.)
- Three days later the oocytes are examined to see which ones have been fertilised. Two are selected, to increase the chance that at least one will implant, and inserted into the uterus using a tube.

Human reproduction

1 Fill in the missing words in the gaps in the following passage. (8)

In the testis, sperm is produced in the .... tubules which are lined internally with the germinal epithelium, consisting mainly of cells called .... . These cells increase mitotically and some of them will differentiate into .... which undergo meiosis, each producing four haploid .... which then differentiate into mature sperm cells.

The sperm cells consist of a flagellum and a headpiece containing two prominent structures, the nucleus and the .... . Between the headpiece and the flagellum is a midpiece which is almost filled with .... . The germinal epithelium also contains the .... cells which nourish the developing sperm. Between the tubules are the interstitial cells which produce the male hormone, ...

WJEC B3 JUNE 2001

2 The drawing below shows a cross section through a seminiferous tubule.

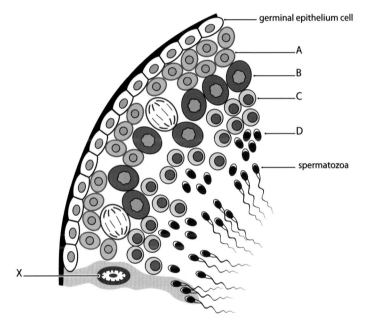

(a)(i) Label cells A–D. (2)

(ii) Name the cell labelled X in the diagram. (1)

(iii) What is the function of the cell labelled X? (1)

(b)(i) State the type of cell division involved in the production of cell A. (1)

(ii) Explain why there are more spermatozoa than cell type A in the tubule. (1)

WJEC BY5 JUNE 2011

3   The diagram shows the various stages of oogenesis in a section of the ovary.

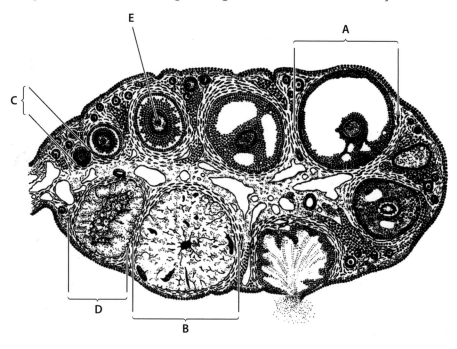

(a)   Name the stages labelled A, B and C. (3)

(b)   Explain why B changes in appearance to become D. (1)

(c)(i) State the ploidy of the cell labelled E. (1)

  (ii) Name one stage in the development of the male gamete which has the same ploidy. (1)

WJEC A2 JUNE 1999

4   The diagram shows the sequence of events which take place when the nucleus of a sperm enters the cytoplasm of an egg.

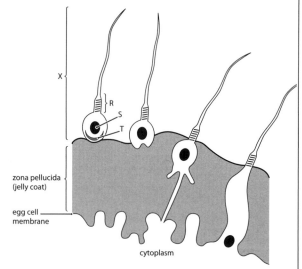

(a)   Name the part of the reproductive tract in which these events take place. (1)

(b)(i) Complete the table to show the names of R and S in the diagram, a structure found in each, and the function of these structures. (6)

	Name	Structure	Function
R			
S			

  (ii) Use the information in the diagram to explain the role of T in the process. (2)

WJEC B3 JAN 1997

BY5

Sexual reproduction in plants

The flowering plants or Angiosperms are the most successful of all terrestrial plants. The flower is the organ of reproduction and usually contains both male and female parts. In Angiosperms the female part, the ovule, is never exposed but is enclosed within a modified leaf, the carpel. A key feature of the success of flowering plants is their relationship with animals. Pollen grains have no power of independent movement and have to be transferred to the female part of the flower to ensure fertilisation. Flowering plants have evolved the strategy of attracting animals, particularly insects, to their flowers, feeding them and exploiting their mobility to transfer pollen from flower to flower. Some plants are pollinated by the action of wind.

By the end of this topic you should be able to:

- Describe the basic structure and functions of the parts of the flower.
- Compare an insect- and a wind-pollinated flower.
- Explain what is meant by pollination and describe how cross-pollination results in far greater genetic variation compared with self-pollination.
- Describe the process of double fertilisation in flowering plants.
- Describe the development of the fruit and seed.
- Describe the structure of the seed.
- Describe the requirements for germination and how food reserves are mobilised from the food store to the embryo plant.

YOU SHOULD KNOW ›››

››› the names of the parts of the flower and their functions

››› the meaning of the term pollination

››› the difference between self- and cross-pollination

››› the relative advantages and disadvantages of the two methods of pollination

››› the differences between insect- and wind-pollinated flowers

▼ **Study point**

The carpel is made up of three parts: the stigma, style and ovary.

Examiner tip
Be prepared to label a diagram of a flower and explain the function of its parts.

Flower structure

Structure of an insect-pollinated flower

Flowering plants are diploid, and meiosis takes place within the reproductive tissues to produce haploid reproductive structures or spores.

- Meiosis takes place in the anther to produce the male spores or pollen grains which contain haploid gametes.

- The female spores are the ovules, which are made in the ovary. The female gametes develop inside the ovule.

- Flowering plants must transfer the pollen grains from the male anther to the female part of a plant of the same species. This is called pollination. A pollen grain has a tough resistant wall to prevent it from drying out during this transfer. When the male and female gametes fuse it is called fertilisation. The fertilised ovule becomes the seed.

- The design of a flower is related to its method of pollination. Insect-pollinated flowers have, amongst other features, bright colours and a scent, whereas wind-pollinated flowers, such as grasses, tend to be green and have no scent.

The following describes the structure of a typical insect-pollinated flower. A flower is made up of four sets of modified leaves arranged from the outside to the centre:

- The outermost ring of structures is the sepals. They are usually green and protect the flower in bud.

- Inside the sepals is the ring of petals. These are brightly coloured to attract insects. They usually have a scent and may produce nectar, again to attract insects.

- Inside the petals are the male parts of the plant, the stamens. Each stamen consists of a long filament at the end of which are the anthers which produce pollen grains. As well as supporting the anther the filament contains vascular tissue, which transports food materials necessary for the formation of pollen grains. The anther is usually made up of four pollen sacs arranged in two pairs, side by side. When mature, the pollen sacs split to release the pollen.

- In the centre of the flower are one or more carpels. These are the female part of the flower. Each carpel is a closed structure inside which one or more ovules develop. The lower part of the carpel, which surrounds the ovules, is called the ovary and bears at its apex a stalk-like structure, the style. This ends in a receptive surface, the stigma.

▶ *Flower structure*

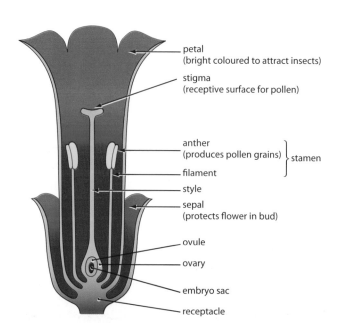

petal
(bright coloured to attract insects)

stigma
(receptive surface for pollen)

anther
(produces pollen grains) } stamen

filament

style

sepal
(protects flower in bud)

ovule

ovary

embryo sac

receptacle

Pollination

Pollination is the transfer of pollen grains from the anther to the stigma of a plant of the same species. Pollination is necessary so that the pollen grains, containing the male gametes, are brought into contact with the female part of the flower so that fertilisation can be achieved.

There are two types of pollination:

- Self-pollination. In some species self-pollination occurs and the pollen from the anthers of a flower need only be transferred to the stigma of the same flower or another flower on the same plant.

- Cross-pollination. In the majority of species cross-pollination occurs where pollen is transferred from the anthers of one flower to the stigma of another flower on another plant of the same species.

The genetic implications of self- and cross-pollination

Self-pollination results in inbreeding and a consequent reduction in the degree of variation in the population. There is also a greater chance of two undesirable recessive alleles being brought together at fertilisation. However, there are advantages to inbreeding because it can preserve good genomes which may be suited to a relatively stable environment.

Therefore the two forms of pollination have very different genetic consequences:

- Self-pollination leads to self-fertilisation, cross-pollination to cross-fertilisation.

- Self-fertilised species depend on random assortment and crossing over during meiosis, and on mutation to bring about variation in the genomes of male and female gametes.

- Self-fertilised species display less genetic variation than cross-fertilised species that are produced from gametes from two different individuals.

- Outbreeding is of greater evolutionary significance because in the struggle for survival some genomes are more successful than others.

Different flowering plant species employ a variety of methods to ensure that cross-pollination takes place. These include the stamen and stigma ripening at different times, being at different levels within the flower, or there may be separate male and female flowers.

Flowers are adapted for cross-pollination by either insects or wind

- In insect pollination, for example, bees feed on the sugary nectar using their long tongues to reach the nectar at the base of the female part of the flower. As the bee enters the flower, the anthers brush against the back of the bee leaving the sticky pollen behind. When the bee enters another flower, it brushes some of the pollen against the ripe stigma, and cross-pollination has taken place.

- In wind-pollinated flowers, such as grasses, the anthers hang outside the flower so that the wind can blow away the small, smooth and light pollen. The feathery stigmas hang outside the flowers and provide a large surface area for catching pollen grains that are blown into their path.

Table comparing insect- and wind-pollinated flowers

Insect-pollinated flowers	Wind-pollinated flowers
Colourful petals, scent and nectar	Small, green and inconspicuous, no scent, petals usually absent
Anthers within the flower	Anthers hanging outside the flower
Stigma within the flower	Large, feathery stigmas
Small quantities of sticky pollen	Large quantities of small, smooth, light pollen

9

Knowledge check

Link the appropriate terms 1–4 with the statements A–D.

1. Anther.
2. Petal.
3. Sepal.
4. Stigma.

A. Attracts insects.
B. Where pollen grains are produced.
C. The receptive surface for pollen.
D. Encloses and protects the flower in the bud.

▼ Study point

You are not required to know any details of the methods employed by plants to ensure that cross-pollination takes place.

▼ Honeybee pollinating a flower

▼ Grass flowers

YOU SHOULD KNOW »»

»» the structure of the pollen grain and ovule

»» the names of the nuclei in the pollen grain and pollen tube

»» the names of the three main nuclei in the embryo sac

Key Term

Dehiscence = to burst open releasing pollen grains.

▼ **Study point**

The gametes are the nuclei. In the male the nuclei are contained within the pollen grain. In the female the nuclei are contained within the ovule.

Examiner tip
Candidates often confuse pollination and fertilisation. Make sure you understand the difference.

▼ **Study point**

The ovule consists of the outer integuments surrounding an embryo sac containing the nuclei.

▼ **Study point**

It is not necessary to know the names of all eight nuclei. You need only know the female egg nucleus and the two polar nuclei.

Gamete development

Development of the male gamete

In the anther, diploid cells undergo meiosis to form haploid pollen grains. A pollen grain is surrounded by a tough wall that is resistant to desiccation. This enables pollen grains to be transferred from one flower to another without drying out.

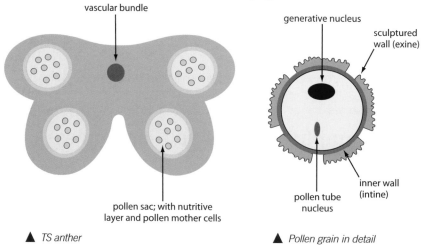

▲ *TS anther*　　　　　▲ *Pollen grain in detail*

Inside the pollen grain the haploid nucleus undergoes mitosis to produce two nuclei, a generative nucleus and a tube nucleus. The generative nucleus later gives rise to the two male nuclei.

When the pollen is mature, the outer layers of the anthers dry out and tensions are set up in lateral grooves. Eventually dehiscence occurs and the edges of the pollen sacs curl away exposing the pollen grains. In insect-pollinated flowers these will be carried to the stigma by insects such as bees.

Development of the female gamete

- The ovules are produced in the ovary with the female gamete or egg nucleus developing inside the ovule.

- In the ovule a mother cell undergoes meiosis to produce a haploid embryo sac, within which eight nuclei form by mitosis. The ovule is contained within the ovary.

▼ *Mature ovule within the carpel*

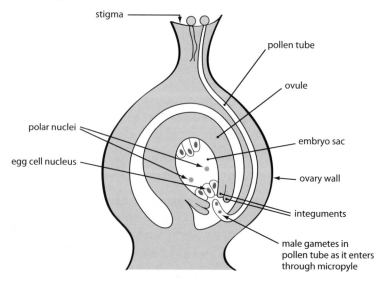

Fertilisation

This is the process where a male gamete fuses with a female gamete to produce a zygote. In flowering plants the ovule is protected within the ovary. The male gamete is the nucleus contained in the pollen grain and can only reach the female nucleus in the ovule by means of a pollen tube.

- When a compatible pollen grain lands on the stigma, the stigma produces a sugary solution in which the pollen grain germinates, producing a pollen tube.

- The pollen tube grows down the style. It secretes enzymes as it goes, digesting its way through the tissues of the style. It may also gain nutrients from the digested products.

- The pollen tube nucleus is positioned at the tip of the tube, with the two male nuclei, derived by mitosis from the generative nucleus in the pollen grain, close behind.

- The pollen tube grows through the gap between the integuments, called the micropyle and passes into the embryo sac.

- The pollen tube nucleus disintegrates presumably having completed its function of controlling the growth of the pollen tube.

- The tip of the pollen tube bursts open releasing the male gametes into the embryo sac and the two male nuclei enter.

- One of the male gametes fuses with the female nucleus to form a zygote.

- The other male gamete fuses with both polar nuclei to form a triploid endosperm nucleus.

- Thus, a double fertilisation occurs, a process unique to flowering plants.

Development of the fruit and seed

Following fertilisation, the development of the seed and fruit takes place. The seed develops from the fertilised ovule and contains an embryonic plant and a food store.

- The diploid zygote divides by mitosis to form the embryo, consisting of a plumule (developing shoot), a radicle (developing root) and one or two seed leaves or cotyledons.

- The triploid endosperm nucleus develops into a food store to provide reserves for the developing embryo.

- The integuments become the seed coat or testa.

- The ovule becomes the seed.

- The ovary becomes the fruit.

▼ *Broad bean fruit and seeds*

YOU SHOULD KNOW ›››

››› the role of enzymes in digesting a pathway for the pollen tube

››› the fusion of male and female nuclei in the process of double fertilisation

Examiner tip
In a given diagram be prepared to draw the pathway of growth of the pollen tube.

10

Knowledge check

Link the appropriate terms 1–4 with the statements A–D.

1. Micropyle.

2. Zygote.

3. Triploid endosperm nucleus.

4. Embryo sac.

A. Region which contains the female nucleus and polar nuclei.

B. The gap through which the pollen tube enters.

C. The result of the fusion of one of the male gametes and the female egg nucleus.

D. The result of the fusion between a male gamete and the polar nuclei.

Key Term

Dormancy = a period when active growth is suspended. Germination occurs when specific conditions are met.

▼ **Study point**

Flowering plants are divided into two main groups: monocotyledons and dicotyledons. The monocotyledons are important as they include cereals.

Knowledge check

Link the appropriate terms 1–5 with the statements A–E.

1. Ovary.
2. Ovule.
3. Integuments.
4. Triploid endosperm nucleus.
5. Embryo.

A. Becomes the seed.
B. Becomes the testa.
C. Develops into the fruit.
D. Develops from the zygote.
E. Becomes the food store.

Structure of the seed

The broad bean is classed as a dicotyledon, as it has two seed leaves or cotyledons, whereas the maize is classed as a monocotyledon, as it has only one cotyledon. In the broad bean the food store has been absorbed into the cotyledons but in the maize, typically of cereal grains, the food store surrounds the seed leaves.

▶ *Broad bean seed (Vicia faba).*

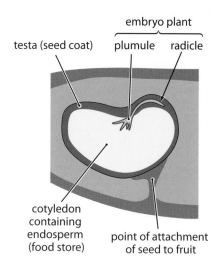

Germination of *Vicia faba*

After a period of **dormancy** and when environmental factors are favourable, stored food will be mobilised and the seed will germinate. The three main requirements for successful germination are:

- A suitable temperature – the optimum temperature for germination is the optimum for the enzymes involved in the process of germination. The temperature varies from species to species.
- Water – needed for the mobilisation of enzymes, vacuolation of cells and for transport.
- Oxygen – respiration releases energy, in the form of ATP, available for metabolism and growth.

▶ *Young seedling germinated*

▼ *Germination sequence*

Mobilisation of food reserves during germination

- Food reserves in seeds are insoluble in water and cannot as such be transported in the seedling.

- The reserves must be broken down into relatively simple soluble substances which dissolve in water and are then transported to the growing apices of the young shoot or plumule and the young root or radicle.

- Water is taken up rapidly by the seed in the initial stages, causing the tissues to swell as well as mobilising the enzymes.

- The seed coat ruptures as the radicle pushes its way through first. The radicle will grow downwards and the plumule upwards.

- The enzyme, amylase, hydrolyses starch into maltose; proteases convert proteins to amino acids. The soluble products are transported to growing points.

- During germination the cotyledons of the broad bean remain below ground.

- The plumule is bent over in the shape of a hook as it pushes its way up through the soil. This protects the tip from damage by soil abrasion.

- If the seed has been planted at the correct depth in the soil, when the plumule emerges it unfurls and begins to make food for itself by photosynthesis. By now the food reserves in the cotyledons will have been depleted.

The graph shows the changes in the dry mass of seeds as they are germinating. The dry mass of the endosperm, the embryo as it develops into a seedling, and the total for the seed are shown.

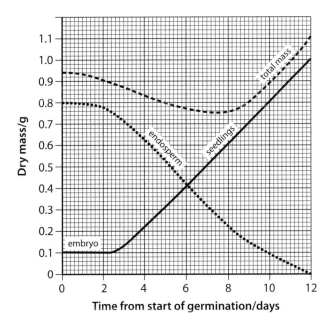

▶ Maize fruit (Zea mays)

Knowledge check

12

Identify the missing word or words.

The three main requirements for germination are water, a suitable temperature and ••••. Water is needed for the mobilisation of ••••. The young root or •••• grows first to provide anchorage and obtain water. The food store or •••• is hydrolysed by enzymes to supply soluble products for the growth of the embryo. The young shoot or •••• grows upwards through the soil and when above soil level makes food by the process of •••• as the food store has almost depleted.

Examiner tip

Be prepared to explain the relative changes in the dry mass of the embryo/seedling and endosperm.

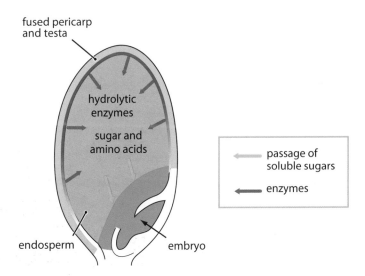

109

Sexual reproduction in plants

1   (a) Diagram 1 represents a section of a flower.   Diagram 2

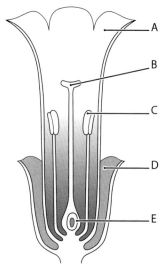

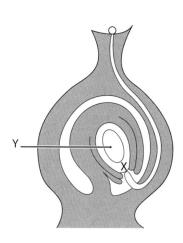

   (i) Name the parts of the flower labelled A–E. (5)

   (ii) State two features, shown in the diagram, which suggest that the flower is insect pollinated rather than wind pollinated. (2)

  (b)   Diagram 2 represents the female reproductive system of this flower.

   (i) Describe how the pollen tube passes through the tissues. (3)

   (ii) Name the region labelled X through which the pollen tube enters. (1)

   (iii) Name the structure Y shown in the diagram. (1)

   (iv) After fertilisation the structure will develop into the fruit and seed. Complete the table to describe which regions develop into the fruit, testa, endosperm and embryo plant. (4)

Fruit	
Testa	
Endosperm	
Embryo plant	

WJEC BI5 JUNE 2007

2   The diagram shows a germinating pollen grain.

  (a)   Name the structures labelled 1–4. (4)

  (b)   State precisely what happens to the structures labelled 3. (2)

  (c)   Name the term used to describe the events you have outlined in (b). (1)

  (d)   Apart from their role in the reproduction of plants, pollen grains may be directly or indirectly useful or disadvantageous. Give one example in each case. (2)

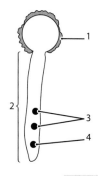

WJEC B3 JUNE 2001

3 The diagram shows the nuclei K to T present in the ovary of a pollinated flower, the diploid number of which is 12.

(a) Complete the table to show which of the nuclei K to R will fuse with S to T at fertilisation, the function of the fusion product and the number of chromosomes it will contain. (6)

Nucleus	Fuses with	Function of fusion product	Number of chromosomes in fusion product
S			
T			

(b) After fertilisation the structure labelled Z swells.

(i) Name the structure which is produced. (1)

(ii) Describe how this structure might help to ensure the survival of the species. (2)

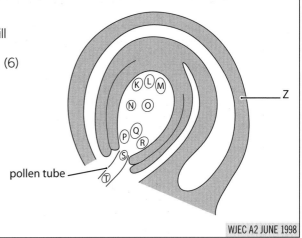

pollen tube

WJEC A2 JUNE 1998

4 (a) The graph shows the changes in the dry mass of seeds as they are germinating. The dry mass of the endosperm, the embryo as it develops into a seedling, and the total for the seed are shown.

Explain the relative changes in the dry mass of the embryo, seedling and endosperm. (4)

(b) The embryos were carefully removed from 40 seeds which were not germinating. The seeds were then divided into two equal groups and treated as follows:

Group A were soaked in water.

Group B were soaked in water to which embryos from germinating seeds had been added.

Petri dishes were prepared with agar jelly containing starch. The soaked seeds from both groups were then placed on the agar. After 24 hours, the seeds were removed and iodine solution was poured over the surface of the agar. The mean diameter of starch-free areas of agar was recorded for each group. The results are shown below.

	Mean diameter of starch-free area (mm)
Seeds soaked in water (group A)	4.4
Seeds soaked in water to which embryos from germinating seeds had been added (group B)	7.1

(i) Explain how the starch-free area of agar has been formed. (3)

(ii) Suggest an explanation for the difference in the results of the two groups of seeds. (1)

(c) The main food reserve in the broad bean seed is not the endosperm. Name the structures that store the food in this seed. (1)

WJEC BI5 JUNE 2003

BY5
Inheritance

Sexual reproduction introduces genetic variation amongst individuals in a population. If a species is to survive in a constantly changing environment and to colonise new habitats, sources of variation are essential.

As we saw in the previous topic it is meiosis which is the main source of introducing genetic variation. The various sources of variation help to bring about natural selection which has resulted in the vast range of species that inhabit Earth.

In order to study the way in which characteristics are passed from one generation to the next it is necessary to study the work of Gregor Mendel (1822–84). He was the first person to work out the ways in which genes are inherited. He formulated two laws which form the basis of the science of genetics. This was an amazing feat as scientists of the time had no knowledge of DNA, genes or chromosomes. His experiments involved using pea plants the characteristics of which are controlled by single genes which behave independently. More recent work has shown that there are exceptions to the rules set out by Mendel. These exceptions include co-dominance, linkage and sex linkage.

Genetic variation may also arise as a result of mutation, whereby completely new alleles arise. Mutations may occur naturally but the rate of occurrence increases when organisms are in contact with ionising radiation and mutagenic chemicals.

Topic contents

By the end of this topic you should be able to:
- Define genetic terms.
- State Mendel's laws of inheritance.
- Carry out monohybrid and dihybrid genetic crosses.
- Carry out a statistical test known as a Chi² test.
- Solve problems involving co-dominance and linkage.
- Describe haemophilia as an example of sex linkage.
- Describe gene mutations using sickle-cell anaemia as an example.
- Describe chromosome mutations using Down's syndrome as an example.
- Explain the importance of mutations as a source of variation.
- Explain the effect of ionising radiation and mutagens on mutations.

Genetic terms

- Genotype is the term that describes the genetic make-up of an organism. It also describes all the **alleles** that an organism contains.

- Phenotype is the observable characteristics of an organism.

- **Genes** have three main characteristics:
  - They can separate and combine.
  - They can mutate.
  - They code for the production of specific polypeptides.

- **Alleles** occupy a similar gene-position, or 'locus', on homologous chromosomes.

  If a gene determines a particular inherited characteristic, the alleles which make up the gene may exist in two forms. For example, in a gene which determines fur colour in mice, the two alternative alleles may be for black and white fur. 'Black' and 'white' are the two alleles for the 'fur colour' gene.

- For any one locus on a chromosome, there are theoretically three different allele combinations.
  - Heterozygous – having different alleles for a given gene, that is, a dominant allele and a recessive allele are present together. Each of these alleles is carried on a different chromosome within a pair of homologous chromosomes.
  - Homozygous dominant – having the same two dominant alleles present for a given gene.
  - Homozygous recessive – having the same two recessive alleles present for a given gene.

In the simplest situations, a particular characteristic is controlled by a single gene. If an organism is heterozygous for this gene, the dominant allele will determine the form in which the characteristic is actually expressed. The outcome (that is the phenotype) of a heterozygous condition (that is, the genotype) will therefore be the same as that for a homozygous dominant condition.

YOU SHOULD KNOW ›››

››› the difference between genes and alleles

››› how to carry out a genetic cross using a matrix

››› explain that the expected ratio of a dihybrid cross is 9:3:3:1

››› how to use the Chi^2 test to compare observed and expected results of a genetic cross

Key Terms

Allele = one of the different forms of a gene.

Gene = section of DNA on a chromosome coding for a particular polypeptide.

▼ **Study point**

An understanding of genetics depends on the way chromosomes behave during meiosis. Consider referring back to page 88 before starting this topic.

▼ *Summary of genetic terms*

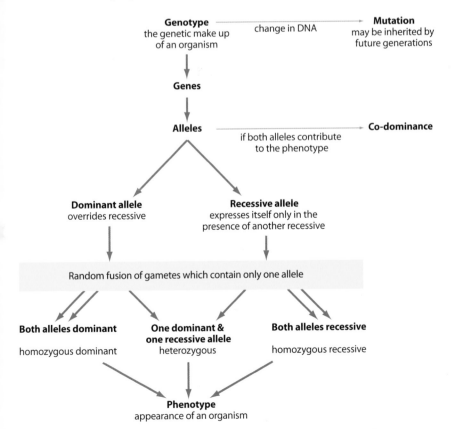

Genotype
the genetic make up of an organism
→ change in DNA →
Mutation
may be inherited by future generations

↓

Genes

↓

Alleles
if both alleles contribute to the phenotype →
Co-dominance

Dominant allele
overrides recessive

Recessive allele
expresses itself only in the presence of another recessive

Random fusion of gametes which contain only one allele

Both alleles dominant
homozygous dominant

One dominant & one recessive allele
heterozygous

Both alleles recessive
homozygous recessive

Phenotype
appearance of an organism

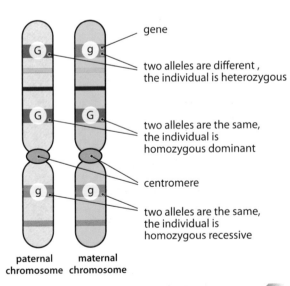

gene

two alleles are different , the individual is heterozygous

two alleles are the same, the individual is homozygous dominant

centromere

two alleles are the same, the individual is homozygous recessive

paternal chromosome   maternal chromosome

▲ *Genes and alleles*

Examiner tip
It is essential that you learn the definitions of these genetic terms.

Monohybrid inheritance

Monohybrid inheritance involves the inheritance of a single characteristic, such as plant height or seed texture. It concerns the inheritance of two alleles involving a single gene.

Mendel's early experiments were based on selecting pea plants of two varieties which showed clearly separable characteristics such as tall and dwarf plants or round and wrinkled seeds.

Consider the following cross involving tall and dwarf plants.

The gene for plant height has two alleles: Tall (T) and dwarf (t).

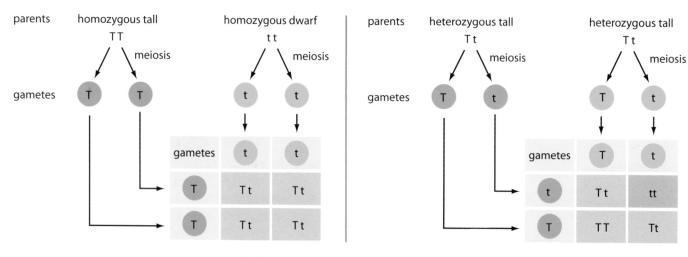

▲ *Monohybrid cross*

▼ **Study point**

In monohybrid crosses two heterozygous individuals will produce offspring with a phenotypic ratio of three dominant to one recessive.

Examiner tip

Once you have practised a number of crosses it is very easy to miss out stages or explanations. This may make your explanations impossible for others to follow. In an exam, even if you achieve the expected outcome, you may not gain full credit. So always carry out these instructions in their entirety.

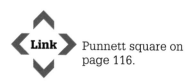

Link Punnett square on page 116.

As a result of carrying out his experiments, Mendel formulated his first law of inheritance, the law of segregation, which states that:

> *'The characteristics of an organism are determined by factors (alleles) which occur in pairs. Only one of a pair of factors (alleles) can be present in a single gamete.'*

Instructions for working out a genetic cross from data provided in a question.

1 Look carefully at the information. For example, regarding the phenotypes of the parents, and whether the parents are homozygous or heterozygous.

2 Choose suitable symbols for the alleles, unless they are provided in the question.

   a Choose a single letter to represent each characteristic.

   b Choose the first letter of one of the contrasting features.

   c If possible, choose a letter in which the higher and lower case forms differ in shape as well as size.

   d Let the higher case letter represent the dominant feature and the lower case letter the recessive one.

3 Represent the parents with the appropriate pairs of letters. Label them clearly as 'parents' and state their phenotypes.

4 State the gametes produced by each parent. Circle the gametes and label them clearly.

5 Use a matrix, called a Punnett square, to show the results of the random crossing of the gametes.

6 State the phenotype of each different genotype and indicate the ratio of each type.

7 Make sure that you have actually answered the question.

Test cross or backcross

This is a method used in genetics to determine whether a particular dominant characteristic observed in an organism is determined by one or two dominant alleles.

For example, a prize black bull bought at a market by a farmer would be expected to be pure-breeding, homozygous dominant (BB). It is not possible to tell this merely by the appearance of the bull. It could be a heterozygous bull (Bb). The phenotype is identical in both cases.

The backcross consists of crossing the bull with a known 'recessive' genotype, a white cow. (The double recessive phenotype has a known genotype because only one allele combination can produce it.)

If the resulting offspring are all black then the bull is pure breeding or homozygous. If the resulting offspring include both white and black forms then the bull was heterozygous.

Dihybrid inheritance

This involves the inheritance of two separate genes. Mendel knew from his early experiments with monohybrid crosses that round seed shape was dominant to wrinkled, and that yellow colour was dominant to green. He used plants which differed by having two pairs of contrasting characters. He carried out the genetic cross as follows.

- Homozygous plants with the two dominant characters, round and yellow seeds were crossed with homozygous plants with the two recessive characters wrinkled and green seeds.
- He found that all the F1 generation had round, yellow seeds.
- When plants grown from these seeds were self-pollinated the seeds produced were of four different types of shape and colour of seed coat.
- He collected and counted the seeds and found there were four types as shown in the table.

Characteristic	Round, yellow	Round, green	Wrinkled, yellow	Wrinkled, green
Totals	315	108	101	32

Each total can be divided by the double recessive total to give an approximate whole number ratio between the phenotypes. The four totals in the table are in the ratio of 9:3:3:1, proportions now known as the dihybrid ratio.

This led Mendel to formulate his second law, which states that:

'Either one of a pair of contrasted characters may combine with either of another pair.'

With our present knowledge of genetics this statement can be rewritten as:

'Each member of an allelic pair may combine randomly with either of another pair.'

The genetic cross for Mendel's experiment may be represented as follows in the form of a Punnet square:

parental phenotypes	pure-breeding round yellow	pure-breeding wrinkled green
parental genotypes (2n)	**RRYY**	**rryy**
gametes (n)	all **RY**	all **ry**
F1 genotype (2n)	all **RrYy**	
F2 parental genotype	**RrYy**	**RrYy**
gametes (n)	**RY Ry rY ry**	**RY Ry rY ry**

R represents round seed (dominant)   **r** represents wrinkled (recessive)
Y represents yellow seed (dominant)   **y** represents green seed (recessive)

♀ \ ♂	**RY**	**Ry**	**rY**	**ry**
RY	**RRYY** round yellow	**RRyY** round yellow	**rRYY** round yellow	**rRyY** round yellow
Ry	**RRYy** round yellow	**RRyy** round green	**rRYy** round yellow	**rRyy** round green
rY	**RrYY** round yellow	**RryY** round yellow	**rrYY** wrinkled yellow	**rryY** wrinkled yellow
ry	**RrYy** round yellow	**Rryy** round green	**rrYy** wrinkled yellow	**rryy** wrinkled green

F2 genotypes (2n) and phenotypes   **9** round yellow   **3** wrinkled yellow
    3 round green   **1** wrinkled green

Link Continuous and discontinuous variation are encountered on page 128.

Continuous and discontinuous variation are encountered on page 128.

▼ Study point

The description of probability is to aid your understanding that the results of conventional genetic crosses are due to chance. You would not be required to reproduce this description in a theory exam.

▼ Study point

In a genetic cross between two heterozygous parents resulting in 96 offspring the probability of the number of double recessive offspring, wrinkled and green is six. This is obtained by dividing 96 by 16.

◄ *Genetic cross*

Mendel was fortunate in his choice of pea plant characters because these particular characters are controlled by single genes. Pea plants are either tall or dwarf, flower colours are clear-cut and easy to tell apart. This is an example of discontinuous variation. However, most characters are controlled by a number of genes, for instance height in humans. People are not just tall or short but show a range of heights. This is an example of continuous variation.

Probability

The presentation of a breeding experiment is a prediction of the likely outcome. What is actually observed may not agree precisely with the prediction. Consider the situation where a coin is tossed 100 times. It would be expected to land heads on 50 occasions and tails on 50 occasions. In practice it would be unusual to obtain this result in the first 100 attempts. If the coin lands 60 heads (H) and 40 tails (T) is this due to a chance deviation from the expected result or is the coin biased in some way?

If two unbiased coins are tossed there are four possible combinations:

    HH or HT or TH or TT

- Rule of addition:

Consider one of the coins. When this is tossed it is certain to give either H or T. Thus the probability of getting either one result or another result is obtained by *adding* their independent probabilities. The probability of getting H is ½ and the probability of getting T is also ½.

Thus the probability of getting one or the other is
    ½ + ½ = 1 or 100% certainty

- Rule of multiplication:

Now consider both coins. The probability that there will be H on both the first and the second coin is obtained by multiplying the two independent probabilities. In this case the probability of getting H on the first coin is ½, and the probability of getting H on the second coin is also ½.

Thus the probability of HH is
    ½ × ½ = ¼

The result of your Punnett square for a monohybrid cross shows a 3:1 ratio in the appearance of dominant and recessive F2 phenotypes. This can be used to calculate the probability of the cross when the four alleles, round, green, yellow and wrinkled are involved.

- the probability of the four alleles appearing in any of the F2 offspring is:
    round (dominant) ¾   yellow (dominant) ¾
    wrinkled (recessive) ¼   green (recessive) ¼

- The probability of combinations of alleles appearing in the F2 is as follows:
  – round and yellow = ¾ × ¾ = 9/16
  – round and green = ¾ × ¼ = 3/16
  – wrinkled and yellow = ¼ × ¾ = 3/16
  – wrinkled and green = ¼ × ¼ = 1/16

A statistical test – Chi²

The expected ratio of phenotypes in the offspring of a dihybrid cross is 9:3:3:1. This ratio represents the probability of getting these phenotypes. It would be surprising if the numbers came out exactly in this ratio. So how close do the observed results have to be to the expected, and have the differences between them happened by chance, or are they so different that something unexpected is taking place? To answer this question scientists use a statistical test called the Chi-squared test.

Consider the following F2 results obtained from the cross between plants with round, yellow seeds and those with wrinkled, green seeds described on page 116.

Characteristic	Round, yellow	Round, green	Wrinkled, yellow	Wrinkled, green
Totals	315	108	101	32

Statisticians carry out the following procedure:

4. Calculate the expected values (E).
5. This is the total number of seeds divided by the number of possible types, for example, for round, yellow seeds $\frac{556 \times 9}{16} = 312.75$
6. Calculate the differences between the observed (O) and expected (E) results.
7. Square the differences.
8. Use the formula $= \Sigma \frac{(O-E)^2}{E}$

Complete the table.

Phenotype	Observed (O)	Expected (E)	Difference (O–E)	$(O-E)^2$	$\frac{(O-E)^2}{E}$
Round, yellow	315	313	2	4	0.01
Round, green	108	104	4	16	0.15
Wrinkled, yellow	101	104	−3	9	0.08
Wrinkled, green	32	35	−3	9	0.26

Total the values in the last column.

$$0.01 + 0.15 + 0.08 + 0.26 = 0.50$$

Work out the degrees of freedom. This is a measure of the spread of the data.

It is always one less than the number of classes of data. In the example there are four different phenotype combinations, so there are three degrees of freedom.

To find out if this value is significant or non-significant it is necessary to use a Chi² table.

Number of classes	Degrees of freedom	Chi²			
		Probability that deviation is due to chance alone			
		0.99(99%)	0.50 (50%)	0.10 (10%)	0.05 (5%)
2	1	0.00	0.45	2.71	3.84
3	2	0.02	1.39	4.61	5.99
4	3	0.12	2.37	6.25	7.82
5	4	0.30	3.36	7.78	9.49

Statisticians consider that if the probability is greater than 5% the deviation is said to be non-significant. In other words, the deviation is due to chance alone. If χ^2 is equivalent to a probability value of less than the 5% level, the deviation is said to be significant. That is, some factor other than chance is influencing the results.

Looking along the row for three degrees of freedom it can be seen that the Chi² value of 0.50 lies between 2.37 and 0.12 which is equivalent to a probability between 0.50 (50%) and 0.99 (99%). This means that the deviation from the 9:3:3:1 ratio is non-significant and is simply the result of statistical chance.

Study point

This is the only statistical test you are required to use at A2 level.

Examiner tip

Try out the statistical test by making up your own expected results, work out the Chi² and discover whether your results are significant or non-significant.

Study point

The figures have been rounded for ease of calculation.

Study point

The degree of freedom is simply one less than the number of classes of data. In a dihybrid cross there are four categories of data. Therefore the degree of freedom is 4–1 = 3.

Study point

In Biology if the significance is at or below the 5% level then the result is said to be significant. A useful phrase to use is 'The result is significant at the 5% level and something other than chance is affecting the result'.

Co-dominance

Not all characteristics are controlled by a single gene which behaves independently, as observed in Mendel's experiments. One example is co-dominance. Instead of one allele being dominant and the other recessive, both alleles are dominant, that is, the alleles express themselves equally in the phenotype.

In most cases the heterozygote shows a phenotype intermediate between those of the two homozygotes. Examples of co-dominance are:

- Shorthorn cattle have the genotypes and phenotypes RR (red), RW (roan) and WW (white) coat colour.

- AB blood groups

- Snapdragon plants which have the homozygous genotypes RR and WW produce red or white flowers. One allele codes for an enzyme that catalyses the formation of red pigment in flowers. The other allele codes for an altered enzyme, which lacks this catalytic activity and so does not produce the pigment. However, if the two homozygous plants are crossed, the offspring are pink. That is, the two parents produce an intermediate offspring.

▼ **Study point**

In co-dominance both alleles at a locus on a chromosome are equally dominant.

▼ **Study point**

You are not expected to memorise examples of co-dominance. In an exam question you will be told that co-dominance is involved.

▼ **Study point**

Snapdragons show incomplete dominance, i.e. the phenotype of the heterozygote is a blend of the two homozygotes.

▲ Snapdragon flowers

The genetic diagram for these crosses is the same as that illustrating Mendel's first law but in the F1 all individuals have the intermediate phenotype.

There are two methods of representing the letters of the genotype:

	Method 1		Method 2	
Parental phenotypes	red flowers	× white flowers	red flowers	× white flowers
Parental genotypes	RR	WW	$C^R C^R$	$C^W C^W$
Gametes	R	W	C^R	C^W
F1 genotype		RW		$C^R C^W$
F1 phenotype			All pink	

14

Knowledge check

Identify the missing word.

Each gene has two different forms called alleles. If the two alleles on a homologous pair of chromosomes are the same they are said to be ••••, but if they are different they are said to be ••••. When the effect of an allele is not apparent on the phenotype when paired with a dominant allele, it is said to be ••••. When two alleles both contribute equally to the phenotype they are said to be ••••.

Sex determination

Humans have 46 chromosomes arranged in 23 pairs. The first 22 pairs are the autosomes; the last pair are the sex chromosomes.

Human chromosomes (a total of 46)

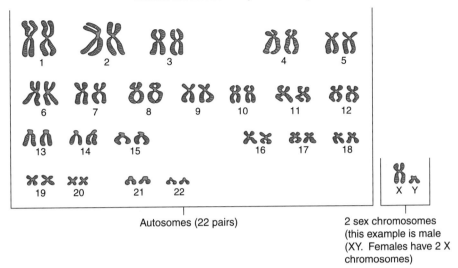

Autosomes (22 pairs)

2 sex chromosomes (this example is male (XY. Females have 2 X chromosomes)

▲ *Human chromosomes*

- In humans the male has a dissimilar pair of sex chromosomes, called X and Y, whilst the female has a pair of two similar X chromosomes.
- All the female's eggs contain an X chromosome.
- Half the male's sperm contains an X chromosome and the other half contains a Y chromosome.
- At fertilisation the egg may join with either an X-carrying sperm or a Y-carrying sperm. This gives an equal chance of the child being a boy or a girl.

Parental phenotype: male   female

Parental genotypes: XY   XX

Gametes: XY   X

		Male gametes	
		X	Y
Female	X	XX	XY
gametes	X	XX	XY

Offspring phenotypes: 50% male 50% female

Study point

As the X chromosome is much longer than the Y chromosome, for most of the length of the former there is no equivalent portion of the Y chromosome.

Sex linkage

Some alleles are carried on the X chromosome and are described as sex linked.

- The Y chromosome is much smaller than the X and carries very few alleles. Therefore in the male any recessive alleles carried on the X chromosome will express themselves in the phenotype. This is because they are unpaired and so there is no dominant gene present. This special form of inheritance is known as sex linkage, an important feature of which is that the male cannot hand on the allele to his sons as they must receive the Y chromosome to become male. On the other hand, all his daughters must receive the recessive allele from him. Females who are heterozygous for sex-linked recessive traits are known as carriers and have a 50% chance of handing on the recessive allele to their sons.

Key Term

Carrier = an individual with one normal allele and one potential harmful recessive allele. The individual is phenotypically normal.

▼ **Study point**

The males have a Y chromosome and this could only have been inherited from their fathers. Their X chromosome must therefore have come from their mothers.

▼ **Study point**

Haemophilia is no longer present in the royal family, as King Edward VII, the son of Queen Victoria, from whom they are descended, did not have or carry the alleles for haemophilia. (The mutation presumably appeared in Victoria or one of her immediate female ancestors.)

Haemophilia is caused by a recessive allele on the X chromosome. The gene that codes for Factor VIII, an important protein involved in blood clotting, is a sex-linked gene located on the X chromosome.

- Haemophilia is a potentially lethal condition. It is the result of an individual being unable to produce one of the many clotting factors. The inability of the blood to clot leads to slow and persistent bleeding.

- It is now possible to extract the particular clotting factor from donated blood allowing haemophiliacs to lead near-normal lives. (Although the risk of passing the disease on to their children remains.)

- This condition occurs almost exclusively in males.

- When the recessive allele occurs in males it expresses itself because the Y chromosome cannot carry any corresponding dominant allele.

- For the condition to arise in females it requires the double recessive state and as the recessive allele is relatively rare in the population, this is unlikely to occur.

- To obtain an affected female, the father must be affected and the mother either affected or a **carrier**.

If **H** is the allele for normal blood clotting, h is the allele for haemophilia. The possible genotypes are:

$X^H X^H$ female, normal

$X^H X^h$ female carrier

$X^h X^h$ female haemophiliac

$X^H Y$ male, normal

$X^h Y$ male, haemophiliac

Consider a cross between a normal female and a haemophiliac male.

Parental genotypes: $X^H X^H$ × $X^h Y$

Gametes: X^H × $X^h Y$

		Male gametes	
		X^h	Y
Female	X^H	$X^H X^h$	$X^H Y$
gametes	X^H	$X^H X^h$	$X^H Y$

Offspring phenotypes: 50% carrier females
50% normal males

Family pedigree charts are sometimes used to trace the inheritance of sex-linked conditions such as haemophilia.

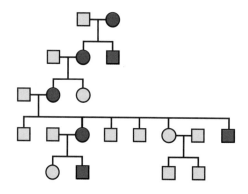

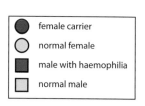

- ● female carrier
- ○ normal female
- ■ male with haemophilia
- □ normal male

Linkage

Linkage occurs when two different genes are found on the same chromosome. They are inherited together, and pass into the gametes together. At fertilisation the linked genes then pass into the offspring together.

The crosses and ratios considered so far have involved two pairs of contrasting characters found on *different* chromosomes. Crosses involving linkage do not follow the typical Mendelian pattern and consequently Mendelian ratios will not be obtained.

Recombination takes place when alleles are exchanged between homologous chromosomes as a result of crossing over. The further apart two genes are on a chromosome, the more chance there is of crossing over taking place.

genes A + B are linked since they are on the same chromosome

parents   AaBb × aabb

some crossing over will occur here and B and b are exchanged

non-cross overs   cross overs

linked genes pass into the same gamete

gametes

F1

no crossing over — parental types   crossing over — recombinants

▲ *Crossing over*

In meiosis, linked genes are passed on together to the gametes so that most of the F2 progeny inherit the characteristics determined by the linked genes. When crossing over occurs, an opportunity is provided for linked genes to be separated and give rise to recombinants. However, crossing over may take place in only a small proportion of the cells undergoing meiosis, between 5 and 10%. Therefore few of the gametes will contain recombinant genes.

▼ **Study point**

Most gene mutations rarely show up in the phenotype as they are recessive.

▼ **Study point**

Bacteria are widely used in experiments as they have a short life cycle and a greater rate of mutation.

▼ **Study point**

Although mutations occur randomly, they occur with a set frequency. The rate varies from species to species but is typically one mutation per 100,000 genes per generation.

Examiner tip
You are not expected to know about the different forms of gene mutation.

Mutations

A mutation is a change in the amount, arrangement or structure in the DNA of an organism:

- It may affect a single gene or a whole chromosome.
- Most mutations occur in somatic (body) cells.
- Only those mutations which occur in the formation of gametes can be inherited.
- Mutations are spontaneous random events which may provide a source of material for natural selection pressures and therefore evolution.
- Mutation rates are normally very small, therefore mutation has less impact on evolution than other sources of variation.
- In general, organisms with short life cycles and more frequent meiosis show a greater rate of mutation.
- The rate of mutations occurring can be increased by ionising radiation and mutagenic chemicals.

Mutations can happen in two ways:

1. DNA is not copied properly before cell division.
   - Sometimes mistakes are made in the copying process so that new chromosomes are faulty.
   - Usually they are small errors, involving only one gene, so they are called gene mutations or point mutations.

2. Chromosomes are damaged and break.
   - If chromosomes break they will normally repair themselves (the DNA will rejoin) but they may not repair themselves correctly. This can lead to large changes in the structure of the DNA and may affect a large number of genes. These are called chromosome mutations.

Gene mutations

A change in the structure of a DNA molecule, producing a different allele of a gene, is a gene mutation. Any gene can mutate but rates vary from one gene to another within an organism. Gene mutations are changes in the base pairs within the genes. They can take the form of duplication, insertion, deletion, inversion or substitution of bases. Whatever the change, the result is the formation of a modified polypeptide.

How can mutations cause a change in the phenotype?

During protein synthesis the sequence of DNA triplets of bases is transcribed into the mRNA codons and is then translated into a sequence of amino acids that make up a polypeptide. A single change in one of the bases in the DNA could result in a change in the amino acid sequence of the polypeptide. The sequence of events may be described as follows:

- The genetic code, which ultimately determines an organism's characteristics, is made up of a specific sequence of nucleotides on the DNA molecule.
- Any change to one or more of these nucleotides, or any rearrangement of the sequence, will produce a different sequence of amino acids in the protein it makes as translation machinery is still acting correctly.
- The protein made is often an enzyme which may then be unable to catalyse a specific reaction. For example, a specific enzyme is necessary to convert a chemical precursor into the skin pigment, melanin. If a gene mutation results in the inability to produce this enzyme, the organism will lack a pigment. The organism is referred to as an albino.

Sickle-cell anaemia

A gene mutation (substitution) in the gene producing haemoglobin results in a defect called sickle-cell anaemia. The replacement of just one base in the DNA molecule results in a different amino acid being incorporated into two of the polypeptide chains which make up the haemoglobin molecule. The abnormal haemoglobin causes red blood cells to become sickle-shaped. These abnormal shaped red blood cells are less able to carry oxygen, resulting in anaemia and possible death. Haemoglobin S is produced instead of normal haemoglobin by a single base chain that causes valine to be substituted for glutamic acid at the sixth position in the β globulin chain. DNA codes for glutamic acid are CTT or CTC. Two of the codes for valine are CAT and CAC. In either case the substitution of A for T as the second base would bring about the formation of haemoglobin S.

The mutant allele is co-dominant. In the homozygous state the individual suffers the disease but in the heterozygous state the individual has 30–40% sickle cells, the rest are normal. The heterozygous condition is referred to as sickle-cell trait.

▼ *Normal and sickle-cell red blood cells*

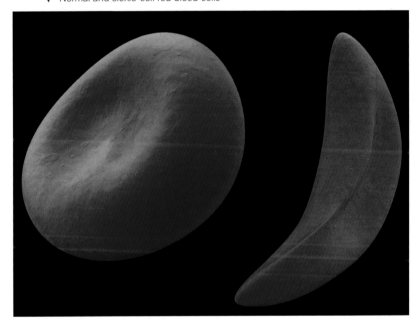

Chromosome mutations

These are mutations that cause changes in the structure or number of whole chromosomes in cells. They are most likely to occur during meiosis, when the process can go wrong as the paired chromosomes line up on the crowded equator at metaphase I and are pulled apart in anaphase I. Errors can result in the chromosomes not being shared equally between the daughter cells.

Changes in structure

During prophase I of meiosis, homologous chromosomes pair up and exchange of material takes place at chiasmata. Errors arise when chromosomes rejoin with the corresponding pieces of chromosome on its homologous partner. Often the homologous chromosomes end up with a different gene sequence. This makes it impossible for pairing up in meiosis to take place.

Key Terms

Non-disjunction = a faulty cell division where one of the cells receives two copies of a chromosome while the other gets none.

Polyploidy = an increase in the number of complete sets of chromosomes.

▼ Study point

Down's syndrome occurs in approximately one in 700 births. The incidence of the mutation is related to the age of the mother; a result of the higher chance of mutation occurring during the formation of oocytes in older ovaries.

Changes in numbers

Non-disjunction is a process in which faulty cell division means that one of the daughter cells receives two copies of a chromosome while the other gets none. In Down's syndrome, chromosome number 21 is affected. If this happens in an ovary, it results in an oocyte with either no chromosome 21 or with two copies instead of one. Oocytes with no chromosome 21 die but those with two copies survive and may be fertilised. The resulting zygote has three chromosome 21s with a total of 47 chromosomes. This condition is known as trisomy 21 and the zygote will develop into a child with Down's syndrome.

▼ *Chromosomes of Down's syndrome*

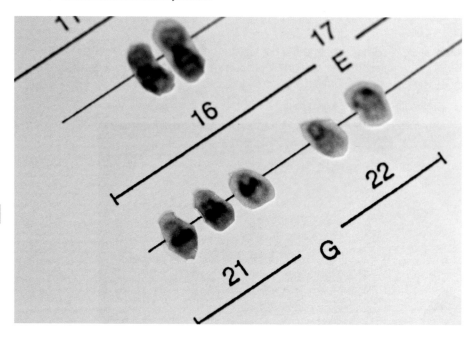

Changes in sets of chromosomes

Occasionally a mutation can affect whole sets of chromosomes. This is known as **polyploidy**.

A defect in meiosis may result in a gamete receiving two sets of chromosomes. When this diploid gamete is fertilised by a normal haploid gamete the zygote will be triploid, that is, having three sets of chromosomes. If two diploid gametes fuse then a tetraploid will be produced. Tetraploidy may also happen after fertilisation if, during mitosis, the two sets of chromosomes double but fail to separate.

Polyploidy is common in flowering plants and is associated with beneficial characteristics, such as disease resistance. Tomatoes and wheat are polyploids. Triploids are usually sterile as they cannot form homologous pairs.

Mutagens and the mutation rate

Mutations happen naturally. However, scientists have found that the mutation rate is increased if organisms are exposed to mutagens. These are factors in the environment which include:

- X-rays, gamma radiation and UV light.
- Chemicals, such as polycyclic hydrocarbons in cigarette smoke.

Carcinogens

Any agent that causes cancer is called a carcinogen and is described as carcinogenic. Some mutagens are carcinogenic.

Carcinogens affect the DNA in cells, resulting in mutations. Mutations that occur in body or somatic cells often have no effect on an organism. Most mutated cells are recognised as foreign by the body's immune system and are destroyed.

Occasionally the mutation may affect the regulation of cell division. Cancers are thought to start when changes take place in these genes. If a cell with such a mutation escapes the attack of the immune system, it can produce a collection of cells called a tumour. Tumours are usually harmless or benign but sometimes the tumour cells are able to spread around the body and invade other tissues. This type of tumour is described as malignant and the diseases caused by such tumours are cancers.

Tobacco smoke contains a number of harmful chemicals that affect human health. These include tar, nicotine and carbon monoxide. Tar is a mixture of many toxic chemicals. It collects in the lungs as the tobacco smoke cools. Tar contains carcinogens which affect the DNA in the cells of the alveoli.

About 25% of all cancer deaths in developed countries are due to carcinogens in the tar of tobacco smoke.

Oncogenes

Most cells need to divide to ensure dead or worn out cells are replaced. Normally, genes control cell division, and division is halted when sufficient cells have been produced for growth and repair. The interaction of two types of genes, proto-oncogenes and tumour suppressor genes, is involved in this process.

Proto-oncogenes stimulate cell division whereas tumour suppressor genes slow down cell division. A gene mutation can cause proto-oncogenes to mutate into **oncogenes** resulting in cells dividing too rapidly and a tumour or cancer may develop. Similarly, carcinogens, for example, in tobacco smoke, can cause these genes to mutate, so that they do not carry out their normal function of suppressing cell division. This leads to uncontrolled cell division resulting in the formation of tumours.

Why are mutations important?

Mutations are important because they increase variation in a population. Most mutations are harmful to the organism concerned. Beneficial mutations are very rare but they may give a **selective advantage** to an organism.

- If a mutation is in a body cell, it may cause cancer. For example, increased exposure to UV light is linked to skin cancer.

- If the mutation is in a gamete, it will not affect the individual producing the gamete, but will affect the zygote that develops from it, that is, the offspring.

- These mutations cause sudden and distinct differences between individuals. They are therefore the basis of discontinuous variation.

- There are potential advantages from mutations that are beneficial and may increase variation. However, most mutations are recessive to the normal allele. A recessive mutant allele must await replication in the gene pool over many generations before chance brings recessive alleles together, resulting in their expression.

Key Terms

Oncogene = a mutated gene that causes cancer.

Selective advantage = characteristic of an organism that enables it to survive and reproduce better than other organisms in a population in a given environment.

▼ Study point

Mutations occurring during gamete formation may be inherited and may result in distinct differences. These are the basis of discontinuous variation.

15 Knowledge check

Link the appropriate terms 1–4 with the statements A–D.

1. Carcinogen.
2. Sickle-cell anaemia.
3. Non-disjunction.
4. Down's syndrome.

A. A gene mutation.
B. Substances that cause cancer.
C. A chromosome mutation.
D. Chromosomes shared unequally between daughter cells.

Examiner tip

Mutations arise spontaneously during DNA replication.
It is incorrect to say that mutagens cause mutations. Increased exposure to mutagens increases the *rate* of mutations occurring.

Inheritance

1 (a) State what is meant by the term 'allele'. (1)

(b) Colouration in cockatiels is determined by a number of different genes.

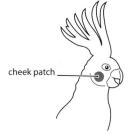

cheek patch

(i) One gene determines the presence or absence of red cheek patches as shown in the diagram.

The allele for red cheek patches R is dominant to that for no cheek patches r. Show how two birds with red cheek patches could produce offspring with no cheek patches. (3)

(ii) Another gene determines the main colour of the feathers covering the body of cockatiels. Its alleles show co-dominance. One allele produces silver colouration S while the other produces grey colouration G. Heterozygous birds are silvery-grey. Use a suitable genetic diagram to show the result of crossing a heterozygous bird with a grey bird. (4)

(iii) Using the information given in (i) and (ii) state the gene type of a silver bird with no cheek patches. (1)

(c) Another gene determines the presence of feathers with a dark edge. This gene is sex-linked and the dark edge is caused by a recessive allele **e**. In birds, unlike humans, the male **XX** has two sex chromosomes that are the same length and each one is, therefore, able to carry the allele. The female **XY** has one shorter sex chromosome that cannot carry this allele.

Using this information and your own knowledge, state all the possible gene types of each of the following birds: (3)

(i) female with dark edged feathers

(ii) male with dark edged feathers

(iii) male with plain feathers

(d) Pigments that produce different coloured feathers are proteins. Explain how different alleles can give rise to the synthesis of different pigments. (3)

WJEC BI5 JUNE 2003

---

2 Duchenne muscular dystrophy (DMD) is a degenerative muscular disease. It is caused by a sex-linked recessive allele. A family pedigree showing inheritance is shown on the right.

(a) Explain fully what is meant by the term sex-linked recessive allele. (3)

(b) Use the key below to answer the following questions.

Key X^N normal allele
X^n muscular dystrophy allele
Y male chromosome

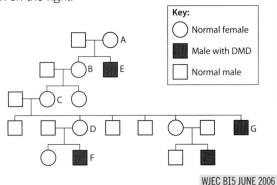

Key:
◯ Normal female
■ Male with DMD
☐ Normal male

(i) State the probable genotype of A, B, C and D. (1)

(ii) State the genotype of E, F and G. (1)

(iii) State the genotype of all the normal males. (1)

WJEC BI5 JUNE 2006

---

3 A maize plant homozygous for smooth, coloured grain was cross-pollinated with a plant homozygous for wrinkled, colourless grain. The F1 plants all produced smooth, coloured grain. On cross-pollinating the F1 plants, it was found that most of the F2 generation resembled the original plants, 73% producing smooth, coloured grain and 22% producing wrinkled, colourless grain.

(a) Which of the characteristics described above are dominant and which are recessive? (2)

(b) What else can be deduced about the alleles for texture and colour of the grains? (1)

(c)(i) State the probable phenotypes of the remaining 5% F2 plants **not** described above. (1)

(ii) Suggest how these phenotypes arose. (1)

(d) Using appropriate symbols to represent the alleles, give the genotype of an:

(i) F1 plant. (1)

(ii) F2 plant you described in (b). (1)

WJEC BY5 JUNE 2012

BY5 Variation and evolution

In the long term, if a species is to survive in a constantly changing environment and to colonise new environments, sources of variation are essential. The genotype of an organism gives it the potential to show a particular characteristic. Most characters are controlled by a number of genes and the differences in the character are not clear-cut. The degree to which the characteristic is shown is also affected by the organism's environment.

Darwin's observations of variation within a population and the tendency for the adult population to be stable in size led him to put forward his theory of natural selection. He proposed selection as the force that causes changes in populations.

Population genetics is concerned with the factors that determine the frequencies of alleles in populations of organisms.

In theory, any individual in a population is capable of breeding with any other. However, breeding sub-units may become separated in some way. They may become isolated, and evolve along separate lines. If, reunited after many generations, and the sub-units are found to be incapable of breeding successfully with each other, they have become a separate species. Separation by geographical features, habitat changes, changes in body form and changes in breeding mechanisms may lead to the formation of new species.

By the end of this topic you should be able to:

- Explain that variation is the result of a combination of genetic and environmental factors.
- Describe continuous and discontinuous variation.
- Describe competition for breeding success and survival.
- Explain how population genetics is concerned with how reproductive success affects allele frequency within a gene pool.
- Describe Darwin's theory of natural selection.
- Explain how isolation can result in speciation.
- Describe geographic and reproductive isolation mechanisms.

Topic contents

▼ **Study point**

Environmental factors also play a part in a characteristic such as height. Individuals that are genetically predetermined to be the same height actually grow to different heights due to variations in environmental factors such as diet.

▼ **Study point**

Variety in asexually reproducing organisms can only be increased by mutation. Sexually reproducing organisms increase variation as a result of meiosis, fusion of gametes in addition to mutations.

Genetic variation

Variation is the result of a combination of genetic and environmental factors. Firstly, variation due to genetic factors will be considered.

Genetic variation is also known as heritable variation. As a result of sexual reproduction, variation may be increased when the genotype of one parent is mixed with that of the other. The sexual process has three inbuilt methods of creating variety:

- The mixing of two different parental genotypes where cross-fertilisation occurs.
- The random distribution of chromosomes during metaphase I of meiosis.
- The crossing over between homologous chromosomes during prophase I of meiosis.

Although these processes may establish a new combination of alleles in one generation, it is mutation that generates long-lasting variation of a novel kind. However, as previously stated, the occurrence of a useful mutation is a very rare event.

There are two types of genetic variation.

Continuous variation

Most characters are controlled by a number of genes and the differences in the character are not clear cut. A character, within a population, showing a gradation from one extreme to another shows continuous variation. An example is height. If an individual has inherited a number of alleles for tallness from the parents, that individual has the potential to grow tall.

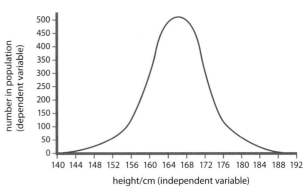

▲ *Normal distribution curve*

An organism will inherit genes, giving it a theoretical maximum size, but whether or not this is reached will depend upon nutrition during the growth period and other environmental factors. Thus, if organisms of identical genotype are subject to different environmental influences, they show considerable variety. Because these influences are varied, they are largely responsible for continuous variation in a population.

Discontinuous variation

Characters that are clear-cut and easy to tell apart are controlled by a single gene. There are no intermediate types. For example, light and dark forms in the peppered moth, the ABO blood grouping system, where the gene has more than two alleles.

▼ *Light and dark forms of peppered moth*

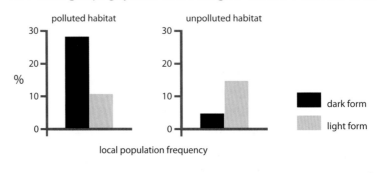

▲ *Discontinuous variation*

Non-heritable variation

Environmental influences play a role in determining phenotypic variation. The environment affects the way an organism's genes are expressed. Environmental factors in humans may include diet and exercise, whereas plants are affected by temperature, light and available nutrients. For example, plants require light to convert a precursor to the green pigment, chlorophyll. If a seed germinates in the dark, the seedling is non-coloured with white leaves. It is said to be etiolated.

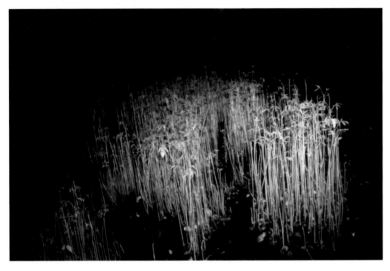

▲ *Seedlings germinating in a cave*

Competition for breeding success and survival

Although all organisms have the reproductive potential to increase their population numbers from generation to generation, this does not happen. This is because as a population increases, various environmental factors come into play to limit the numbers. Organisms must compete for limited resources. For example, plants compete for light, space, mineral ions; animals compete for food, shelter, etc.

There are two types of competition:

• Intra-specific competition – competition between individuals of the same species. This is the basis of the origin of species by natural selection which is studied in detail on page 133.

• Inter-specific competition – competition between individuals of different species competing for the same resources.

Selection pressure

Variation within a population of organisms means that some will have characteristics that give them an advantage in the 'struggle for survival'.

Consider a population of rabbits. The female may produce several litters each year with between two and ten rabbits in each litter. If all the rabbits survived to become adults and they, in turn, reproduced successfully, the rabbit population would increase rapidly.

Eventually, as the increasing amount of rabbits eat more and more of the vegetation such as grass; food would become in short supply.

YOU SHOULD KNOW ›››

››› the difference between inter- and intra-specific competition

››› that organisms with a selective advantage are more likely to survive

▼ **Study point**

Environmental factors have no influence on discontinuous variation.

▼ **Study point**

Variation is due to a combination of genetic differences and environmental influences. It is often difficult to distinguish between these two effects.

◀ **Link** ▶ Competition is studied in detail in BY4 page 46.

▼ **Study point**

In any population the number of young produced is far greater than the number which will survive to become adults. Many young die before maturity and so do not reproduce. There is 'a struggle for survival'.

Key Term

Selection pressure = the environmental force altering the frequency of alleles in a population.

▼ Study point

Selection pressures increase the chances of some alleles being passed on to the next generation, and decrease the chance of others being inherited.

◀ Link ▶ Natural selection, genetic drift and gene pool are concepts discussed on pages 131 and 133.

16

Knowledge check

Link the appropriate terms 1–4 with the statements A–D.

1. Selective advantage.
2. Discontinuous.
3. Selection pressure.
4. Interspecific.

A. Variation due to characters controlled by a single gene.
B. Competition between individuals of different species.
C. An environmental force altering the frequency of alleles in a population.
D. Characteristic that enables an organism to survive and reproduce better than other organisms in a population in a given environment.

Overcrowding would take place allowing diseases to spread. Predators, such as foxes, would increase. These environmental factors act to reduce the rate of growth of the rabbit population. Only a small proportion of the young rabbits will develop into adults and reproduce, so population growth slows. Over a period of time the population will oscillate about a mean level.

What determines which individuals die and which survive? Is it a matter of good fortune or are some individuals born with a better chance of survival than others?

Not all alleles of a population are likely to be passed to the next generation. Only certain individuals are reproductively successful and so pass on their alleles.

In rabbits, coat colour may vary. Most rabbits have alleles which give the normal brown colour. A small number may be homozygous for the recessive allele which gives a white coat. A white rabbit will stand out and is more likely to be killed by a predator such as a fox. As the white rabbit is unlikely to survive to become a mature adult, the chances of it reproducing and passing on its allele for white coat are very small. The allele for white coat will remain rare in the population. However, if the rabbit lives in the Arctic it would be more likely to survive as it will be camouflaged against the snow. Consequently the allele for white coat will increase in the population.

Selection pressure is an abstract force that shapes organisms as they evolve due to mutation, natural selection, and genetic drift. A selection pressure usually acts in a relatively consistent fashion over long timeframes, and actually impacts on the reproductive or survival rates of a species. Potential sources of selection pressure may include availability of prey, presence of predators, environmental stresses, competition with other species, and intra-specific competition.

Predation by foxes is an example of a selection pressure. The effect of such selection pressures on the frequency of alleles in a population is called natural selection. Predation increases 'fitness' in the prey. For example, foxes kill the weakest rabbits.

Selection, in the context of evolution, is the process by which organisms that are better adapted to their environment survive and breed, while those less well adapted fail to do so. These better adapted organisms are more likely to pass on their characteristics to succeeding generations. The organism's environment exerts a selection pressure and this determines the spread of any allele within the gene pool.

Population genetics

A **population** of organisms reproducing sexually contains a large amount of genetic variation. All the alleles of all the genes of all the individuals in a population at any one time are known as the **gene pool**.

Population genetics is concerned with determining the relative proportions of the various genotypes present in a population, from which can be calculated the relative proportions of alleles in the population. This is known as **allele frequency**.

Each organism contains just one of the many possible sets of alleles that can be formed from the pool. The gene pool remains stable if the environment is stable. However, if the environment changes, some phenotypes will be advantageous and will be selected for, whilst others will be disadvantageous, and will be selected against. Thus a gene pool is constantly changing, some alleles becoming more frequent and others less frequent. In some circumstances alleles may be totally lost from the gene pool.

The Hardy–Weinberg principle provides a mathematical equation that can be used to calculate the frequencies of the alleles of a particular gene in a population.

The principle states that in a large, randomly mating population, assuming the absence of migration, mutation and selection, the gene and genotype frequencies remain constant. That is, the proportion of dominant and recessive alleles of a particular gene remains the same. It is not altered by interbreeding.

One useful application of the Hardy–Weinberg principle is that if the frequency of one of the alleles in a gene pool is known, the Hardy–Weinberg equation can be used to calculate the expected proportions of the genotypes in the population.

The Hardy–Weinberg principle demonstrates that a large proportion of recessive alleles exist in the heterozygotes. Heterozygotes are a reservoir of genetic variability.

The Hardy–Weinberg principle is used to calculate allele and genotype frequencies in a population. It can therefore be used to predict the number of defective individuals in a population.

The Hardy–Weinberg equation may be expressed as follows:

$$p^2 + 2pq + q^2 = 1$$

Consider a pair of alleles Aa:

let p = frequency of A, and q = frequency of a.

In the population $p + q = 1$.

Assuming random mating then in the next generation

$$AA = p^2; Aa = 2pq; aa = q^2.$$

Consider the following example:

A recessive allele confers resistance to an insecticide in a particular insect species. Explain how the allele is distributed if 36% of the insect population is resistant.

Allele frequency is represented as a decimal fraction.

Since a gene has two alleles, their combined frequency = 1.

$rr = 36\%$ or 0.36 i.e. $q^2 = 0.36$ $q = \sqrt{0.36} = 0.6$

Since $p + q = 1$ $p = 0.4$ $p^2 = 0.16$

$2pq = 2 \times 0.4 \times 0.6 = 0.48$ or 48%

Therefore allele distribution is as follows:

RR $(p^2) = 0.16$ (16%) Rr $(2pq) = 0.48$ (48%) rr $(q^2) = 0.36$ (36%)

Key Terms

Population = a group of interbreeding individuals of the same species, occupying the same habitat at the same time.

Gene pool = all the alleles in a population at any one time.

Allele frequency = the number of times an allele occurs within the gene pool.

▼ **Study point**

You are not required to study the Hardy–Weinberg principle and will not be tested in an exam question. It has been included to help explain this difficult topic.

▼ **Study point**

The Hardy–Weinberg equation could be used to calculate the allele frequency of a defective allele causing a genetic disease such as cystic fibrosis in the gene pool of the human population.

Key Term

Genetic drift = chance variations in allele frequencies in a population.

Darwin's finches are studied in BY2.

Certain factors can act upon a genetic equilibrium and bring about significant changes to the frequency of some of the alleles and change the composition of the gene pool. These factors include **genetic drift**, mutations and natural selection.

Sometimes variations in allele frequencies in populations occur by chance. This is known as random genetic drift. It may be an important evolutionary mechanism in small or isolated populations.

Say an allele occurs in 1% of the members of a species. In a large population, of say 1,000,000, then 10,000 individuals may be expected to possess the allele. By chance, the population of individuals with the allele will not be significantly altered in the next generation. If, however, the population is much smaller, say 1000 individuals, only ten will carry the allele. By chance, these ten may fail to mate and pass on the allele and so the allele will be lost from the population altogether.

An important case of genetic drift is when a few individuals become isolated from the rest of the species and start a new population; for example, when a few individuals colonise an isolated island or some new habitat.

These founder members of the new population are a small sample of the population from which they originated. By chance they may have a very different allele frequency. While the founder population remains small, it may undergo genetic drift and become even more different from the large parental population. This process is called the founder effect. The effect undoubtedly contributed to the evolutionary divergence of Darwin's finches after strays from the South American mainland reached the remote Galapagos Islands.

► *Animals found on the Galapagos Islands*

Evolution and selection

Evolution is the process by which new species are formed from pre-existing ones over a period of time. The basis of contemporary thought surrounding the theory of evolution was first put forward by Alfred Wallace and Charles Darwin. In 1859 Darwin proposed **natural selection** as the force that causes changes in populations. More recently biologists have realised that natural selection can also maintain variation and therefore stabilise a population.

Charles Darwin (1809–1882) was employed as a naturalist and member of a scientific survey which sailed to South America and Australia in 1832. He visited a small group of volcanic islands called the Galapagos Islands. These are situated about 600 miles off the coast of Ecuador. When these islands were originally formed by volcanic activity, no life existed there. Any plants or animals must have reached the islands by sea or air from the mainland. Darwin studied many different animals on the islands and was amazed by the variety of life-forms that existed there.

▲ *Galapagos giant tortoise*

Darwin's observations of variation within a population and the tendency for the adult population to be stable in size led to the development of the idea of natural selection. The theory proposes that those organisms that are better adapted to their environment are more likely to survive and reproduce to produce offspring that are successful.

The theory is based on the following observations:

- In any population there is variation.
- Individuals within a population have the potential to produce large numbers of offspring, yet the number of adults tends to stay the same from one generation to the next.

From these observations, two deductions were made:

- There is a struggle for survival (competition) with only the 'fittest' surviving.
- The individuals that survive and reproduce pass on to their offspring the characteristics that enable them to succeed (that is, a selective advantage).

In time, a group of individuals that once belonged to the same species may give rise to two different groups that are sufficiently distinct to belong to two separate species.

If the environment or conditions change, then the features needed to survive in it will change, so natural selection is a continuous process.

YOU SHOULD KNOW ›››

››› Darwin's theory of natural selection

 Key Term

Natural selection = a process that encourages the transmission of favourable alleles and hinders the transmission of unfavourable ones and contributes to evolution.

▼ **Study point**

To this point a study has been made of how genes and alleles are passed between individuals in a population. This section considers the genes and alleles of an entire population.

 **How Science Works**

Darwin made observations that led to an explanation in the form of a hypothesis.

▼ **Study point**

Darwin proposed natural selection as the force that causes changes within populations.

Types of selection

▼ **Study point**

You are not required to know the three categories of selection. The description has been included to explain how allele frequency changes when the environment changes.

There are three types of natural selection: stabilising selection, directional selection and disruptive selection.

Natural selection does not always result in change. If an organism has a favourable phenotype it is more likely to produce offspring very similar to itself. If the environment is stable and does not change then the extreme variations tend to be eliminated since they confer no apparent advantage. This is called stabilising selection.

▼ **Study point**

The allele frequency in a population will remain constant from one generation to the next unless an allele leads to a phenotype with an advantage or a disadvantage compared with other phenotypes.

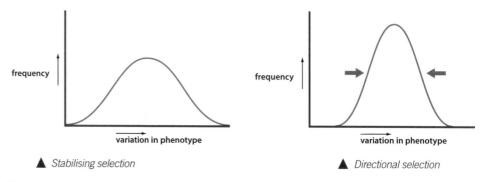

▲ *Stabilising selection* ▲ *Directional selection*

If the environment changes then it may favour organisms at one extreme of the phenotypes. Consider the following hypothetical situation.

▼ **Study point**

The allele for 'small fins' remains in the gene pool as it is present in the heterozygous condition.

A lake exists where for thousands of years a species of small fish lives. The fish have a range of fin lengths, typically shown by the normal distribution curve. In the lake the species have no predator, such as a bigger fish. In a nearby lake lives a bigger fish, a potential predator. A weather situation occurs when it rains for a number of weeks. The two lakes become partially united by a stream which becomes a river deep enough for the predator to swim through. The big fish acts as a selection pressure. The small fish with big fins have a selective advantage in that they can swim faster than members of the same species with smaller fins. They survive, reproduce and pass on the alleles for large fins to the next generation. Eventually the population will all have large fins.

▼ *Directional selection*

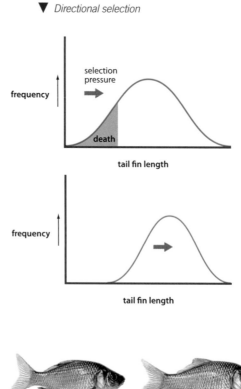

Isolation and speciation

Populations are groups of interbreeding individuals of the same species occupying the same habitat. In theory, any individual in a population is capable of breeding with any other. However, breeding sub-units may become separated in some way, i.e. become **isolated**, and evolve along separate lines. If, reunited after many generations, the sub-units were found to be incapable of breeding successfully with each other; they would have become a separate species. Separation by geographical features, habitat changes, changes in body form and changes in breeding mechanisms may lead to the formation of new species.

Speciation

Within a population of one **species** there are groups of interbreeding individuals. Within each population there are breeding sub-units called **demes**. Individuals within a deme tend to breed with each other more often than they do with individuals of other demes. New species arise when some barrier to reproduction occurs so that the gene pool is divided and the flow of genes between separate demes may cease. Such a barrier, which effectively prevents gene exchange between demes, is called an isolating mechanism. If the separation is long term, eventually the two groups will be so different that two new species incapable of interbreeding are formed. The separate species will each have their own gene pool. This process is called **speciation**.

Isolation leading to speciation

For new species to develop from a population, some form of isolating mechanism is required. There are two main forms of isolating mechanisms.

Geographical isolation

This occurs when the population becomes physically split into separate demes. The physical barrier may be a mountain or a river or any feature which prevents the population of the same species from interbreeding. The evolution of a new species is very probable, given time. This sort of speciation is known as allopatric speciation.

Consider an isolation model:

- A population of birds with short flight range feed and breed only in the cool conditions of a valley and the lower slopes of two mountains a considerable distance apart. The birds are only able to breed at a certain temperature provided by the cool conditions. The mountain peaks are too cold for the birds to survive.

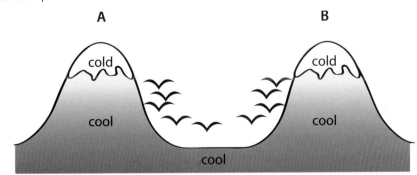

▲ *Isolation model*

Key Terms

Isolation = occurs when a barrier prevents two populations from breeding with one another.

Species = a group of similar organisms that can interbreed to produce fertile offspring.

Deme = a breeding sub-unit.

Speciation = the evolution of new species from existing species.

Examiner tip

Candidates tend to waffle in their responses to this topic. The learning of definitions is essential and the use of a model helps focus on the concept.

Key Term

Hybrid = the offspring resulting from cross breeding of different species.

Knowledge check

Link the appropriate terms 1–5 with the statements A–E.

1. Isolation.
2. Hybrid.
3. Species.
4. Speciation.
5. Gene pool.

A. All the alleles in a population at any one time.

B. The evolution of new species from existing species.

C. A group of similar organisms that can interbreed to produce fertile offspring.

D. The offspring resulting from cross breeding of different species.

E. When a barrier prevents two populations from breeding with one another.

▼ *Zebronkey*

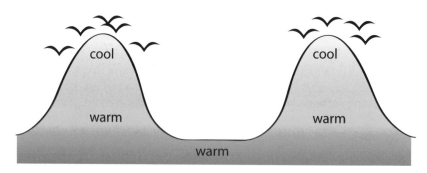

The climate then changes and it becomes warmer. The birds tend to inhabit the nearest mountain and become confined to the cool mountain peaks. The birds are split into two separate breeding populations or demes, each with their own gene pool. Over a very prolonged period of isolation the birds may be subjected to different selection pressures. Because of the effect of natural selection on each gene pool, the two populations may become sufficiently genetically different to prevent interbreeding.

- It may be that those birds isolated on mountain top A adapted to feed on insects in crevices. Birds with long beaks fed successfully and so survived to reproduce and passed on this favourable characteristic. On mountain top B the birds had fruit on which to feed and so had a different beak type.

- If the climate reverts to the original temperature and the birds are again able to inhabit the valley and lower mountain slopes they come into contact with each other. Over time the appearance may have altered and the different-shaped beaks may result in a different mating call. The birds are no longer attracted to each other. If the two populations have established a different gene pool and can no longer interbreed, then two separate species have evolved.

Reproductive isolation

This occurs when organisms inhabiting the same area become reproductively isolated into two groups when there are no physical barriers. Species formation occurring in demes in the same geographic area is known as sympatric speciation. Reproductive isolation can be important in preventing the dilution effect of gene flow into the gene pool from other populations.

The barriers to breeding include the following mechanisms:

- Behavioural isolation – in animals with elaborate courtship behaviour, the steps in the display of one subspecies fail to attract the necessary response in a potential partner of another subspecies.

- Mechanical isolation – the genitalia of the two groups may be incompatible.

- Gametic isolation – in flowering plants pollination may be prevented because the pollen grain fails to germinate on the stigma, whereas in animals sperm may fail to survive in the oviduct of the partner.

- Hybrid inviability – despite fertilisation taking place, development of the embryo may not occur. This may be because the chromosomes no longer match each other, as is the case with polyploidy.

- Hybrid sterility – when individuals of different species breed, the sets of chromosomes from each parent are different. These sets are unable to pair up during meiosis and so the offspring are unable to produce gametes. The **hybrid** is therefore sterile and the species is reproductively isolated.

An example of hybrid sterility is a 'zebronkey'. This is the name given to the offspring which results from the mating of a zebra with a donkey. The zebronkey is sterile as it has 52 chromosomes that are unable to form homologous pairs.

Variation and evolution

1 In an experiment a zebra was crossed with a donkey to produce a hybrid called a zebronkey. The diagram shows the parental phenotype, the chromosomes contributed by each parent and the offspring phenotype. (The animals are not drawn to the same scale.)

common zebra

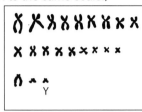
gamete

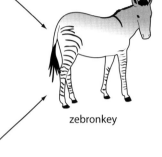
zebronkey

donkey

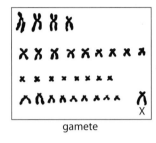
gamete

(a)(i) Describe two differences in parental phenotype. (2)

   (ii) State the sex of the zebronkey. (1)

   (iii) How many chromosomes would you expect to find in a zebronkey skin cell? (1)

(b) Use the information in the diagram to explain why zebronkeys cannot produce fertile offspring. (3)

(c) Suggest why horse breeders are interested in producing hybrids between different members of the horse family. (1)

WJEC A2 JUNE 1995

---

2 The loganberry arose as a result of a cross between a Californian blackberry and a raspberry. The diagram shows the relationship between these three species.

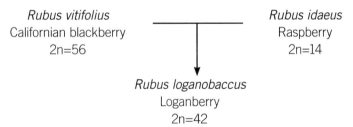

Rubus vitifolius
Californian blackberry
2n=56

Rubus idaeus
Raspberry
2n=14

Rubus loganobaccus
Loganberry
2n=42

(a) State the genetic term which can be used to describe a hybrid organism of this type. (1)

(b) Suggest how the cross between the blackberry and raspberry gave rise to the loganberry. (2)

(c) This type of hybrid is usually infertile and propagated from cuttings. However, sometimes new plants, which are fertile, do arise spontaneously. Suggest how this happens. (1)

WJEC B3 JAN 1999

---

3 Thousands of years ago in Africa, Lake Nabugabob became separated from Lake Victoria. There are five species of cichlid fish of the genus *Haplochromis* in Lake Nabugabob, each descended from a different species in the main lake, Lake Victoria.

(a) Explain why the fish from each lake can be described as different species. (2)

(b) Explain how the splitting of the fish population into Lake Nabugabob and Lake Victoria populations has led to the formation of a separate species. (4)

WJEC BI5 JUNE 2006

4   Read the passage below and then answer the questions:

Scientists assume that past population crashes are the reason why some species show little genetic variation between individuals. This lack of genetic variation may put a species at greater risk of extinction.

In Illinois, USA, the population of prairie grouse has fallen from 10 million birds a century ago to less than 50 today, as farmers convert prairie to cornfields.

Researchers extracted DNA from 15 museum specimens collected before the population crash and 32 specimens collected recently from a nature reserve.

Identical sections of DNA were compared.

Present day specimens showed an average of 3.67 different alleles per section compared with 5.12 alleles per section in museum specimens.

Adapted from *New Scientist* 23 August 1997

(a)   Suggest three reasons for the fall in population of prairie grouse 'from 10 million birds a century ago to less than 50 today as farmers convert prairie to cornfields'. (3)

(b)(i) Suggest 'why some species show little genetic variation between individuals' immediately after a crash. (1)

(ii) Explain how the comparison between numbers of alleles in museum specimens and present day specimens can be used to support the assumption made by conservationists. (2)

(iii) Suggest why some scientists consider that the conclusions based on these data may not be valid. (1)

WJEC B3 JAN 1999

5 (a)   Explain what is meant by the term 'survival of the fittest'. (2)

(b)   Shell colour and pattern in the land snail, *Cepaea nemoralis*, is genetically determined. Shells may be brown, green or pink. In addition, the whole shell may have up to five dark bands on it. Thrushes eat these snails, which they select by sight.

The table below shows the distribution of some shell types in three different habitats.

Shell type	% of each shell type present in different areas		
	Grassland	Rough herbage (nettles, long grass and dead stems)	Woodland floor (dead leaves, soil and twigs)
Brown	10	23	54
Green	58	19	12
Pink	7	8	4
Banded	25	50	30

(i) Name the shell type with the greatest survival value on the woodland floor. (1)

(Ii) Explain the relative abundance in grassland and rough herbage of snails with

1. Green shells. (1)

2. Pink shells. (1)

(IIi) Explain the relative abundance of banded snails in grassland, rough herbage and woodland. (2)

(iv) In winter the snails hibernate just beneath the soil with the mouth of the shell up and covered with white mucus. The thrushes dig out such prey from the soil. Suggest why you would not expect selection to operate on shell colour under these circumstances. (1)

(v) During very hot summers pink shells and pale-coloured shells are more frequent.

1. Suggest one factor, apart from predation, which might influence selection under these conditions. (1)

2. Suggest one possible selective advantage to the snails of pale coloured shells. (1)

WJEC B2 JAN 1998

Applications of reproduction and genetics

Genetic engineering enables scientists to manipulate DNA in a variety of ways. The quality of farm animals and crops may be improved by laboratory-based techniques. Animal stocks may be increased by cloning of embryos and the transfer of genetic material. Plant micropropagation provides a rapid method of producing large numbers of genetically identical plants.

In human genetics advances have been made as a result of the Human Genome Project. This has resulted in the location, identification and sequencing of genes in human DNA. This has tremendous potential for the treatment of genetic diseases, such as cystic fibrosis, but also raises a number of ethical issues. Medical advances are also made using cells cultured in the laboratory. Therapeutic stem cell cloning has enormous medical potential. However, use of human embryos to provide a supply of stem cells for use in research is controversial.

Recombinant DNA technology has a number of important applications such as the production of products such as insulin on a large scale. The insertion of genes into plants to improve yield and introduce disease and pest resistance has obvious benefits, but there remains concern about the development of these genetically modified crops.

The technique of genetic fingerprinting can be used to provide forensic evidence at a crime scene and the use of the polymerase chain reaction enables even minute DNA samples to be duplicated in order to provide larger samples for testing. However, there is concern over the misuse of this vast amount of stored data.

By the end of this topic you should be able to:

- Describe embryo cloning and cloning by nuclear transplants.
- Describe tissue culture of animals and the ethical issues surrounding the use of human stem cells.
- Describe plant tissue culture or micropropagation of plants.
- Describe the aims of the Human Genome Project.
- Describe the potential uses of the data obtained.
- Describe the symptoms and treatment of cystic fibrosis.
- Discuss the implications of genetic counselling and genetic screening.
- Describe recombinant DNA technology with particular reference to the production of insulin.
- Describe examples of genetically modified organisms.
- Describe the processes of genetic fingerprinting and the polymerase chain reaction.
- Discuss the ethical issues surrounding gene ownership, gene therapy and recombinant DNA technology.

Topic contents

Key Terms

Clone = a group of genetically identical organisms formed from a single parent as a result of asexual reproduction or by artificial means.

***In vitro* fertilisation** = a technique which involves mixing the egg or oocyte with sperm in a dish where fertilisation takes place.

▲ *Two identical sheep*

18

Knowledge check

Identify the missing word or words.

When an egg and sperm are fused in a Petri dish this is known as ••••
•••• fertilisation. The fertilised egg is allowed to divide by •••• into a ball of cells. The cells are split and the young embryos are implanted into the uterus of another sheep called a ••••. This technique is called •••• cloning.

Cloning of animals

In the past, conventional breeding techniques have been used to improve farm animals, crops and ornamental plants. However, selection and cross breeding is laborious, time consuming and sometimes unpredictable. The quality of farm animals may be improved by laboratory-based breeding techniques involving embryos. The technique of embryo surgery has also enabled farmers to increase their stock.

Embryo cloning

This technique has been used to produce genetically identical individuals and has made it possible for farmers to increase the numbers of their animals. Eggs are taken from high milk yielding cows and are fertilised in a Petri dish using sperm from the best bulls. This is known as ***in vitro* fertilisation** (commonly called 'test-tube fertilisation'). The fertilised egg divides to form a ball of cells. This group of cells or young embryos is split into separate cells. Each of these cells will then develop into a new embryo, genetically identical (**clone**) to the original. The embryos are then transplanted into other cows called surrogates.

▼ *Stages in embryo cloning*

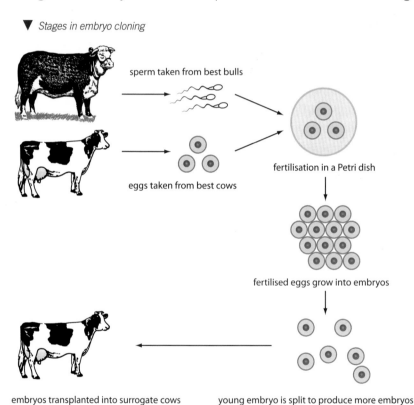

sperm taken from best bulls

fertilisation in a Petri dish

eggs taken from best cows

fertilised eggs grow into embryos

embryos transplanted into surrogate cows

young embryo is split to produce more embryos

Cloning by nuclear transfer

This technique allows clones to be produced from one individual. It involves transplanting a nucleus from a somatic or body cell into an egg cell. The procedure may be described as follows:

- Cells are taken from the tissues of the udder of a sheep (the donor) and cultured in a medium which stops division.

- An unfertilised egg is removed from a different sheep (the recipient) and the nucleus is removed, leaving an egg cell without a nucleus.

- The donor and recipient cells are fused together using a gentle electric pulse, and allowed to divide to the eight-cell stage producing a ball of cells.

- The developing embryo is implanted into the uterus of another sheep (the host or surrogate).
- The lamb born is genetically identical to the original donor sheep.

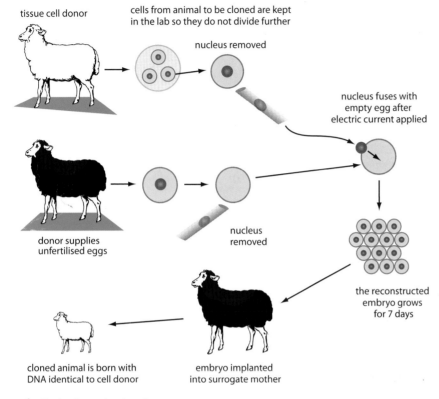

▲ *Cloning by nuclear transfer*

The technique of cloning animals has a number of advantageous features. It has enabled desirable qualities to be preserved for future generations. Embryo cloning allows many genetically identical copies of an animal to be produced. If a high milk yield mutation occurred in a cow, making her significantly better than other members of the herd, cross breeding with a bull would reshuffle her genes with a consequent loss of her unique characteristic. Cloning is the only technique that will conserve her unique features for future generations. Other advantages are:

- Cell culture is useful for production of cells in quantity, e.g. cancer cells for medical research, monoclonal antibodies.

- The production of a single, identical, genetic line of cells with desirable characteristics may be used to maintain genetic stocks.

However, there are disadvantages. They include:

- In mammals the technique is very expensive and unreliable.
- There may be the inadvertent selection of disadvantageous alleles.
- Progeny may show long-term/unforeseen effects such as premature aging.

Cells from young animals and cancer cells can be induced to divide *in vitro*. A few cells retain their ability to divide even in an adult, for example new cells to heal wounds. Most cells, however, **differentiate** into cells which have specific functions, such as nerve or muscle cells, and most of these specialised cells do not normally divide again.

- The technique of growing cells in a laboratory is called tissue culture. The medium in which the cells are grown has to be precisely controlled, and conditions such as water potential and temperature have to be carefully monitored. Animal cells in tissue culture develop into mature cells of the same type as the cell from which the culture was started. Of course, all the cells are identical and contain identical genes to the parent cell.

Key Term

Differentiate = cells become specialised for different functions.

▲ *Cloning technique*

19 **Knowledge check**

Identify the missing word or words.

Cloning by •••• •••• involves the removal of the nucleus from the cells of the •••• of a donor and transplanting it into the enucleated unfertilised egg cell of a recipient. The donor and recipient cells are •••• together and allowed to divide. The developing embryo is implanted into the uterus of another sheep. The lamb born is genetically identical to the •••• sheep.

Link The ethical issues involved with cloning are studied in more detail on page 142.

▼ **Study point**

Cloning is also used to conserve rare breeds, where embryos of young animals are bisected and successfully transplanted into a surrogate mother of a common breed to produce a new individual of the rare type.

Key Terms

Stem cell = an undifferentiated cell capable of dividing to give rise to cells which can develop into different types of specialised cells.

Ethics = a set of standards that are followed by a particular group of individuals and are designed to regulate their behaviour. They determine what is acceptable.

▼ Study point

Cell cultures have been used for some time for medical and research purposes, for example in the culture of viruses for vaccine production and also in the production of monoclonal antibodies. New techniques, such as cell replacement therapy and tissue engineering, are being developed.

How Science Works

Scientists must consider ethical issues in the treatment of humans and other organisms.

Examiner tip

Consider writing an essay entitled 'What are the arguments for and against tissue culture?' Plan your essay by making two columns and inserting the points in note form.

- Tissue engineering involves inducing living cells to grow on a framework of synthetic material to produce a tissue such as skin tissue. This has obvious applications for the treatment of extensive, deep burns. An artificial skin called 'Apligraf' is now widely used in place of skin grafts.

- Other applications of tissue engineering include blood vessel replacement, bone and cartilage repair, and the treatment of degenerative nerve diseases. Central to this area of research is the use of **stem cells**. Stem cells are undifferentiated dividing cells that are found in adult animal tissues and need to be constantly replaced. They are found in selective tissue such as the bone marrow. They can develop into any other types of cell given the correct conditions. They have therefore been used to treat a variety of genetic disorders. Stem cells are also found at the earliest stage of embryo development, before the cells have differentiated. These are called embryonic stem cells.

- Therapeutic stem cell cloning has enormous medical potential. Cloned stem cells could be used to generate organs for transplantation. This would prevent immune rejection and reduce the problem of organ shortages.

The technique may be described in simple terms as follows:

- A mature cell is taken from the patient and the nucleus is removed.
- The nucleus is removed from a human ovum.
- The mature cell nucleus is transferred into the 'empty' ovum.
- The ovum, containing the patient's DNA, divides to form a ball of stem cells.
- Stem cells are isolated and cultured with appropriate growth factors, allowing them to grow into the required organ or tissue.

Tissue culture

Ethics and the use of stem cells

There is considerable controversy surrounding the use of stem cells. At present, embryonic stem cell research is allowed in the UK under licence. On 9 March 2009, President Barack Obama issued an Executive Order entitled 'Removing Barriers to Responsible Scientific Research Involving Human Stem Cells', the previous administration having banned stem cell research.

- The supply of embryos comes from the surplus embryos which were not placed into a female's uterus during fertility treatment. Once the stem cells are removed these embryos would be destroyed. Some consider it unacceptable to use embryos for this purpose even if there was never any chance of the embryo being allowed to develop. Others consider that the potential benefits outweigh the **ethical** concerns. The human stem cells could be used to treat Parkinson's disease, Alzheimer's disease, heart disease, liver diseases, diabetes, multiple sclerosis and some cancers.

- As previously stated, human embryos are not the only source of stem cells. They can also be obtained from the bone marrow of human adults and no consent is required. However, at the present time cells from this source have more restricted medical applications.

- Opponents also argue that embryonic stem cell technologies are a slippery slope to reproductive cloning and can fundamentally devalue human life. Human cloning is illegal in the UK but it is feared that any research knowledge gained could be used to clone humans in another country.

Micropropagation (plant tissue culture)

Micropropagation involves the cloning of plants. It is an extremely cost-effective way of producing large numbers of genetically identical plants which are clones of a single parent.

The technique of micropropagation is based on the ability of differentiated plant cells to give rise to all the different cells of the adult plant. In other words, many plant cells are **totipotent.** Under the right conditions many plant cells can develop into any other cell.

At the tip of the roots and shoots of plants are areas called **meristems.** If cells are removed from the meristem and placed in suitable conditions, new, genetically identical, plants will develop.

These steps are generally followed in micropropagation:

1. A plant with the desired characteristics is selected.
2. A sterile scalpel is used to remove the meristem from the shoot.
3. The meristem is cut into small pieces called explants.
4. The explants are placed onto a sterile, aerated nutrient medium, such as agar jelly.
5. The cells are allowed to divide by mitosis producing a mass of undifferentiated cells, called a callus.
6. The callus is subdivided and each piece is allowed to differentiate into a plantlet.
7. When they have reached a suitable size the plantlets are transplanted into sterile soil.

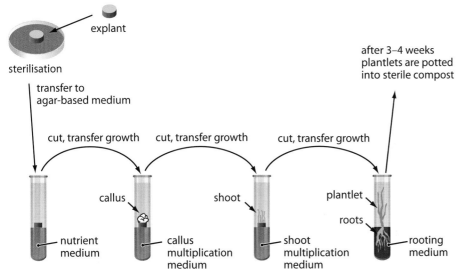

▲ Stages in micropropagation

Plant tissue culture has many advantages over the more traditional methods of propagation such as taking cuttings. These advantages include:

- Large numbers of plants can be grown in sterile controlled conditions ensuring a greater survival rate than would be the case if seeds were planted outside.
- It is less time-consuming as it cuts out the requirement for pollination, seed production and seasonal restrictions on germination.
- Good quality stock is selected, possessing qualities such as resistance to disease or high yield. By this means plant diseases can be eliminated.

YOU SHOULD KNOW ›››

››› the technique of plant tissue culture

››› that many plant cells are totipotent

››› the advantages and disadvantages of plant tissue culture

Key Terms

Totipotent (cells) = cell which can mature into any body cell.

Meristem = growing points where cells divide rapidly by mitosis.

▼ Study point

Not all plant cells are totipotent. Xylem and phloem are highly specialised for their particular functions.

▼ Study point

Conventional methods of plant propagation, such as grafting and taking cuttings, have been used for centuries. Using plant tissue culture, cells are taken from stock plants that have desirable characteristics and have commercial value.

- The crop is uniform since the plants are genetically identical. From a commercial viewpoint this is very important.
- Large numbers of plants can be stored in a small area with reduced heating and lighting costs.
- Unique genotypes can be preserved.
- Reduced space is required for transport.

Although the process is very cost effective overall there are certain disadvantages.

- Sterile conditions have to be maintained, otherwise bacterial or fungal contamination of the culture medium may result, with subsequent loss of plants.
- The plants are genetically unstable with an increased rate of mutation in medium-grown cells leading to abnormality in the plantlets. Regular inspection is needed to remove any defective individuals, thus labour costs are higher than with traditional propagation methods.

YOU SHOULD KNOW ›››

››› the main aims of the Human Genome Project

››› the potential benefits of the project

››› the ethical issues surrounding the data obtained

The Human Genome Project

The project began in 1990 and was originally planned to last 15 years, but rapid technological advances accelerated the completion date to 2003. The main aims of the project were to:

- Identify all the approximately 20,000–25,000 genes in human DNA.
- Determine the sequences of the 3 billion chemical base pairs that make up human DNA.
- Store this information in databases.
- Improve tools for data analysis.
- Transfer related technologies to the private sector.
- Address the ethical, legal, and social issues that may arise from the project.

Though the project itself is complete, it will take many years to analyse all the data.

▼ Study point

The human genome is described as 'all the DNA sequences contained in the chromosomes of an organism'.

▼ Study point

Knowing the base sequence of a normal, functioning gene makes it possible to eliminate all risk of the disease by correcting or replacing the faulty allele in humans.

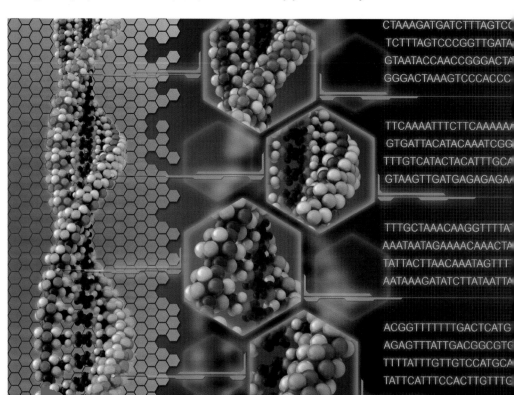

```
CTAAAGATGATCTTTAGTCC
TCTTTAGTCCCGGTTGATA
GTAATACCAACCGGGACTA
GGGACTAAAGTCCCACCC

TTCAAAATTTCTTCAAAAA
GTGATTACATACAAATCGG
TTTGTCATACTACATTTGCA
GTAAGTTGATGAGAGAGAA

TTTGCTAAACAAGGTTTTA
AAATAATAGAAAACAAACTA
TATTACTTAACAAATAGTTT
AATAAAGATATCTTATAATTA

ACGGTTTTTTTGACTCATG
AGAGTTTATTGACGGCGTC
TTTTATTTGTTGTCCATGCA
TATTCATTTCCACTTGTTTC
```

Beneficial applications of the project

The information enables scientists to know exactly which sections of DNA, on which chromosomes, are responsible for the many different inherited diseases. The process takes place as follows:

- A DNA sample is obtained from a patient and scanned for mutated sequences.

- **Gene probes** are used to seek their complement among the three billion base pairs of the individual's genome.

- If the mutated sequence is present, the probe will bind to it and flag the mutation.

Another method of DNA testing involves comparing the sequence of DNA bases in a patient's gene to a normal version of the gene. The cost of testing can be very expensive and depends on the sizes of the genes and the numbers of mutations tested.

The following are some of the main uses of genetic testing:

- Carrier screening, which involves identifying unaffected individuals who carry one copy of a gene (recessive) for a disease that requires two copies for the disease to be expressed.

- Pre-implantation genetic diagnosis.

- Pre-natal diagnostic testing.

- New-born baby screening.

- Pre-symptomatic testing for predicting adult-onset disorders such as Huntington's disease.

- Pre-symptomatic testing for estimating the risk of developing adult-onset cancers and Alzheimer's disease.

- Confirmation that an individual has a suspected disease.

- Forensic/identity testing.

Some of these applications may be considered in more detail:

- Using a sample of DNA from a person it is possible to identify whether that person is a carrier of a faulty allele such as that which causes cystic fibrosis. People who are carriers may decide not to have children or to have an antenatal genetic test to check if their child will be born with the disease.

- Some genes that have been identified play a contributory role in diseases later in life, such as Alzheimer's disease and breast cancer. Although genes play a part in disease development, so does the environment, which includes people's diet and whether they smoke, etc. Genetic testing can give an idea of the probability of developing a particular disease. Those people at greatest risk can then be targeted by health authorities, screened at regular intervals and given appropriate advice about how to reduce the risk by changing their lifestyle. Once the base sequence of a gene is known it is then possible to find the protein that it codes for. Once the structure of that protein is known it is possible to design drugs whose molecules would fit it perfectly. It may be possible to design drugs that act against the gene itself.

Key Term

Gene probe = short piece of DNA the sequences of which are complementary to the mutated sequences.

▼ Study point

The incidence of some inherited diseases such as thalassaemia, which is an inherited blood anaemia disease common in some Mediterranean countries, is falling as a result of genetic testing.

▼ Study point

The health trend is a move to prevention rather than cure. The former is far more cost-effective in the long term as well as being beneficial to the population as a whole.

▼ Study point

There is no doubt that genetic research will continue. The challenge is to ensure that ethical guidelines that have been developed are followed enabling genetic engineering to continue in a safe and responsible way.

▼ **Study point**

There are many diseases that are caused by faulty alleles of genes. The aim of gene therapy is to treat a genetic disease by replacing defective genes in the patient's body with copies of a new DNA sequence. About 60% of currently approved gene therapy procedures are targeting cancer with about 25% aiming to treat genetic disorders such as cystic fibrosis.

✚ **How Science Works**

Gene therapy raises ethical issues, particularly the possible long-term consequences of germ-line therapy.

The advantages and limitations of gene testing

- Gene testing has already dramatically improved lives. Some tests are used to clarify a diagnosis and direct a physician toward appropriate treatments, while others allow families to avoid having children with devastating diseases or identify people at high risk for conditions that may be preventable.

- Commercialised gene tests for adult-onset disorders, such as Alzheimer's disease and some cancers, are the subject of most of the debate over gene testing. These tests are targeted to healthy (presymptomatic) people who are identified as being at high risk because of a strong family medical history for the disorder. The tests give only a probability for developing the disorder. One of the most serious limitations of these susceptibility tests is the difficulty in interpreting a positive result, because some people who carry a disease-associated mutation never develop the disease. Scientists believe that these mutations may work together with other unknown mutations or with environmental factors to cause disease.

- A limitation of all medical testing is the possibility for laboratory errors. These might be due to sample misidentification, contamination of the chemicals used for testing, or other factors.

- Many in the medical establishment feel that uncertainties surrounding test interpretation, the current lack of available medical options for these diseases, the tests' potential for provoking anxiety, and risks for discrimination and social stigmatisation could outweigh the benefits of testing.

- There are also a number of social concerns:
    - Who should have access to personal genetic information and how will it be used?
    - Who owns and controls the genetic information?
    - Should parents have the right to have their children tested for adult-onset diseases?
    - Is there a danger of one day producing human clones?

Gene therapy

There are 4000 genetic diseases affecting the human population.

Gene therapy is a technique whereby a defective gene is replaced with a gene cloned from a healthy individual to provide a potential cure for a genetic disorder. The main problem with gene therapy lies in developing a gene delivery system, that is, a means of inserting 'normal' versions of genes into a person's cells and ensuring that they function correctly once they get there.

Gene therapy usually requires a vector or carrier to introduce the DNA. The majority of procedures use viruses as vectors to deliver the selected gene to the target cells. Some use liposomes and others use injection of naked plasma DNA.

There are two possible ways of replacing defective genes:

- Gene therapy involving somatic cell therapy targets cells in the affected tissues. This method may be therapeutic, but the genetic changes are not inherited.

- Germ-line therapy, involves the introduction of corrective genes into germ-line cells, that is, the gene is replaced in the egg and will enable genetic corrections to be inherited.

Cystic fibrosis

Cystic fibrosis is due to a defective autosomal recessive allele. It is a common disease and affects approximately 8500 people in the UK. Sufferers produce a thick, sticky mucus from the epithelial cells lining certain passageways in the body. These secretions lead to a number of problems:

- The pancreatic duct becomes blocked, preventing pancreatic enzymes from reaching the duodenum and so food digestion is incomplete.

- The bronchioles and alveoli of the lungs become clogged, causing congestion and difficulty in breathing. The mucus is difficult to remove and leads to recurrent infections.

To relieve the distress with breathing, frequent daily chest physiotherapy massage is needed to keep the airways open. The sufferer also has impaired digestion and a limited absorption of food. Children with the condition have large appetites to try to compensate.

To inherit the disease both parents must be carriers of the defective recessive allele. Carriers can be identified using a simple blood test. The normal gene codes for the production of a protein found in the cell membrane. This protein, called cystic fibrosis trans-membrane regulator (CFTR), transports chloride ions out of cells into mucus. Sodium ions follow out of the cells and water passes out of the cell by osmosis. This makes the mucus that lines the air passages a watery consistency. The protein of cystic fibrosis sufferers lacks just one amino acid and so cannot perform its transport function.

Microbiologists have succeeded in isolating and cloning the gene which codes for the CFTR protein. There are two methods of delivery into the epithelial cells of the lung.

Using liposomes

- The genes are inserted into **liposomes**. This involves wrapping the gene in lipid molecules that can pass through the membranes of lung epithelial cells.

- An aerosol inhaler is used to add the non-defective gene to the epithelial cells of the lung.

- The liposomes fuse with the phospholipid bilayer of the cell membrane and the DNA enters the cells. These cells start to express the inserted gene by making the protein CFTR.

Using a virus

- The virus is rendered harmless.

- The virus is cultured in epithelial cells along with plasmids with the normal CFTR gene inserted.

- The gene becomes incorporated into the virus DNA.

- The virus is isolated and introduced into the patient by means of an inhaler.

- The virus injects the plasmid DNA which includes the normal CFTR gene, into the epithelial cells of the lungs.

How effective is gene therapy?

There has been limited success with the gene therapy treatment because the effect is short-lived and the treatment may need to be repeated at 30-day intervals. Only a small proportion of the introduced genes are expressed. There may also be an immune response in the patient. However, the advantages of gene therapy far outweigh the disadvantages. To give a child that would be born with a genetic disease the chance of a normal life, or to prevent the development of cancer in an individual are goals that medical science must aspire to.

Key Term

Liposome = minute spheres of lipid molecules, capable of carrying DNA inside them.

▼ Study point

The use of stem cells, rather than mature somatic cells, is longer lasting in patients.

▼ Study point

The treatment does not solve the digestive problems of the patient but has the potential to solve the problem of congested and infected lungs.

▼ Study point

Plasmid DNA containing the therapeutic gene is incubated with the empty liposomes. The negatively charged DNA binds with the positively charged liposomes and the plasmids are absorbed. Liposomes containing plasmid DNA are called lipoplexes.

20

Identify the missing words.

Cystic fibrosis sufferers lack a protein, called CFTR, which transports •••• ions out of cells into mucus. Sodium ions follow out of the cells and •••• passes out of the cell by ••••. This makes the mucus that lines the air passages a watery consistency. The protein of cystic fibrosis sufferers lacks just one •••• •••• and so cannot perform its transport function.

The treatment involves targetting body or •••• cells of the affected tissue. The genes are inserted into lipid molecules called ••••. These are then delivered into the body by means of an ••••.

How Science Works

Genetic screening raises ethical issues. Information obtained needs to be used responsibly.

▶ *Using ultrasound as a guide, a doctor examines the abdominal wall of a pregnant woman to withdraw the fluid. After the amniotic fluid is extracted, the cells it contains are analysed for various chromosomal abnormalities.*

Genetic counselling

If a family has a history of a genetic defect, unaffected members can consult a genetic counsellor for advice on the risk of bearing an affected child. Genetic counselling is closely linked to genetic screening since it provides the genetic counsellor with information for discussion with potential parents. Advice may be based on:

• Whether there is a history of the disorder in the family.

• Whether the parents are closely related.

• The frequency of the faulty gene in the general population.

This information enables people to make personal decisions about themselves or their potential offspring.

Genetic screening

Once it is established that there is a risk of passing on a defective allele, there are means of investigating whether a child is affected before it is born. On the basis of these tests the parents can decide whether or not to have the pregnancy terminated. Techniques involved include:

• A blood test – there is a simple blood test for detecting cystic fibrosis.

• Amniocentesis – this involves withdrawing some of the amniotic fluid at 15–20 weeks, i.e. about halfway through pregnancy. The fluid contains cells that have floated away from the surface of the embryo. These cells may be analysed microscopically.

• Chorionic villus sampling – early in pregnancy (within 8–10 weeks) tiny samples of foetal tissue are withdrawn from the uterus, and cells are cultured and examined under the microscope.

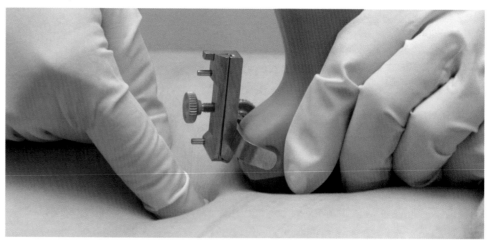

Advantages and disadvantages of gene therapy

Genetic screening produces much controversy and raises many ethical and legal issues. Many believe that this involves an invasion of privacy. Some also believe that if prenatal tests are carried out, finding defective genes will lead to an increase in the number of abortions. Individuals with defects may be placed in a high risk group for insurance purposes to cover the cost of treatment. This would mean that insurance cover would be very expensive or even impossible to obtain.

Couples may find that they are carriers of a genetic disease and must decide if they want to have a child that could be born with a defect.

Another problem involves the regulation of gene therapy in its use solely for reducing defects. Many fear that companies will use gene therapy for the wrong reasons, such as choosing or modifying the characteristics of a child.

Genetic engineering

Genetic engineering allows genes to be manipulated, altered and transferred from one organism to another. Applications of genetic engineering include the transfer of:

- Genes into bacteria, so that they can make useful products such as insulin.
- Genes into plants and animals so that they acquire new characteristics, for example resistance to disease.
- Genes into humans so that they no longer suffer from genetic diseases such as cystic fibrosis.

The process of producing a protein using the DNA technology of gene transfer and **cloning** involves the following stages:

- Isolation of the DNA fragments.
- Insertion of the DNA fragment into a vector.
- The transfer of DNA into suitable host cells.
- Identification of the host cells that have taken up the gene by use of gene markers.
- Cloning of the host cells.

To explain the principles of using gene technology to produce useful molecules on a large scale, the production of insulin is described, using bacteria called *Escherichia coli (E.coli)*.

DNA identification and isolation

First, the gene must be identified and isolated from a **donor DNA** molecule. Two methods of isolation may be used using the enzymes restriction endonuclease or reverse transcriptase.

The gene coding for insulin is located using a gene probe. A gene probe is a specific segment of single-strand DNA that is complementary to a desired gene. For example, if the gene of interest contains the sequence AATCCGACA, then the probe will contain the complementary sequence TTAGGCTGT. When added to the appropriate solution, the probe will match and then bind to the gene of interest.

Using restriction endonuclease

The gene is then isolated from the rest of the DNA in a human cell. An enzyme called restriction endonuclease is used to cut the DNA into small pieces allowing individual genes to be isolated. The enzyme cuts DNA between specific base sequences which the enzyme recognises. Most **restriction enzymes** make a staggered cut in the DNA double helix. The unpaired bases at the cut form **sticky ends**.

Key Terms

Clone = a population of genetically identical cells or organisms.

Donor DNA = a gene that is isolated for insertion.

Restriction enzyme = enzyme which cuts DNA molecules between specific base sequences.

Sticky ends = the two ends of the 'foreign' DNA segment. They have a short row of unpaired bases that match the complementary bases at the two ends of the opened-up plasmid DNA sample.

◄ *Using a gene probe; strand of DNA and ray of laser*

Key Terms

Reverse transcriptase = enzyme used to synthesise DNA from mRNA in specific cells.

Intron = portion of DNA within a gene that does not code for a polypeptide.

▼ Study point

The advantage of using mRNA is that it carries the specific code for the gene and does not carry 'junk DNA' or **introns** found in DNA.

▼ Study point

Human insulin can be used instead of extracting insulin from animals. Also large quantities of product are produced quickly and relatively cheaply.

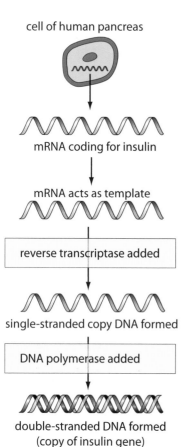

cell of human pancreas

mRNA coding for insulin

mRNA acts as template

reverse transcriptase added

single-stranded copy DNA formed

DNA polymerase added

double-stranded DNA formed
(copy of insulin gene)

The following exercise may help to understand the process.

The bacterium *E.coli* produces an enzyme called EcoR1, this is a restriction endonuclease enzyme. The enzyme causes a reaction that results in the breakage in a strand of DNA. The break always occurs where guanine is next to adenine in a specific sequence of bases on the DNA strand. The diagram shows a small section of the double-stranded DNA from a human.

After the enzyme reaction has taken place the separated piece of double-stranded DNA will be as shown below. The line of cut is staggered with the production of 'sticky ends'.

▼ *Use of restriction enzyme to cut DNA*

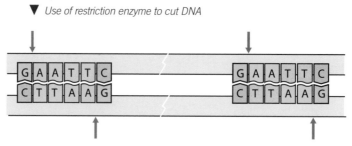

arrows indicate points where the enzyme breaks the strand

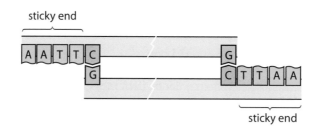

▲ *Production of 'sticky ends'*

If both the four unpaired bases are read at each end from left to right, the bases in one are in the reverse order to those in the other. That is, they are in a palindrome.

Using reverse transcriptase

Locating the correct piece of DNA is not easy, as the cell contains two copies only of the DNA. However, the cell may contain large numbers of molecules of mRNA that has been transcribed from it. This is especially true if cells can be used which are known to synthesise and secrete the required product. The functional mRNA coding for insulin will be present in large quantities in the cytoplasm of the cells of the pancreas.

- This mRNA can be extracted.

- The addition of an enzyme, **reverse transcriptase**, made by a group of viruses called retroviruses, is used to make a DNA copy of the mRNA. This single strand of DNA is called copy DNA or cDNA. Many copies of cDNA are made.

- The addition of DNA polymerase converts this to a double strand for insertion into a plasmid.

Inserting the gene into a vector

To insert the gene into a bacterium a go-between or vector is used. The vector, in this instance, is a **plasmid**, a small, circular piece of DNA found in bacteria. To obtain the plasmids, the bacteria containing them are treated to dissolve their cell walls and the plasmids are separated from the cell debris. The circular DNA molecule making up the plasmid is cut open using the same enzyme, restriction endonuclease. The enzyme makes staggered cuts, called 'sticky ends', which allow the donor DNA to be spliced into the vector DNA. This takes place when the donor and vector DNA are mixed together. The sticky ends are complementary and the C and G bases on their sticky ends pair up. Another group of enzymes, called **DNA ligases**, are used to join the donor and vector DNA together.

The diagram is a simplified representation of a technique used in genetic engineering.

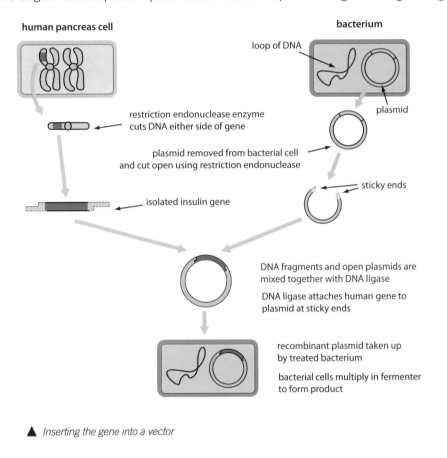

▲ *Inserting the gene into a vector*

Transfer of DNA into the host cell and the use of genetic markers

The recombinant DNA then needs to be transferred into bacterial cells. This involves mixing the plasmids and bacteria together in a medium containing calcium ions allowing the plasmids to pass into the bacteria.

However, only a small proportion, as few as 1%, of the bacterial cells take up the plasmids. It is therefore necessary to identify which bacterial cells have taken up the plasmid, involving the use of antibiotic-resistant genes. The low take-up may be explained as some plasmids close up without incorporating the DNA fragment.

The technique is based on the knowledge that some plasmids carry a gene for antibiotic resistance and this is unaffected by the introduction of the new gene. This is called a marker gene.

Key Terms

Plasmid = circular loop of DNA found in bacteria. The plasmid is known as a vector.

DNA ligase = enzyme which joins together portions of DNA.

Recombinant DNA = DNA which results from the combination of fragments from two different organisms.

▼ Study point

The same restriction enzyme is used to cut open the donor DNA and the plasmid to ensure that the sticky ends are complementary.

How Science Works

The use of a single antibiotic resistant marker to identify bacteria that have taken up plasmids has been largely replaced by other methods such as replica plating using a second antibiotic, fluorescent markers and enzyme markers.

21

Knowledge check

Link the appropriate terms 1–5 with the statements A–E.

1. DNA ligase.
2. Restriction endonuclease.
3. Reverse transcriptase.
4. Plasmid.
5. Marker gene.

A. Circular loop of DNA found in bacteria.

B. Enzyme which joins together portions of DNA.

C. Enzyme used to synthesise DNA from mRNA in specific cells.

D. Enzyme which cuts DNA molecules at specific base sequences.

E. Gene for antibiotic resistance

Key Term

Transgenic = an organism that has had its genotype altered producing a new strain of organism. Also known as genetically modified organisms.

The Ti plasmid from the soil bacterium, *Agrobacterium tumefaciens*, causes tumours called galls in plants.

1. Plasmid extracted from the bacterium.

2. Restriction enzyme is used to cut the plasmid and remove the tumour-forming gene.

3. A section of DNA containing the gene for disease resistance is located. Using the same restriction enzyme the DNA is cut to isolate the gene.

4. The gene is inserted into the plasmid, replacing the tumour-forming gene. DNA ligase is used to join the donor and vector DNA together.

gene for disease resistance →

The plasmid is inserted back into the bacterium.

5. The bacterial cell is introduced into plant cell. The bacterial cell divides and gene is inserted into plant chromosome.

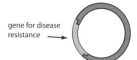

6. The transgenic plant cells are grown by tissue culture in a Petri dish.

All the bacterial cells are grown on a medium that contains the antibiotic, ampicillin. Bacterial cells that have taken up the plasmids will have acquired the gene for ampicillin resistance. These bacterial cells are able to break down the antibiotic and survive.

Using the bacteria that have taken up a piece of foreign DNA successfully, the foreign DNA replicates along with the rest of the plasmid every time the bacterial cell divides. Cloning of the recombinant containing bacteria, results in the production of multiple copies of the recombinant gene. That is, the bacteria divide repeatedly and give rise to a large population of bacterial cells all of which contain replicas of the foreign DNA.

The genetically modified bacteria are cultured on a large scale using a fermenter and produce insulin which is extracted and purified.

Genetically modified organisms

Using the techniques described in the previous section the genetic make-up of plants and animals can be altered by the transfer of genes between individuals of the same species or between individuals of different species. An organism that has had its genotype altered is called a **transgenic** organism.

Genetically modified crops

Bacteria are readily introduced into plants. Certain species naturally attack damaged plants and cause the plant cells to multiply and form a tumour. The bacteria do this by inserting genes from their own plasmids into one of the plant's chromosomes. The plasmid gene links with the DNA of the plant but stimulates the growth of a tumour. Scientists can replace the tumour-forming genes in the bacterial plasmids with useful genes.

◀ *Inserting plasmids into a plant*

The following describes two examples of transgenic plants or GM crops.

Soya beans

In many countries soya beans are very important as a source of food. They are used as an ingredient in a wide range of foods such as flour, protein and oil. About 60% of food products such as bread, biscuits, baby foods, soya milk, etc., are soya based. Certain varieties of soya plants have been modified to be tolerant to a weed-killer. This allows the weed-killer to be sprayed onto the crop without affecting it but it kills all the weeds. The weed-killer breaks down in the soil into harmless components.

Tomatoes

Tomatoes ripen naturally as they produce an enzyme which breaks down the pectin in their cell walls. Tomatoes sold at the supermarket need to be firm and at their best when displayed. This creates a problem for supermarkets that need to transport tomatoes long distances from their supplier. Scientists have developed a genetically modified tomato called 'FlavrSavr'. A gene has been introduced into the tomato plant having a base sequence complementary to that of the gene producing the enzyme. The mRNA transcribed from this inserted gene is therefore complementary to the mRNA strand of the original gene. The two combine to form a double strand. This prevents the mRNA of the original gene from being translated and effectively blocks the production of the enzyme. The result is that FlavrSavr tomatoes have a longer shelf life and a better taste.

Benefits and concerns

Since the introduction of GM crops at the end of the 20th century, there has been an increase in public concern and some scepticism regarding the research carried out by government agencies. Generally, GM foods have had a bad press. Questions are asked such as 'Are there potential risks in producing GM crops? Will the products and ingredients made from GM crops be labelled? Will the nutritional properties be affected? Will the environment be affected?'

People are opposed to GM crops for the following reasons:

- There are concerns that the GM plants through pollination will transfer their genes to wild relatives or similar crops growing nearby with unforeseen effects. For example, plants with introduced genes that enable them to resist insect attack will quickly lead to the establishment of a resistant population of insect pests. Long-term field trials will establish whether these concerns are well founded.

- GM crops contain marker genes. Some marker genes confer antibiotic resistance. There is concern that these genes may be transferred to the bacteria in the intestine of the consumer.

- Plant breeding may fall into the hands of just a few commercial companies, and the varieties they offer to the farmer will be reduced. This could make crops more susceptible to attack by pests and diseases and lead to a reduction in the use of important old varieties of their wild relatives.

- If GM crops are to be grown commercially in the UK, organic farm produce will be compromised. Pollen from GM crops, spread on the wind and by insects, could find its way into organic fields and beehives.

As a result many retailers have banned GM ingredients from their own brand products. This will remain until public confidence in the long-term use of GM crops is restored.

On a worldwide scale there is no doubt that GM crops have tremendous potential value. There are numerous examples of the benefits of GM crops:

- Solving food shortages in various parts of the world; perhaps also enabling crops to be grown in drought areas.

- Producing improved food with improved flavour and better keeping qualities.

- Reducing the harmful effects of modern farming by introducing nitrogen-fixing genes into crops such as rice and wheat, reducing the use of artificial fertilisers.

- Introducing genes that confer resistance to insects, weeds and diseases.

- Real benefits from improved animal production might be seen in the Third World. For example, it may one day be possible to introduce disease resistance into otherwise vulnerable animals. The Bovine Genome Project could result in, for instance, resistance to trypanosomiasis being introduced into more productive breeds of cattle from their naturally resistant African counterparts.

How Science Works

It is important to consider the moral, ethical and social issues connected with genetic engineering.

▼ Study point

List reasons for and against GM crops.

Genetic fingerprinting

Key Term

Electrophoresis = exposing the fragments of DNA to an electric current in a gel trough.

DNA Fingerprinting

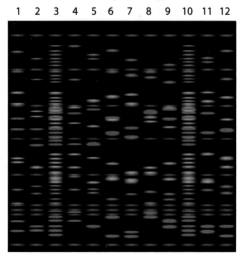

▼ *Genetic fingerprinting*

A person's DNA profile is known as their 'genetic fingerprint'. An individual's genetic fingerprint is unique. The technique of genetic fingerprinting can be used to provide forensic evidence and also determine parents in paternity cases. Since body cells contain the same DNA, tissues such as blood, hair, skin cells or semen can be used.

About 90% of the DNA of the human chromosome has no known function. Individuals acquire different sequences of this non-functional DNA. They vary in length but consist of sequences of bases, 20–40 bases long, often repeated many times. These unique lengths of non-coding DNA, known as hyper-variable regions (HVR) or short tandem repeats (STRs), are passed on to the offspring. It is the number of times that these lengths of non-coding DNA are repeated that is used to show the differences between individuals.

1. The DNA is extracted from the sample and cut into small fragments using restriction endonucleases.

2. The DNA fragments are separated by a technique known as **electrophoresis.** Since the fragments are negatively charged, they move towards the positive terminal. The smaller the fragment, the faster it moves and the DNA becomes separated into bands according to the size of the fragments.

3. The trough is covered with a nylon membrane and the fragments are transferred to the membrane by a process called Southern blotting.

4. Radioactive DNA probes (now largely replaced by non-radioactive or chemi-luminescent probes) are used to attach to specific parts of the fragments and any unbound fragments are washed off.

5. The nylon membrane with DNA fragments attached is placed under X-ray film and the radioactive probes expose the film.

6. This autoradiograph reveals a pattern of light and dark bands (the dark band indicates where a radioactive probe is present) which are unique to individuals and is called a genetic fingerprint.

The bands in a fingerprint are inherited from both parents: these can be used in paternity suits and can also be used to convict criminals. To do this, white blood cells are taken from the mother and the possible father. The bands of the mother are subtracted from the child's pattern. If the man is the true father, he must possess all the remaining bands in the child's genetic fingerprint.

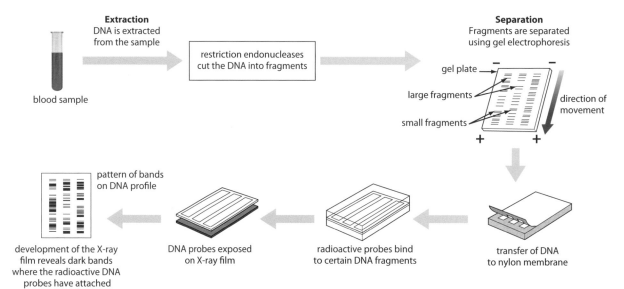

Polymerase chain reaction

PCR is really semi-conservative replication of DNA in a test-tube. The sample of DNA is dissolved in a buffer and mixed with the enzyme, DNA polymerase, nucleotides and short pieces of DNA called **primers**, which act as signals to the DNA polymerase to start copying.

The stages in the process are as follows:

1. The original DNA (target DNA) is heated to 95°C and it separates into two single strands.

2. The solution is cooled to 55°C triggering the primers to join to the complementary base sequences on each of the single strands of DNA. This in turn triggers DNA replication.

3. The solution is heated to 70°C and DNA polymerase (which is not denatured at this temperature) catalyses the synthesis of a complementary strand for each of the single strands of DNA, producing two identical double strands of DNA.

4. Steps 1–3 are repeated many times, doubling the quantity of DNA produced each time.

▼ *Polymerase chain reaction*

heat to 95°C; the two strands separate

↓

add the primers and cool to 55°C
so that they bind to the DNA

↓

raise temperature to 70°C. The DNA polymerase
enzyme copies each strand, starting at the primers

↓

the process is repeated until sufficient DNA is made

Issues of privacy

Scientists are confronted with vast quantities of data, a large proportion of which is genetic fingerprinting information. This information is used for phylogenetic studies, forensic science, paternity studies, etc. This raises concerns regarding the storage of this information as well as who has access to the data. Will insurance companies use the data to determine life and health insurance premiums?

On the wider issue of biodiversity of human beings, efforts are being made to store genetic material from the many races and tribes of the world before isolated tribes are intermixed and lost. This is scientifically useful, but careful ethical standards need to be maintained in order that genetic privacy is maintained and that no misuse of the information occurs in the future.

◣ Key Term

Primer = short sequences of nucleotides.

▼ Study point

It is important that the fragments of DNA used in PCR are not contaminated with any other biological material as the contaminants may contain DNA which would also be copied.

▼ Study point

Forensic scientists often use PCR when producing a genetic fingerprint to increase the quantity of DNA because the sample obtained at a crime scene may be very small.

22 Knowledge check

Link the appropriate temperatures 1–3 with the descriptions A–C.

1. 95°C.
2. 55°C.
3. 70°C.

A. DNA polymerase catalyses the synthesis of a complementary strand.

B. DNA separates into two single strands.

C. Primers are triggered.

The advantages and disadvantages of genetic engineering

There are economic issues associated with the new techniques which are technically complicated and therefore very expensive on an industrial scale. However, there are numerous advantages:

- The large-scale production of complex proteins or peptides that cannot be made by other methods.
- The production of higher yielding crops with superior keeping qualities, introducing resistance to disease.
- The health benefits for treating genetic diseases.

However, there are concerns that the development of genetic engineering will introduce the possibilities of misuse:

- Germ-line gene therapy is controversial as it involves replacing the defective allele with healthy alleles inside the fertilised egg. Some genes have no apparent function other than to control or 'switch off' other genes on the same chromosome. Tampering with genes in the fertilised egg could result in unforeseen effects in future generations.
- There are a number of potential hazards associated with genetic engineering and it is impossible to predict what the consequences might be of releasing genetically engineered organisms into the environment.

The potential hazards are:

- A new gene, on insertion, may disrupt normal gene function. For example, a potentially dangerous micro-organism with a new gene may become a dangerous pathogen if it is released into the environment.
- Bacteria readily exchange genetic material. The recombinant DNA might get into other organisms. For example, herbicide resistance might be transferred to a weed species.
- The deliberate use of antibiotic resistant genes in *E. coli*, which lives in the human gut, and the possibility that these genes could be accidentally transferred to human pathogens.
- The possibility of transfer of DNA with linked pathogenic genes, for example oncogenes increasing cancer risks.

Examiner tip

Consider making a list of the advantages and disadvantages and ethical issues involved with DNA technology. Then answer the following essay 'What are the advantages and disadvantages of DNA technology? Discuss this by referring to specific examples wherever possible.'

▼ Study point

The main ethical question is whether scientists have the right to alter the genotype of future generations. Do scientists know enough about how genes interact with each other?

▼ Study point

Despite legislation restricting the production and field testing of transgenic plants and animals, there remain reservations about the long-term effects of the manipulation of the human genome and the production of genetically modified organisms.

Applications of reproduction and genetics

1(a) Modern farming practice has been very successful in the artificial selection of cattle for dairy herds. A common breed is the large, black and white Friesian, the cows of which produce a high milk yield. Both cows and bulls normally have their horns removed.

Name a feature in the description of Friesian cattle which provides an example of:

(i) Continuous variation. (1)

(ii) Discontinuous variation. (1)

(iii) Non-inheritable characteristic. (1)

(b) Outline how cattle are bred selectively to produce a higher milk yield. (2)

(c) A possible consequence of selective breeding is that some breeds of cattle may become extinct.

(i) Why is it important to conserve rare breeds? (2)

(ii) Suggest what genetic problems might arise when maintaining a very small population of a rare breed over many generations. (2)

(d) To what extent might genetic counselling be regarded as a form of artificial selection in humans? (2)

WJEC A2 JUNE 1991

2 The diagram shows a method used to clone sheep.

(a)(i) State the scientific term used to describe:

I the developmental stage of the embryo transferred to the uterus of ewe T. (1)

II ewe T. (1)

(ii) Name the first process which takes place in the uterus of ewe T after embryo transfer. (1)

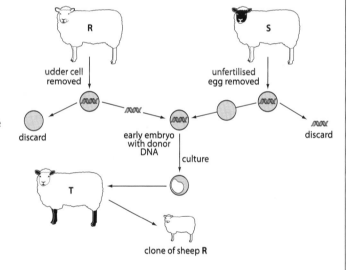

(b) Scientists used ewes from different pure breeding varieties in order to check that the procedure was successful at each stage and that the lamb produced was a clone of R.

Suggest what could have been deduced about the procedure if the lamb had been born:

(i) With a black face. (1)

(ii) With black legs. (1)

(c)(i) Suggest one reason why scientists did not think that it would be possible to clone sheep from udder cells. (1)

(ii) Some scientists do not regard sheep produced in this way as a pure clone. Suggest one reason for this. (1)

(d) Suggest one reason why it would be undesirable to produce all farm animals in this way. (1)

WJEC B3 JUNE 1998

3 Cauliflowers can be grown from seed, or clones of plants can be produced by micropropagation.

(a) What is meant by the phrase 'clones of plants can be produced by micropropagation'? (3)

(b) Explain why sieve tubes cannot be used in micropropagation. (1)

(c)(i) State two advantages of producing crops, such as cauliflowers, asexually. (2)

(ii) State two disadvantages of producing crops asexually. (2)

(d) Plant geneticists have noticed that during micropropagation of cauliflowers the number of chromosomes in the cells of some of the plants produced is 36 and not 18 as in the parent plant.

(i) What type of mutation is shown by the above example? (1)

(ii) Using your knowledge of nuclear division, suggest how the number of chromosomes has doubled in these plants. (1)

(iii) The cauliflower plants, which have three of each chromosome type in each of their cells, are sterile. Using your knowledge of nuclear division suggest why this is the case. (2)

(e) Trials have been carried out to genetically modify cauliflowers in order to make their leaves much greener than normal. 'Green genes' were introduced into cauliflower cells by either attaching them to part of a cauliflower virus (which has been rendered harmless) or to a bacterial plasmid. Suggest three reasons why there are concerns about this technology. (3)

WJEC BI5 JUNE 2005

4 The bacterium *Escherichia coli* produces an enzyme called EcoRI. This enzyme causes a reaction that results in a breakage in a strand of DNA. The break always occurs where guanine is adjacent to adenine in a specific sequence of bases on the DNA strand.

The diagram below shows a small section of the double-stranded DNA from a human. Part of the base sequence is labelled on strand I.

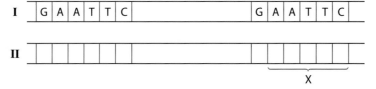

(a) Write the base sequence that would appear in the boxes on strand II. (1)

(b) Indicate where the enzyme would break strands I and II. (1)

(c)(i) Draw the separated piece of double-stranded DNA after the enzyme reaction has taken place. (1)

(ii) What is the most obvious feature of the sequence of bases in your drawing? (1)

(d) After the reaction, what name is given to region X? (1)

(e) Name the group of enzymes to which EcoRI belongs. (1)

(f) Genetic engineering makes use of the above technique to open the circular DNA in a bacterium. If a human gene, which codes for a valuable protein, occurs between the base sequences in the diagram, the fragment you have drawn can be joined into the bacterial structure. This enables the bacterium to synthesise the human protein.

(i) Name this bacterial structure. (1)

(ii) Name the enzyme used to fix the fragment into the bacterial structure. (1)

(g) An alternative technique is to collect human cells which produce this protein and extract the mRNA which codes for it from the cytoplasm. In the presence of free nucleotides and an enzyme the corresponding length of single-stranded DNA is formed.

(i) Name this type of enzyme. (1)

(ii) Another enzyme is used to turn this single strand into a double strand. Name this enzyme. (1)

(iii) Suggest one advantage of this technique over the method shown in the diagram. (1)

(h) Name a major international project that is likely to be helpful to genetic engineers in the future. Explain how it will help. (2)

WJEC BI1 JAN 2007

5 The diagram represents part of the process in the production of a crop plant resistant to the broad-spectrum herbicide, glyphosate. M represents the gene for glyphosate resistance.

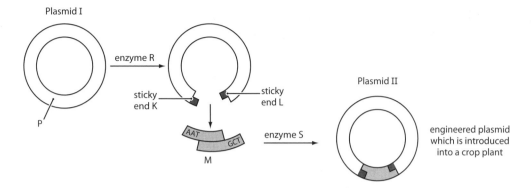

(a)(i) Name the specific biological molecule P which forms the plasmid. (1)

(ii) Name the enzyme types represented by R and S. (2)

(iii) The diagram shows the sticky ends on M in detail. Enter the base sequence you would expect to find on sticky end K and L of the plasmid. (2)

(b)(i) Suggest one advantage to farmers of growing crops resistant to glyphosate. (1)

(ii) Suggest one disadvantage of this particular strategy. (1)

WJEC A2 JUNE 1997

6 Read the following passage:

Tomatoes are often hard and flavourless because they are picked when green and firm enough to transport. They are then ripened by spraying with ethylene. This turns the tomatoes red but does not improve the flavour. Scientists have tried to slow the ripening process so that fruit can ripen on the vine and still maintain firmness for transport.

To stop the tomatoes turning soft too soon, scientists devised a way to block the enzyme polygalacturonase which eventually causes the fruit to rot.

(a) Suggest one reason why the activity of polygalacturonase 'eventually causes the fruit to rot'. (1)

(b) The passage continues:

Scientists inserted into the plant a gene, the sequence of which is the exact opposite of the gene which produces the enzyme polygalacturonase, an 'antisense' version of the gene. This gene was named the 'FlavrSavr' gene. The diagram shows how 'FlavrSavr' prevents tomatoes from rotting.

Adapted from *New Scientist* 28 May 1994

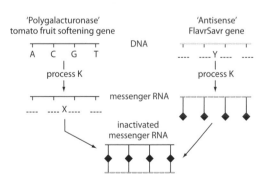

(i) State the codes to be found at X (polygalacturonase mRNA) and Y ('antisense' DNA). (2)

(ii) Name the process K which is shown in the diagram. (1)

(iii) With the aid of the diagram suggest how the 'antisense' 'FlavrSavr' gene slows down the process of tomato fruit softening. (3)

(c) Suggest one precaution scientists may have taken before recommending that genetically engineered tomatoes were safe for public consumption. (1)

WJEC A2 JUNE 1998

BY5

Energy and ecosystems

Ecology is the study of how living organisms interact with each other and with the environment. Although humans have existed on Earth for a relatively short period of time, they have had a far greater influence on the environment than any other species. The study of ecology is vital in order to collect data about the environment and how it is changing. Decisions have to be made based on the data, so the data has to be accurate and reliable. People need to be well informed in order to make important decisions that may have consequences for future generations.

The study of the flow of energy through the ecosystem is known as ecological energetics. The source of energy in an ecosystem is sunlight, and this is converted to chemical energy by the process of photosynthesis. The energy then passes along the food chain, at each stage of which some of the energy is lost as heat. Only approximately 10% of the energy available is transferred from one trophic level to the next. Consequently, food chains are no longer than five trophic levels. Then there is insufficient energy to support a large enough breeding population.

Ecosystems are dynamic and subject to change. Organisms interact with each other and the environment. Succession is the change in structure and composition of species of a community over time.

Topic contents

By the end of this topic you should be able to:

- Describe the flow of energy through the ecosystem.
- Explain primary and secondary productivity.
- Explain why herbivores have a lower secondary productivity than carnivores.
- Describe pyramids of energy as the best representation of quantitative data.
- Explain what is meant by succession.
- Describe the difference between primary and secondary succession.

Energy flow through the ecosystem

The ultimate source of energy for any ecosystem is sunlight. Plants convert sunlight energy into chemical energy by the process of photosynthesis. This energy is passed from organism to organism through food chains.

The study of the flow of energy through the **ecosystem** is known as ecological energetics. The following description summarises the flow of energy through the ecosystem:

- Green plants are called producers and trap solar energy and manufacture sugars from simple raw materials by the process of photosynthesis.

- The sun's energy is passed from one feeding or **trophic** level to another through the ecosystem.

- Herbivores (primary consumers) are animals that feed on plants. Carnivores are animals that feed on other animals.

- Each of these groups forms a feeding or trophic level with energy passing from each level to a higher one as material is eaten.

- Eventually the energy leaves the system as heat.

- Only a small amount of the total energy that reaches the plant as light is incorporated into plant tissues. As energy is passed along the food chain there is a large loss at each level.

- At each level energy is lost through respiration, and through the excretion of waste products, so the amount of energy is reduced.

- The sequence from plant to herbivore to carnivore is a food chain and is the route by which energy passes between trophic levels.

- It is the loss of energy at each level which limits the length of a food chain, so the number of links in a chain is normally limited to four or five.

- On the death of producers and consumers, some energy remains locked up in the organic compounds of which they are made. Detritivores and decomposers feed as saprobionts and contribute to the recycling of nutrients.

  - Detritivores are organisms such as earthworms which feed on small fragments of organic debris, called detritus, made up of non-living organic material, such as fallen leaves and the remains of dead organisms.

  - Decomposers are microbes such as bacteria and fungi that obtain nutrients from dead organisms and faeces. They complete the process of decomposition started by detritivores.

Key Terms

Ecosystem = a natural unit of living (biotic) components in a given area, as well as the non-living (abiotic) factors with which they interact.

Trophic = feeding.

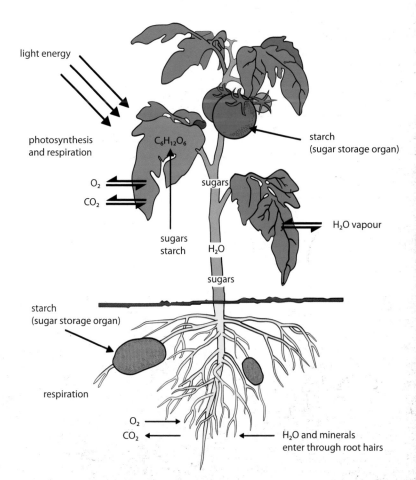

▶ Photosynthesis

Energy flow though producers

- The energy flowing from one organism to another in the food chain originates as sunlight.
- A large proportion of the energy that falls on a plant is not absorbed.
- If it is assumed that 100 units of energy per unit time reach the leaves of a crop plant, the diagram below shows what happens to the energy.

23

Knowledge check

Link the appropriate terms 1–4 with the statements A–D.

1. Gross primary productivity.
2. Net primary productivity.
3. Secondary productivity.
4. Photosynthetic efficiency.

A. The efficiency of a plant to trap light energy.
B. The rate at which energy is stored in plants.
C. The rate at which organic matter is produced by plants.
D. The rate at which consumers accumulate energy in body tissue.

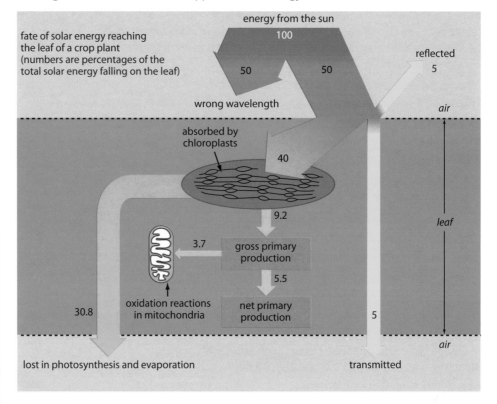

▲ *Energy loss in plants*

Photosynthetic efficiency (PE) indicates the ability of a plant to trap light energy and can be shown by the equation:

$$PE = \frac{\text{Quantity of light energy incorporated into product}}{\text{Quantity of energy falling on the plant}}$$

In plants this may be as low as 1%, slightly greater in crop plants, with sugarcane having a photosynthetic efficiency of 7–8%. The efficiency depends on external factors such as light intensity and temperature.

Gross primary productivity (GPP) is the rate at which products, such as glucose, are formed. A substantial amount of gross production is used up in respiration by the plant.

GPP – respiration = net production.

That which is left over after respiration is called net primary productivity (NPP). This represents the food available to primary consumers. In crop plants this represents the yield which may be harvested.

Secondary productivity is the rate at which consumers accumulate energy in the form of cells or tissues.

Examiner tip
Be prepared to carry out calculations in exam questions

Energy flow through consumers

Consumers have a conversion efficiency of about 10%, that is, for every 100 grams of plant material taken in or ingested, only about 10 grams is incorporated into herbivore biomass. This means that only part of the NPP of the ecosystem is transferred to the primary consumers.

The energy transfer between each trophic level may be calculated using the following equation:

$$\text{Energy transfer} = \frac{\text{Energy available after transfer}}{\text{Energy available before transfer}} \times 100$$

Herbivores are not able to eat all the vegetation available to them.

Consider a cow feeding on grass in a field:

- Some of the plant material is not eaten by the cow. Cattle grazing a field will eat the grasses and edible weeds but do not eat the roots and often leave the woody parts of the plants.

- Cows feed on plant material that contains cellulose, which they are unable to digest without the aid of bacteria. This passes out of the body as faeces containing a high proportion of undigested matter. (In terms of the ecosystem this energy is not wasted as it is available to decomposers.)

 Ruminants in BY2.

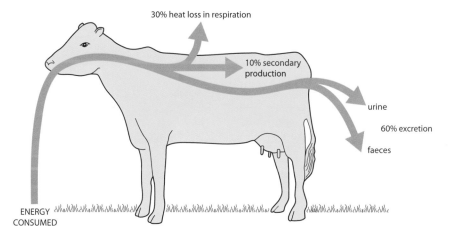

▲ *Energy flow through bullock*

- Some of the food material in the field is being eaten by other herbivores such as rabbits.

Herbivores have a lower secondary productivity than carnivores. That is, carnivores are more efficient at energy conversion than herbivores. They have a much higher secondary productivity. This is because their protein-rich diet is more readily and efficiently digested. Only about 20% of the energy intake is lost in the faeces and urine of carnivores compared with a loss of about 60% in herbivores.

YOU SHOULD KNOW ›››

››› that pyramids of energy may be used to represent feeding relationships

››› the meaning of the term 'succession'

››› the difference between a primary and secondary succession

Key Terms

Biomass = the mass of living material present at a given time.

Succession = the change in structure and composition of species of a community over time.

Climax community = a community that has reached equilibrium with its environment and no further change occurs.

Pyramids of energy

- The number of organisms, their **biomass** or the amount of energy contained in each trophic level, can be represented in diagrams with a bar for each level. These are known as pyramids of numbers, biomass and energy respectively.

- The diagram below shows two different pyramids for the same ecosystem

The pyramid of numbers is relatively easy to measure but does not take into account size or juvenile forms. It may also be impossible to draw to scale. Pyramids of biomass are difficult to measure accurately and give no indication of total productivity. Also both methods can give inverted pyramids.

- The most accurate way of representing feeding relationships in a community is to use a pyramid of energy, which provides a quantitative account of the feeding relationships in a community.

- A pyramid of energy shows the quantity of energy transferred from one trophic level to the next, per unit area or volume, per unit time. This represents the total energy requirement of each successive trophic level in a food chain.

- As material passes up through the food chain, energy is lost in respiration as heat, and in excretion, so the size of the bars decreases sharply. Since only some of the energy is passed on from one level to the next, energy pyramids are never inverted as in biomass pyramids.

- Pyramids of energy enable ease of comparison of the efficiency of energy transfer to be made from one trophic level to the next between different communities.

▼ *Ecological pyramids*

	pyramid of numbers	pyramid of energy
insectivorous bird	20	38 MJ
hoverfly larva	58 000	400 MJ
greenfly	88 000 000	4920 MJ
wheat	10 000 000	350 000 MJ

Community and succession

The distribution of species does not necessarily remain the same over long periods of time. Ecosystems are dynamic and subject to change. Organisms and their environment interact, if one changes so does the other. A change in the environment affects the organisms, and a change in the organisms affects the environment.

- Primary **succession** refers to the introduction of plants/animals into areas that have not previously supported a community, for example bare rock, or the site of volcanic eruption.

- Secondary succession refers to the reintroduction of organisms into a bare habitat previously occupied by plants and animals. If the original vegetation is removed, for example by fire, or by tree felling, the area rapidly becomes re-colonised by a succession of different plants and animals.

In any area, over time, new organisms replace existing ones, that is species diversity increases until a stable state is reached. All successions usually involve changes in community structure and function until a community reaches a climax of succession known as the **climax community**, for example a mature woodland.

Consider the colonisation of bare rock. The first organisms to colonise the bare rock are algae and lichens. These plants are called pioneer species and form a pioneer community. Lichens slowly erode the rock. This together with the weathering of the rock and the accumulation of dead and decomposing organic material leads to the formation of a primitive soil. Wind-blown spores allow mosses to appear and, as the soil develops, grasses become established. As the soil builds up deep-rooted shrubs appear. Over a very long time trees such as oak become established. This is then known as the climax community. This is a stable condition dominated by long-lived plants.

The different stages in a succession when particular species dominate are called **seres**.

bare rock colonised by algae, fungi and lichens → pioneer community of heather and mosses → herbs and low-growing shrubs

taller shrubs

oak/beech forest ← birch and pine saplings

◀ *Succession*

In a secondary succession, seeds, spores and organs of vegetative reproduction may remain in the soil and dispersal of plants and migration of animals will assist in colonisation of the habitat.

Human interference can affect a succession and may prevent the natural development of the climax community:

- Grazing by sheep.
- Farming of land.
- Deforestation and soil erosion.

Heather moors are subject to management to provide ideal conditions for game birds such as the red grouse. Adult grouse feed mainly on young, succulent heather shoots. The main form of management is by burning, which is carried out about every twelve years, usually in the autumn or early winter.

The diagram shows a profile of the four growth phases in the life cycle of heather, *Calluna vulgaris.*

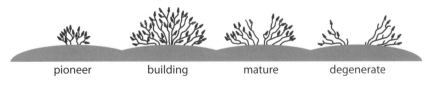

pioneer   building   mature   degenerate

▲ *Grouse management*

The pioneer phase would supply the best food supply for the adult grouse; the building phase would provide the best shelter for nesting. Without management the heather would pass through the mature to the degenerate phase and conditions would become unsuitable for the breeding of grouse.

Key Term

Sere = stage in succession.

▼ Study point

It should be realised that a community consists of animals as well as plants and that the animals have undergone a similar succession dictated by the plant types present at each stage.

24

Knowledge check

Link the appropriate terms 1–5 with the statements A–E.

1. Primary succession.
2. Secondary succession.
3. Seres.
4. Climax community.
5. Pioneer

A. The recolonisation of land where vegetation has been destroyed by fire.
B. First organisms to colonise bare rock.
C. A stable community where there is no further change.
D. The colonisation of bare rock.
E. The different stages in a succession.

Energy and ecosystems

1 The diagram represents the energy flow in $KJ\,m^{-2}\,year^{-1}$ through the community in one area of sea in the English Channel.

(a) Only 0.5% of the energy at the sea surface is fixed by the phytoplankton. Suggest two reasons for the 'loss' of energy at this stage. (2)

(b) Calculate:

  (i) The net primary production. (2)

  (i) The total energy available to decomposers. (1)

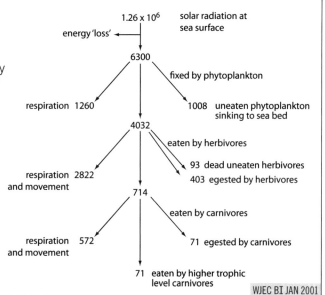

WJEC BI JAN 2001

2 (a) The energy flow through the herbivores can be expressed by the following equation:

$$C1 = C2 + R2 + E2$$

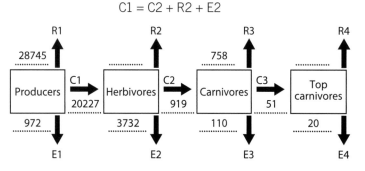

  (i) Calculate the respiratory loss by the herbivores. (1)

  (ii) Give the equation that expresses the energy flow through the carnivores. (1)

(b) The values given are for a small wood and are in $KJ\,m^{-2}\,year^{-1}$. The area of the wood is 25,000 m^2.

  (i) Calculate the total amount of energy 'expelled' by this ecosystem in one year. (2)

  (ii) Describe what happens to this expelled energy. (2)

WJEC BI2 JAN 2004

3 The diagram below shows the fate of solar energy that falls upon the vegetation of a field community. All measurements are in $KJ\,m^{-2}\,year^{-1}$.

(a)(i) The arrows X and Y represent the fate of solar energy that falls upon the field but is not used in photosynthesis. Suggest what might happen to this light energy. (2)

  (ii) Use the figures in the diagram to calculate the gross production and net production of the field. (2)

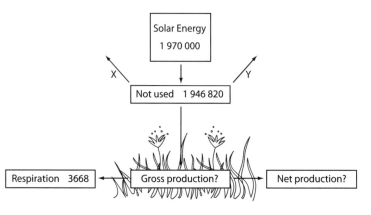

(b)   Energy flow between the animals in the field is shown below.

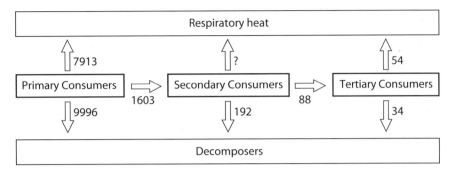

(i) Calculate the energy lost as heat by the secondary consumers. (1)

(ii) What products of the primary consumers will be available to decomposers as sources of energy? (1)

(c)   The principles of energy transfer through food chains can be used to compare the efficiency of different farming methods.

The table compares food use and rate of growth in cattle and rabbits.

	Cattle	Rabbits
Number of animals	1	300
Total body weight kg	600	600
Daily food consumption kg	7.5	30
Time taken to eat 1 ton of hay days	120	30
Daily weight gain kg	0.9	3.6
Total weight gain per tonne of hay kg	108	108
Daily heat loss kJ	84000	336000

(i) Which animal is the more efficient converter of hay into meat? (1)

(ii) Give a reason for your choice. (1)

(iii) Why do the rabbits lose more heat than the cow? (1)

(iv) Give one way in which a rabbit farmer might be able to reduce the heat loss and explain how this practice would affect meat production in the rabbits. (2)

WJEC BI2 JUNE 2006

4   Volcanic eruptions under the surface of the sea occasionally produce new islands such as Surtsey which formed 40km off the coast of Iceland. Krakatoa is an island 25km from the tropical island of Java in Asia. In 1850 it suffered a violent volcanic eruption and all life on the island was destroyed.

The table shows the number of flowering plant species that colonised the islands in the twelve years after the eruptions.

Number of years after eruption	Number of flowering plant species	
	Surtsey	Krakatoa
3	2	14
6	7	31
9	15	41
12	26	48

(a)   What is meant by the term succession? (1)

(b)   Suggest two reasons for the faster rate of colonisation on Krakatoa. (2)

(c)   The pioneer plants became established on the bare rocks of the island after the eruptions. They helped to make the conditions more suitable for other plants. Suggest how this process occurred. (2)

(d)   Give two reasons why the increase in the number and variety of flowering plants allowed the diversity of insects to increase. (2)

WJEC BI2 JUNE 2003

BY5

Effects of human activities

The increase in human population has meant that more food has to be produced to support this increase. In agriculture an increase in land use and overfishing of the oceans has led to a conflict between production and conservation. The use of pesticides and fertilisers has improved crop yield but environmental issues arise from their use. Overuse of antibiotics and pesticides has led to resistance in a number of pests.

Human activities are altering ecosystems upon which humans and other species depend. In the oceans fish stocks are being depleted by overharvesting. Massive destruction of habitats throughout the world has been brought about by agriculture, urban development, deforestation, mining and environmental pollution.

It is now recognised that each species may represent an important asset to humans; as a potential food source, or as a source of medical treatment. The conservation of species also ensures the conservation of existing gene pools. For ethical reasons it is important to conserve potentially useful genes for future generations of humans as well as for the survival of the species itself.

Humans also recognise the need to have a greater responsibility for the Earth as a whole. The increase in greenhouse gases is a major concern and is thought to be the cause of global warming. The increased demand for fossil fuels to provide energy for industrial nations is a serious concern. The development of biofuels from the monoculture of crops such as sugarcane is one attempt at helping to solve the problem. However, using food crops in this way is likely to push prices up, affecting food supplies for less prosperous nations. The solution to the problem may lie with the advances made in genetics, for example, the production of drought-resistant crops by genetic engineering.

Whatever the outcome it is essential that informed political decisions are made from knowledge based on sound scientific principles.

Topic contents

By the end of this topic you should be able to:

- Describe how human activity influences the environment at a local and global level.
- Describe how resistance develops in selected organisms.
- Describe the methods of artificial selection and their genetic consequences.
- Describe the effect of human activity on biodiversity and attempts to minimise the effects.
- Explain the effects of changes in agriculture.
- Describe the effects of deforestation and managed forestry.
- Describe attempts to prevent overfishing and the occurrence of eutrophication as a result of fish farming.
- Describe how the use of fertilisers can lead to water pollution.
- Explain how increasing levels of CO_2 are causing the greenhouse effect and global warming.
- Explain the impact of biofuel production.

Resistance

The process of evolution is normally very slow but the effect of human influence on the environment has created new selection pressures that have accelerated certain processes. Examples are warfarin resistance in rats and antibiotic **resistance** in bacteria.

Warfarin resistance in rats

The pesticide 'warfarin', which is an anticoagulant, has been used on a large scale to control the rat (*Rattus norvegicus*) population. Rats have become resistant to warfarin. There is a link between their diet and the degree of resistance.

A dominant allele R at a single locus in rats confers resistance. However, this allele also confers a requirement for vitamin K:

- Heterozygotes (Rr) are resistant to warfarin and have only a small requirement for vitamin K.
- Homozygotes (RR) are resistant to warfarin but have a massive requirement for vitamin K which is difficult to meet.
- Homozygotes (rr) are killed by warfarin but have a much better chance of survival than RR rats if warfarin is absent from the environment.

This is an example of heterozygote advantage where the heterozygotes are favoured by selection and both alleles Rr will be maintained in the population with all three genotypes RR, Rr and rr being produced in each generation. In the rat population both warfarin-sensitive and warfarin-resistant alleles are maintained in areas where warfarin is used as a selective agent.

Antibiotic resistance

In agriculture many farm animals are reared indoors so that they grow more rapidly. In these crowded conditions there is a greater risk of disease spreading; therefore broad-spectrum antibiotics are often added to animal food in an attempt to prevent disease.

Many bacteria that were previously susceptible to antibiotics have now become resistant. This resistance has arisen by mutations occurring randomly within populations of bacteria which then confer an advantage in the presence of that antibiotic. This may be the ability to produce an enzyme which breaks down the antibiotic. For example, some bacteria produce an enzyme, penicillinase, which renders penicillin ineffective. In the presence of penicillin, non-resistant forms are destroyed. There is a selection pressure favouring the resistant types. The greater the quantity and frequency of penicillin use, the greater the selection pressure. Repeated exposure to antibiotics has led to more bacteria surviving and passing on resistant genes.

The problem has been made worse by the discovery that resistance in bacteria can be transmitted between individuals of the same species. There is evidence that the resistance may be passed from one organism to another on plasmids, during conjugation (sexual reproduction). This means that a disease-causing organism can become resistant to a given antibiotic even before the antibiotic is used against them.

▶ *Conjugation in bacteria*

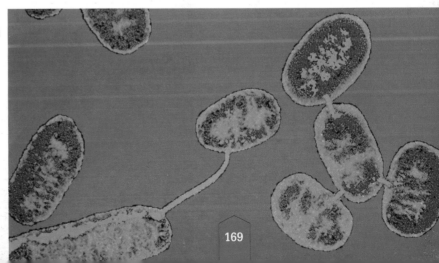

Key Term

Resistance = the ability of an organism to survive exposure to a dose of that poison which would normally be lethal to it.

Link Refer back to mutations on page 122.

Examiner tip
Candidates often incorrectly state that bacteria are immune to antibiotics. Bacteria become resistant to antibiotics.

▼ **Study point**

MRSA (methycillin resistant *Staphylococcus aureus*) has developed a resistance to several antibiotics.

▼ **Study point**

Artificial selection or selective breeding of animals and plants makes use of variations that occur within a population.

Artificial selection

Humans choose organisms showing desirable characters and breed only from these. In terms of genetics, humans rather than the environment determine which alleles are passed on to future generations and which are lost. This process of artificial selection mimics natural selection and provides evidence that selection can lead to the development of characteristics and the production of very distinct forms of organisms, as seen in many domestic animals and plant species.

Artificial selection:

- is carried out by humans to obtain plants or animals with the characteristics humans require.
- may take many years to develop organisms with the required characteristics.
- produces organisms belonging to the same species, which are often described as different breeds or varieties.

There are two basic methods of artificial selection:

- Inbreeding – occurs when the gametes of close relatives fuse. The problem with inbreeding is that it promotes homozygosity. That is, it increases the chance of a harmful recessive gene expressing itself, since there is a greater risk of a double recessive individual occurring. For example, plant species inbred over many generations show a degree of loss of vigour, size and fertility. This is called inbreeding depression. At intervals it is necessary to introduce new genes by outbreeding.
- Outbreeding – occurs by the crossing of unrelated varieties. Outbreeding promotes heterozygosity. It introduces hybrid vigour where the organisms sometimes grow more strongly. It arises when the new sets of chromosomes are complementary in their effects. Occasionally crosses have occurred between plants of different species, e.g. the development of modern wheat.

The following describes a typical breeding programme, to increase milk yield in cattle. To develop cows with an increased milk yield the following steps would be carried out:

1. Test the milk yield of selected high milk yielding cows.
2. Select the cow with the highest milk yield (A).
3. Select a bull descended from a cow with a high milk yield (B).
4. Cross cow A and bull B, and select female calves.
5. Wait for these calves to mature, then test their milk yield.
6. Select the cow with the highest milk yield (C), then repeat these steps over several generations.

Biodiversity

Human activities are altering ecosystems upon which they and other species depend. In the oceans, stocks of many fishes are being depleted by over-harvesting, and some of the most productive and diverse areas, such as coral reefs and estuaries are being severely stressed.

Extinction

Extinction is a natural process that has been taking place since life first evolved. It is the current *rate* of extinction that underlies the biodiversity crisis. Scientists believe that the normal 'background' rate of extinction is one out of every million species per year. It is now estimated that human activity in tropical areas alone has increased extinction rates between 1000 and 10,000 times! Massive destruction of habitats throughout the world has been brought about by agriculture, urban development, forestry, mining, and environmental pollution. Marine life has also been affected. About one third of the planet's marine fish species rely on coral reefs. At the current rate of destruction about half of the reefs could be lost in the next 20 years.

Endangered species

The vast majority of Earth's earlier occupants, including the large and once dominant dinosaurs and tree ferns, have become extinct largely as a result of climatic, geological and biotic changes. At the present time, human activity has taken over as the main cause of species extinction. Many of the larger mammals such as mountain gorillas, giant pandas, tigers and polar bears are threatened. Their decline in numbers has three main causes:

- Loss of habitat.
- Overhunting by humans.
- Competition from introduced species.

Other species are also threatened by additional causes such as:

- Deforestation.
- Pollution.
- Drainage of wetlands.

It is now recognised that each species may represent an important human asset, a potential source of food, useful chemicals, or disease-resistant genes. There is therefore a need for species conservation.

Present-day plants and animals used in agriculture and horticulture have been developed from plants and animals that were originally in the wild. Breeding increases genetic uniformity with the loss of rarer alleles. In the past, breeders may have neglected some important qualities, such as resistance to cold and disease, etc. These need to be added back into highly cultivated varieties, using the wild plants and animals as a gene bank. If habitats and the wildlife that live in them are threatened, this may no longer be possible. There is also concern about the progressive destruction of the tropical rain forests.

Among the many trees and shrubs are some with medicinal properties. The extinction of any plant species before its chemical properties have been investigated could amount to an incalculable loss. In recent years there has been much concern about the loss of gene pools, and legislation has endeavoured to prevent the extinction of endangered species.

▲ *Coral reef*

YOU SHOULD KNOW ›››

››› the reasons why species become endangered

››› the causes of extinction

››› methods of conservation

▼ **Study point**

The conservation of species ensures the conservation of existing gene pools.
For ethical reasons it is important to conserve potentially useful genes for future generations of humans as well as for the survival of the species itself.

Key Term

Ecotourism = responsible travel to natural areas that conserves the environment and improves the well-being of local people.

Examiner tip

Consider an essay entitled: 'What are endangered species? Discuss the reasons why some species have become endangered. Discuss ways in which species be conserved for future generations.'

▼ Study point

In Europe species are preserved in protected areas. Efforts are also being made to conserve the dwindling areas of tropical rain forests. This involves the development of habitats which are legally safeguarded and patrolled by wardens. This gives authorities greater powers to control developments and activities within designated areas.

▼ *Wetlands in Uganda*

The following are some of the steps that have been taken:

- Stocks of seeds of 'traditional' varieties of plants are stored in seed banks.
- The establishment of sperm banks.
- The founding of rare breeds societies to maintain old, less commercial varieties of animals.
- The protection and breeding of endangered species in specialised zoos.
- Reintroduction programmes, e.g. Red Kite in mid Wales.
- Global organisations, such as the World-Wide Fund for Nature, mount continuing campaigns to promote public awareness.
- International co-operation restricting trade, e.g. in ivory and whaling.
- In the UK, the Countryside Commission is the government body that promotes nature conservation. It gives advice to government and to all groups whose activities affect wildlife and their habitats:
    - It produces a range of publications.
    - It proposes schemes of management for each of the major ecosystem types, endeavouring to conserve species diversity.
    - It establishes nature reserves managed by wardens.

Education and legislation have also played their part in conservation.

Legislation has been introduced to protect endangered species and to prevent overgrazing, overfishing, hunting of game, collection of birds' eggs, picking of wild flowers, and plant collecting.

Ecotourism is a recent method introduced to promote conservation. The aims of **ecotourism** are:

- Minimise the negative impacts of tourism.
- Contribute to conservation efforts.
- Employ local people and give money back to the community.
- Educate visitors about the local environment and culture.
- Co-operate with local people to manage natural areas.
- Provide a positive experience for both visitor and host.

▼ *Cable cars in Malaysia*

Agricultural exploitation

Both the efficiency and the intensity of food production are being continually increased to meet the demands to produce more food for human consumption.

Following World War II more land was cultivated, the use of fertilisers and pesticides was increased, and mechanisation was introduced. These changes had a number of environmental implications:

- To make larger fields to enable machinery that was needed to prepare the soil and harvest crops, many hedgerows were removed.
- In the larger fields, single crops were grown, for example wheat or barley. This **monoculture** leads to reduced species diversity. Also, if the same crop is grown on the same plot year after year, yield progressively declines. This is due to two main factors:
  - Mineral depletion – intensive cultivation necessitated a huge increase in the use of inorganic fertilisers.
  - An increase in pests and diseases – necessitating the use of pesticides to remove insects and other pests.

In recent years the views of government, farmers and consumers have changed. People are far more aware of the value of the countryside, not only because it is a source of food, but also because it provides a habitat for plants and animals as well as a place to visit for relaxation and enjoyment. Schemes are in place to encourage farmers to manage their farms for biodiversity. Some land is given over to conservation and the farmers receive a grant to compensate them for reduced income. Since the Environment Act was passed in 1995 the loss of hedgerows has been reversed. Hedges are important as they provide habitats for insects and birds that live and feed on them. They also provide nesting sites for birds. Hedges act as wildlife corridors enabling birds and mammals to move from one area of woodland to another, helping to maintain the biodiversity of the woodlands.

YOU SHOULD KNOW ›››

- ››› the problems associated with monoculture
- ››› why deforestation occurs and its consequences
- ››› the importance of forestry management

Key Term

Monoculture = the simultaneous growth of large numbers of crop plants of similar age and type within a defined area.

▼ Study point

Forests cover about 34% of the world's land surface. However, about half the world's forests have been cut down by deforestation during the last 30 years.

▼ Study point

Yield progressively declines if the same crops are grown in the same field year after year due to mineral depletion and the increase in pests and diseases.

Link Pest control on page 47.

▼ Field of yellow rapeseed, Yunnan Province, China

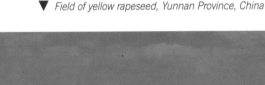

▼ Combine harvesting wheat

Key Term

Soil erosion = the removal of topsoil containing valuable nutrients.

Examiner tip

In answering a question on the effect of human influence on habitats you must give an objective and scientific answer. Too often candidates become carried away with the effects of human activity and do not provide clear and logical arguments supported by appropriate facts and examples.

▼ Study point

Tree roots help to bind soil together. Deforestation contributes to soil erosion by washing the soil away particularly on hillsides.

▼ *Deforestation*

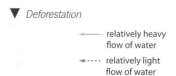

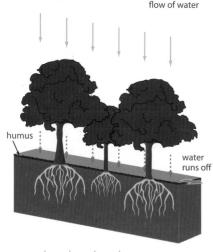

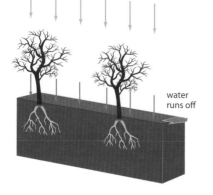

Deforestation

Forest and woodland trees are being cut down faster than they can be replanted or regenerated naturally. Forests help to maintain a balance of carbon dioxide and oxygen in the atmosphere.

▲ *Deforestation in British Columbia*

Reasons for deforestation:

- There is a world demand for timber as a building material.
- Wood is used as a fuel.
- Land is cleared for farming.
- New roads are built to provide a transport infrastructure.
- There is a demand for paper and packaging.

The consequences of deforestation are:

- Climate change: the rate at which carbon dioxide is removed from the atmosphere by the process of photosynthesis is being reduced by cutting down forests. On a global scale this is a massive reduction and contributes to global warming.

- Destruction of natural habitats, leading to a reduction in biodiversity. It is estimated that at least 50% of the Earth's species live in the tropical rain forests, even though they only occupy about 10% of the Earth's land area. If natural habitats are destroyed, this may lead to the loss of medicinal properties of some tropical plants that may become extinct before their clinical properties have been investigated.

- Soil erosion:
  - Digging and ploughing loosens the topsoil, assisting in the process of **soil erosion**.
  - The removal of vegetation affects regional climate mainly by reducing rainfall thus accelerating desertification.
  - Deforestation of the watershed causes lowland flooding.

The removal of vegetation on the higher slopes of valleys results in heavy rain sweeping exposed soil to the flood plains below. On the lower slopes, plants and leaf litter would normally act as a sponge soaking up heavy rainfall, and water would gradually be released into the soil. Instead, due to the absence of plants, only evaporation occurs. This is generally slower than transpiration in returning water vapour to the atmosphere, so soil conditions become wetter.

Forest management

Woodland and forests have been used as a source of timber for thousands of years. With careful management, it is possible to make use of this resource without destroying the ecosystem.

Managed forestry involves sustainable replanting and regeneration:

- In Britain the technique of **coppicing** has been used for thousands of years. This traditional woodland management system is based on the fact that most deciduous trees grow from the base when their trunks are cut down.

- Instead of removing all the trees in an area at one time, **selective cutting** can be used. This technique is valuable on steep slopes where the total removal of trees would leave the soil very vulnerable to erosion. Selective cutting also helps to maintain nutrients in the forest soil, reduces the nutrient loss, and minimises the amount of soil that is washed into nearby waterways.

- **Long rotation time** also increases sustainability.

With good forestry practice, efficiency can be increased in several ways:

- Planting trees the optimum distance apart. Planting trees too close together will result in intra-specific competition. This results in the trees growing tall and thin producing poor quality timber.

- Controlling pests and diseases. If trees grow well, this results in a high quality harvest of timber. This means that fewer trees need to be felled. Best use is made of the land, reducing the total area of land required.

- Cutting timber in such a way that a similar number of trees are removed year after year for long periods of time, the forest ecosystem can be maintained. This means that the habitats are left intact and species are able to live in the forest even though timber is being extracted.

- Preservation of native woodlands. At present woodland covers 10% of the UK but of this area only 1% consists of natural or native woodland. It is essential that these native woodlands are preserved in order to maintain and enhance biodiversity. There is a need to plant more native species to provide a wide range of habitats for the great variety of species that live there.

Key Terms

Coppicing = the cutting down of trees close to the ground and then leaving them for several years to re-grow.

Selective cutting = felling only some of the largest trees, leaving the others in place.

Long rotation time = leaving each part of the forest for many years before re-harvesting it.

▲ *Coppiced poplar trees*

▼ *Thinning and tree spacing*

Key Terms

Overfishing = the rate at which fish are harvested exceeds the rate at which they reproduce.

Drift netting = suspending a net from floats stretched between two boats so that fish swim into it.

Trawling = dragging a large net through the water, catching whatever happens to be in the way.

Overfishing

There has been a dramatic increase in the intensity and efficiency of commercial fishing methods resulting in **overfishing** in many areas of the world. The European Commission has successfully banned the fishing of particular species, enabling the breeding stocks to recover. Legislation limiting the size of fishing fleets, restricting the numbers of days spent at sea, and controlling the mesh size of nets has been less successful as they are difficult to enforce.

Commercial fishing

Some fish, called pelagic fish, live in the upper parts of the water and are caught by **drift netting**. Once caught in the net the fish cannot escape unless they are small enough to fit through the net's mesh.

Fish that live deeper in the water, the mid and bottom-feeders, are caught by **trawling**. The size of the holes in the net is again very important and it is vital for the conservation of fish stocks that nets with a very small mesh are banned as they catch young fish before they have become sufficiently mature to reproduce.

▲ *Commercial fishing boat*

Overfishing can seriously affect not only the fish stocks but also the livelihoods of the fishermen. A delicate balance needs to be struck between catching large numbers of fish so as to make a commercial living and ensuring that there are enough fish left alive to be able to replenish stocks for future years.

Effects of overfishing on other wildlife

The overfishing of a particular species has 'knock-on' effects along the food chain. For example, as herring is eaten by cod, if herring are overfished, the cod population suffers as well. In the Antarctic, fishing for krill is threatening to disrupt the delicate balance of nature in these waters. Krill are small shrimps and are a very important trophic level in the food chain. They are the main source of food for the great whales, and also supplement the diets of seals, penguins, squid and fish. Krill occur in huge swarms many miles across. Since the 1980s six countries, including Japan and Russia, have been harvesting krill. The natural balance in the Antarctic has already been upset by the overexploitation of whales; the heavy fishing of krill will undoubtedly have a serious effect on the whale population.

Measures to reduce overfishing

- Imposing quotas on catches based on scientific estimates of the size of the fish stocks.
- Restricting the net mesh size. Correct mesh size should be used in all nets to ensure that fish of the correct age are caught and to prevent as much as possible 'accidental' catches of other fish. Larger mesh nets allow juvenile fish to escape and so survive to reproduce.
- International agreements limiting catches.
- Enforcing closed seasons for fishing.
- Enforcing exclusion zones.

Fish farming

In the UK trout and salmon are the fish most commonly farmed. These species can be bred and grown to maturity in ponds, lakes and managed enclosures in estuaries, where predation is reduced and food supplies are maintained. For plankton-feeders the growth of phytoplankton can be aided by the addition of artificial fertilisers to the water. Fish grow rapidly when they are reared in the warm waters discharged from factories.

Key Term

Eutrophication = the artificial enrichment of aquatic habitats by excess nutrients, often caused by run-off of fertilisers, resulting in a reduction in the oxygen level of the water.

Link Eutrophication is studied in more detail on page 180.

▲ *Fish farming in a lake*

▲ *Fish farm in Thailand*

Fish farming, however, is the cause of many problems. Farmed salmon are often kept very densely stocked. In this state the fish can more easily become diseased and these diseases can spread to wild fish. Huge amounts of antibiotics are required to keep the fish moderately healthy. The pesticides used to control fish parasites are also known to harm marine invertebrates. There is also the likelihood that the delicate balance of the waterways may be upset. For example, **eutrophication** can result when fish excreta, waste food and fertiliser are carried in the water to the wider community around the rearing pens.

When fish escape, the farmed fish interbreed with wild fish and potentially weaken wild stocks. There is also the problem of pollution in the water and seabed around fish farms. Farmed salmon, which are carnivorous, eat three times their bodyweight in fish feed, which is made from other fish. This is not the best use of resources from an environmental point of view. Another problem with all salmon (wild or farmed) is that they can contain high levels of dioxins and polychlorinated biphenyls (PCBs).

YOU SHOULD KNOW ›››

››› how the delicate balance of the carbon cycle has been affected by the burning of fossil fuels and deforestation

››› the meaning of the terms 'greenhouse effect' and 'global warming'

››› the consequences of global warming

››› how biofuels may be an alternative to fossil fuels

Link The carbon cycle in BY4 page 51.

▼ Study point

It is suggested that if concentrations of greenhouse gases rise at current rates, possible temperature increases during the next 50 years could be in the range 1.5–5.5°C.

Carbon cycle

There has been a rise in carbon dioxide in the atmosphere, particularly over the last 50 years. There are two main reasons for the increase:

- The burning of fossil fuels. This accounts for about 70% of the increase in CO_2, most (76%) coming from industrialised countries.

- Deforestation – accounts for about 30% of the increased CO_2 levels, as about half the world's forests have been removed over the last 30 years. Forests help to maintain the balance of carbon dioxide and oxygen in the atmosphere. This is important because carbon dioxide is a 'greenhouse gas'. It absorbs radiation from the Earth and if it accumulates, it leads to 'global warming'.

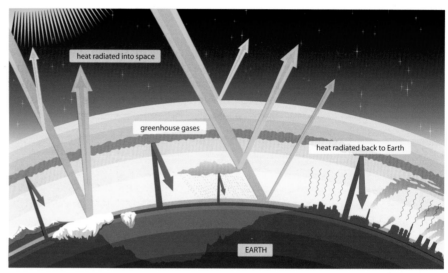

▲ *The greenhouse effect*

- Greenhouse gases form a layer in the atmosphere acting like glass in a greenhouse. These gases allow high-energy solar radiation to pass through to the Earth's surface. Much of this energy is 'bounced back' towards space as low energy heat which is absorbed and trapped by the gases. The greenhouse effect is a natural process without which the average temperature on Earth would be too low to sustain life. In recent years the situation has become much worse due to the increase in industrialisation in countries such as China, and the increase in global transport.

- Global warming may lead to changes in rainfall patterns, a rise in sea level, and a wide range of impacts on plants, wildlife, and humans. When scientists talk about the issue of climate change, their concern is about global warming caused by human activities.

Possible consequence of global warming may be:

- Some melting of polar icecaps resulting in flooding in coastal areas.

- Increased frequency of droughts, hurricanes and cyclones, and also forest fires.

- In tropical areas of the world, decreased availability of water might lead to the formation of deserts.

- Increased crop yields, but insect pest populations might also increase.

- Climate change will have serious effects on world food production with massive reductions in the grain crops of North America and Central Asia. This would have serious economic and political consequences.

- Increasing CO_2 in the oceans decreases the pH, which threatens fish populations, coral reefs, etc.

- Genetic engineering research is ongoing to develop drought-resistant crops. A gene that controls water efficiency in plants has been identified but it will take many years of research to develop the idea further.

Biofuels

Biofuels exist in a variety of forms including wood, wood chippings and straw; biogas (methane) from animals' excrement; ethanol, diesel or other liquid fuels made from processing plant material or waste oil.

▶ *Biofuel alternative to fossil fuel*

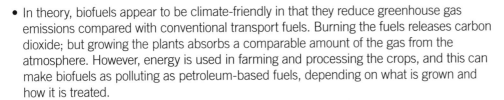

- Ethanol for fuel is made through fermentation, the same process which produces it in wine and beer. Biodiesel is an oil substitute manufactured from oil seed rape. Biogas, mainly methane, is used on a small scale to power generators. Bio-ethanol, an alcohol, is usually mixed with petrol, while biodiesel is either used on its own or in a mixture.

- In theory, biofuels appear to be climate-friendly in that they reduce greenhouse gas emissions compared with conventional transport fuels. Burning the fuels releases carbon dioxide; but growing the plants absorbs a comparable amount of the gas from the atmosphere. However, energy is used in farming and processing the crops, and this can make biofuels as polluting as petroleum-based fuels, depending on what is grown and how it is treated.

- Brazil leads the world in production and use, making about 16 billion litres per year of ethanol from its sugarcane industry; 60% of new cars can run on a fuel mix which includes 85% ethanol.

- From the environmental point of the view, the big issue is biodiversity. With much of the Western world's farmland already consisting of fields of monocultured crops, the fear is that a major adoption of biofuels will reduce habitat for animals and wild plants still further.

- Asian countries may be tempted to replace rainforest with more palm oil plantations. If increased proportions of food crops such as corn or soy are used for fuel, this may push prices up, affecting food supplies for less prosperous populations.

- The mixed picture regarding the climate benefit of biofuels leads some observers to say that the priority should be reducing energy use; they claim that initiatives on biofuels detract attention from this and are more of a financial help to politically important farming lobbies than a serious attempt to cut greenhouse gas emissions.

- There are also technical problems. Although engines can generally cope with the new fuels, current technologies limit production, because only certain parts of specific plants can be used. The tough cellulose in the plant cell walls has to be pre-treated before it can be fermented. It is hoped that the so-called second-generation of biofuels will process the cellulose found in many plants. This should lead to far more efficient production using a much greater range of plants and plant waste.

 Key Term

Biofuel = any kind of fuel that is biological in origin. In recent years, the term biofuel has come to mean ethanol and diesel made from crops including corn, sugarcane and rapeseed.

Examiner tip

Deforestation and biofuels are linked topics in that areas have been cleared in order to produce large fields of monocultured crops.

25

Knowledge check

Link the terms 1–4 with the following statements A–D.

1. Eutrophication.
2. Coppicing.
3. Carbon footprint.
4. Monoculture.

A. Large number of same species of crop plants grown in an area.

B. Annual production of CO_2 to energy use produced by an individual.

C. Technique where trees are cut down close to the ground and left to re-grow for several years.

D. Reduction in oxygen level in a lake resulting from increased level of nitrate.

Link The nitrogen cycle on page 52.

Nitrogen-containing fertilisers

In developed countries agriculture has become more intensive, providing high yields of crops from relatively small areas of land. However, this increase in food production has had a deleterious effect on the environment. The increased use of nitrate-containing fertilisers has had some harmful effects on both aquatic and terrestrial ecosystems.

- Problems caused by excess nitrate in soils. On agricultural land the increased use of fertiliser has reduced species diversity on grassland. Fertilisers increase the growth of grasses and plants such as nettles which shade out smaller plants.

- Problems caused by nitrates leaching into rivers. The leaching of nitrates and phosphates from the surrounding land is a slow, natural process during which the concentration of salts builds up in bodies of water. In lakes and rivers the salts normally accumulate until equilibrium is reached, where they are exactly counterbalanced by the rate at which they are removed. However, sewage and fertilisers are an additional source of these salts and their leaching from the land into the water may result in eutrophication of lakes and rivers.

▲ Eutrophic lake

- Nitrate is highly soluble and is readily leached from soil and washed into rivers from surrounding land. The first effect may be an algal bloom. At this stage the water may become green and light is unable to penetrate to any depth. The plants in the deeper regions of the lake are unable to photosynthesise and therefore die. There is a general decrease in animal species diversity as they rely on the plants for food and shelter. The short-lived algae soon die and are decomposed by saprobiontic bacteria which use a lot of oxygen creating a biochemical oxygen demand (BOD). The water in all but the very upper layers becomes deoxygenated, so that fish and other oxygen-requiring species die. In the final stages of the process of eutrophication anaerobic bacteria in the water may reduce nitrate to nitrite (both nitrate and nitrite are toxic compounds). In view of their toxicity, the EU has set a limit of 11.3 parts per million (ppm) total nitrogen in drinking water. This figure has been exceeded in parts of the UK.

- Where the problem of high nitrate levels in waterways is particularly serious, farmers must comply with strict legislation to reduce the quantity of nitrate they release into the environment. They must:
  - Restrict the amount of fertiliser applied to the soil.
  - Only apply fertiliser at a time when the crops are actively growing.
  - Leave a strip at least 10 metres wide next to watercourses.
  - Dig drainage ditches.

26

Knowledge check

Identify the missing word or words.

Increased nitrate levels in lakes and rivers causes a massive increase in microscopic plants, referred to as an •••• •••••. This means •••• is unable to penetrate to lower depths and plants are unable to carry out the process of •••• and die. The short-lived algae soon die and are decomposed by •••• bacteria using up a lot of dissolved ••••. Anaerobic bacteria then reduce nitrate to ••••.

Effects of human activities

1. Warfarin is used as a rat poison. Resistance to this poison is thought to be controlled by a single dominant allele.

   Before 1967 warfarin was used in all the areas shown on the map. The first incidence of warfarin resistance was recorded near Welshpool. The map shows the spread of the allele for warfarin resistance.

   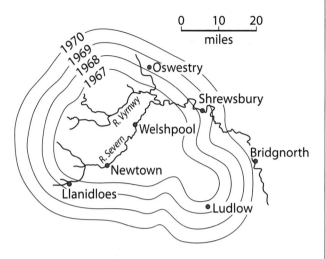

   (a)(i) Explain how the warfarin-resistant allele initially developed. (1)

   (ii) Explain how the allele became common in that population. (3)

   (iii) State two ways in which alleles for the resistance spread through the rat population in the area shown on the map. (2)

   (b) Animals with this allele for resistance need large quantities of vitamin K (which may not be available) in their diet without which they are unlikely to survive and breed. Spread of the resistant population was dependent on the continued use of warfarin. If its use is discontinued, the frequency of the resistant allele in the population is likely to decrease. Explain this statement. (2)

   WJEC BI5 JUNE 2005

2. The North Sea cod is a fish which under ideal conditions has a lifespan in excess of ten years. It starts to breed when it is three years old. The graph below is a plot of data obtained from sample catches in which the age and weight of each fish caught was recorded. The weights for each age group were added together to give the biomass in that age group. Two equal areas of sea were sampled, one which had been moderately fished and the other which had been heavily fished.

   (a)(i) The graph shows that heavy fishing reduces the weight of fish present. Describe one other difference between the two areas. (1)

   (ii) Explain what effect this difference would have on the breeding success of the two populations. (2)

   (b) If similar data were plotted from an area in which there had been no fishing, suggest one way in which the plot would differ from those given in the figure. (1)

   (c) Apart from banning fishing completely, suggest two ways in which the populations shown in the graph could be conserved. (2)

   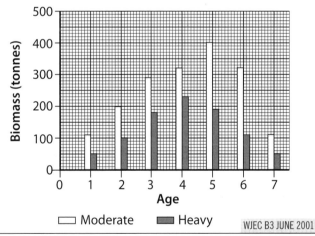

   WJEC B3 JUNE 2001

3. Many of the world's forests have been affected by human activity. Two methods of forestry management that have been used for centuries are 'coppicing' and 'slash and burn'. The latter involves felling and burning trees to create land for agriculture and the resulting ash improves the fertility of the soil. However, gas emissions from biomass burning are vast on a global scale.

   (a) Explain what is meant by the term 'greenhouse effect'. (2)

   (b)(i) Explain why coppicing is less likely to cause soil erosion and increased sediment deposits than the slash and burn method.

   (ii) Explain why slash and burn reduces biodiversity while coppicing increases it. (2)

   WJEC BI2 JAN 2004

4   Read the passage below and use the information and your knowledge to answer the questions that follow.

The rain forests in the developing countries of South East Asia are being destroyed by both roaming farmers and large companies. The roaming farmers, known as 'shifting cultivators', have been blamed for large-scale forest destruction, loss of species and uncontrolled burning.

In shifting cultivation, a plot of forest is felled and burnt, providing fertile ash in which to grow food crops. After one to three years, as weeds flourish and fertility declines, the plot is abandoned for a fallow period of about 20 years.

In Sumatra this traditional method of cultivation has been adapted to make best use of the fallow period. Rubber plant seedlings are planted with food crops and the rubber trees allowed to mature during the fallow period, during which time other wild plant species will grow again. The rubber, a cash crop, can be harvested after 10 years and the land can be made available for felling again after a further 15 years.

When the human population density is high, fallow periods have been reduced and food yields have dropped significantly. In some places the cultivation pattern has been replaced with permanent agriculture, such as rubber plantations.

Adapted from *New Scientist* 15 November 1997

(a)   State two possible reasons, other than agriculture, for the destruction of the rain forests. (2)

(b)   What is the advantage to these farmers of burning felled trees to produce ash before cultivation? (2)

(c)   'Where the human population density is high, fallow periods have been reduced and food yields have dropped significantly. Explain why the food yields have decreased. (2)

(d)   Give two reasons why the pattern of shifting cultivation in Sumatra is of benefit to the farmer. (2)

(e)   A study was carried out in three areas of forest that had different types of agriculture. The number of species of five types of plant (trees, climbers, epiphytes, shrubs and herbaceous plants) were counted in:

  • An area of undisturbed primary forest.

  • An area that was used for traditional agroforest (shifting cultivation, as in Sumatra).

  • A rubber plantation.

The results are shown on the right.

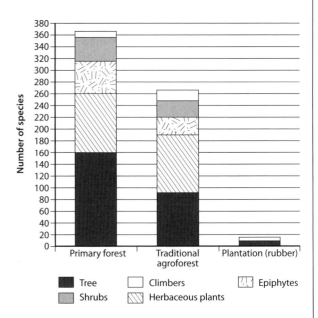

Comment on the species diversity of:

  (i) The plantation compared with the primary forest. (2)

  (ii) The traditional agroforest compared with the primary forest. (3)

(f)   It is often stated that cultivation of the rain forest is totally destructive. Using the information given in the graph and your own knowledge, comment on the validity of this statement. (2)

Adapted from *New Scientist* 15 November 1997

WJEC BI5 JUNE 2003

Exam practice answers

BY4: ATP and Respiration

1. (a) A: phosphates; B: base/adenine; C: ribose/pentose sugar.
   (b) Muscle contraction; active transport; nerve transmission.
   (c) Supplies energy; in all reactions; in all cells.
   (d) Only one enzyme needed; energy released in usable amounts; link between energy production and energy use; easily transported across membranes; easily hydrolysed.

2. (a) A: substrate-level; B: oxidative.
   (b)(i) Decarboxylase.
      (ii) Dehydrogenase.
   (c)(i) X: NAD; Y: FAD.
      (ii) Reduced NAD is associated with three pumps whereas at Y the second carrier is FAD which has two pumps associated with it/carrier system at FAD has two pumps whereas at X there are three pumps.
   (d)

Stage	Number of ATP molecules formed from reduced hydrogen acceptor	Number of ATP molecules formed directly	Total number of ATP molecules formed from each
Link reaction	6	0	6
Krebs cycle	22	2	24

   (e)(i) Acetyl CoA.
      (ii) Two.
      (iii) Pyruvate is converted to acetyl group/acetate; by the removal of carbon dioxide/decarboxylation; acetyl group combines with coenzyme A.

3. (a)(i) A: glycolysis; C: Krebs cycle; D: electron transport chain.
      (ii) P: carbon dioxide; Q: ethanol; R: oxygen; S: water.
      (iii) NAD.
   (b)(i) The hydrogen atoms split into protons and electrons. The electrons provide energy for the pumps; to pump protons across the membrane into the intermembrane space.
      (ii) R to S/oxygen to water.
      (iii) It takes up or removes hydrogen/protons to form water.
      (iv) Protons diffuse from the intermembrane space through the enzyme ATP synthetase and the energy released is used to make ATP from ADP and inorganic phosphate.

4. (a)(i) A: triose phosphate; B: pyruvate/pyruvic acid; C: Acetyl Coenzyme A/Acetyl CoA; D: reduced NAD; E: carbon dioxide; F: oxygen.
      (ii) To provide activation energy/provide energy to split glucose/convert glucose into glucose 6 phosphate.
   (b)(i) Inner mitochondrial membrane/crista.
      (ii) From hydrogen (which is split into protons and electrons).
      (iii) The electrons are used to provide energy to pump protons across the membrane from the matrix into the intermembrane space; an electrochemical gradient is created and protons move down the gradient; through ATP synthetase; to provide energy to convert ADP and inorganic phosphate into ATP.

5. (a) see table below
   (b) Electron transport chain.
   (c) Oxidative phosphorylation is a chemical reaction whereby glucose provides the energy but in photosynthesis the energy originates from light.
   (d)(i) Pyruvate is directly reduced by reduced NAD to lactate.
      (ii) Pyruvate is decarboxylated to ethanal; ethanal is reduced to ethanol.

anaerobic conditions (glycolysis)

6. A glucose is phosphorylated/ATP is added
   B to form hexose phosphate
   C this is split into two 3C triose phosphate molecules
   D which are converted to pyruvate
   E with a net gain of 2 ATP
   F and 2 reduced NAD
   G this takes place in the cytoplasm/glycolysis
   H in the absence of oxygen the Krebs cycle and the electron transport chain cannot take place/ there is no oxygen to act as the final electron acceptor at the end of the ETC.
   I pyruvate is reduced by NADH to lactic acid in animal cells
   J in fungi decarboxylation takes place
   K ethanal is produced
   L ethanal is reduced by NADH to ethanol
   M anaerobic respiration yields a total of 2 ATP
   N because a large amount of energy is tied up in lactic acid/ethanol

---

5. (a)

Stage	Start point	End point	Products			
			ATP	Reduced NAD	Reduced FAD	Carbon dioxide
Glycolysis	Glucose	Pyruvate	✓	✓		
Link reaction	Pyruvate	Acetyl CoA		✓		✓
Krebs cycle	Acetyl CoA	4 carbon compound	✓	✓	✓	✓
Electron transport chain (oxidative phosphorylation)	Reduced NAD or reduced FAD	Water	✓			

BY4: Photosynthesis

1. (a) Thylakoid membrane.
 (b) Photosystems.
 (c) Photophosphorylation.
 (d) (i) Photolysis.
 (ii) Replace electrons lost from photosystem II.
 (iii) Accepted by NADP, which is reduced.
 (iv) Accepting electrons.
 (e) (i) Calvin cycle.
 (ii) Stroma.
 (f) (i) C.
 (ii) Glucose.

2. (a) Absorbs light energy/absorbs light of a specific wavelength/absorbs photons of light.
 (b) (i) 435–440 nm (must have units).
 (ii) Any pigment/chlorophyll a absorbs only a limited part of the spectrum/wavelengths of light; additional pigments increase the range of wavelengths absorbed; increases the efficiency of photosynthesis (any two).
 (c) All wavelengths except green are absorbed/ green wavelength is reflected.
 (d) There is a close correlation between the two/they follow a similar trend; this suggests that the pigments/wavelengths responsible for absorption of light are used in photosynthesis.
 (e) (i) A: light harvesting unit/antenna complex; B: reaction centre.
 (ii) In the reaction centre.

3. (a) Carbon dioxide.
 (b) ATP and reduced NADP.
 (c) ATP at C and F reduced NADP at D.
 (d) Cellulose/energy source/starch/lipids/protein.

4. (a) From the photolysis of water.
 (b) NADP.
 (c) Photosynthesis takes place only in light; Photosynthesis occurs slowly at 5°C; Photosynthesis takes place more quickly at 25°C.
 (d) That photosynthesis is an enzyme-controlled process/light is necessary to split water.

5.

	Oxidative phosphorylation	Cyclic photophosphorylation	Non-cyclic photophosphorylation
Requires light	No	Yes	Yes
Requires oxygen	Yes	No	No
Produces oxygen	No	No	Yes
Number of proton pumps involved	3	1	1
Source of electrons	Reduced NAD/ reduced FAD	PSI	Water/PSII
Final electron acceptor	Oxygen	PSI	NADP/reduced NADP

6. (a) D and K.
 (b) E and J.
 (c) B and L, or C and I
 (d) C and I.

7. A a photon of light strikes chlorophyll/reaction centre/ photosystem
 B chlorophyll A loses an electron
 C in photosystem II
 D the electron is taken up by an electron acceptor and passes down a chain of electron carriers
 E converting ADP to ATP
 F by the process of non-cyclic photophosphorylation
 G the electron is passed to photosystem I
 H an excited electron is lost from photosystem I
 I picked up by an electron acceptor and returned to PSI
 J this is called cyclic photophosphorylation
 K photolysis of water occurs
 L providing an electron to replace that lost from PSII
 M oxygen is released
 N electron from PSI combines with the proton from the splitting of water forming reduced NADP
 O ATP and reduced NADP are available for the light independent reaction

BY4: Microbiology

1. (a) (i) Thin peptidoglycan/muerin cell wall; an additional lipopolysaccharide outer layer.
   (ii) Resistant to penicillin.
   (b) (i) Each cell has reproduced asexually to produce a colony.
   (ii) There may be an underestimate due to merging of colonies.
   (c) Includes both living and dead bacteria.
   (d) Dilution factor equals 10^{-1} and 10^{-2}; 7 colonies counted; $7 \times 100 = 700$.
   (e) (i) To avoid contamination by other micro-organisms.
   (ii) Harmful bacteria/pathogens are less likely to reproduce at this temperature.
   (iii) To prevent contamination from and to the environment.
   (f) Bacterial spores are not destroyed by boiling and are killed only at this high temperature.

2. (a) Suitable temperature/suitable pH/nutrient source/water/oxygen.
   (b) Bacillus: coccus; spirillum (any two).
   (c) (i)

Cell	Colour after staining	Positive or negative
A	violet/purple	positive
B	pink	negative

   (ii) Protein; lipopolysaccharide.

3. (a) (i) To remove heat generated in the process; caused by the metabolism of the bacteria; which could denature the enzymes.
   (ii) To maintain optimum/constant pH.
   (iii) To prevent contamination with unwanted microbes/pathogens.
   (b) Contains nitrogen; needed to synthesise proteins/nucleic acids.
   (c) (i) On the vertical cell line when the curve starts to plateau.
   (ii) This is the end of the growth phase when nutrients are being depleted.
   (iii) Penicillin is released to reduce competition for nutrients.
   (d) To prevent contamination of the environment; to prevent contamination of the culture.

4. (a) Tube 1: obligate aerobes; situated at the top of the test tube in order to absorb maximum oxygen.
   Tube 2: obligate anaerobes; gather at the bottom of the test tube to avoid oxygen.
   Tube 3: facultative anaerobes; gather mostly at the top, since aerobic respiration is the most beneficial; but can survive without oxygen so are found throughout the test tube.
   (b) The bacterium is an obligate anaerobe; oxygen is forced under pressure into the wound; the bacteria cannot metabolise in the presence of oxygen; stop dividing/producing toxin; giving time for antibiotics/immune system to destroy the bacteria.

BY4: Controlling population size

1. (a) W: lag; X: exponential/log; Y: stationary; Z: death.
   (b) (i) On the down slope.
   (ii) The maximum size of population; that can be maintained or supported indefinitely.
   (iii) Availability/competition for food/living space; predation; disease/parasitism; accumulation of toxins.
   (iv) Temperature or weather extremes/flood/fire/natural disasters.
   (v) Dashed line continued in steep downward gradient past carrying capacity line.

2. (a) (i) 10   (ii) 2 to 14.
   (b) (i) Interspecific.
   (ii) $240\,cm^3$.
   (iii) Adding more nutrients/food/bacteria/remove waste.
   (iv) Increase in numbers as there is less competition for food.

3. (a) Putrefaction/ammonification/decay/decomposition.
   (b) Nitrosomonas, Nitrobacter.
   (c) Denitrification; anaerobic conditions.
   (d) (i) Rhizobium.
   (ii) The haemoglobin has an affinity/absorbs oxygen.
   (e) Respiration would demand a high use of oxygen; oxygen is the final electron acceptor in the electron transport chain; and so rapidly converts oxygen to water.

4. A   Nitrogen gas in the atmosphere
   B   Amino acid/protein in plants and animals
   C   Urea in urine/ammonia/nitrite/nitrate in soil
   D   Decomposition/putrefaction
   E   Nitrifying bacteria produce nitrates
   F   Nitrosomonas converts ammonium compounds to nitrites
   G   Nitrobacter converts nitrites to nitrates
   H   Denitrification by Pseudomonas
   I   In anaerobic conditions
   J   Nitrogen fixing bacteria
   K   Azotobacter are free living
   L   Rhizobium in root nodules
   M   Convert nitrogen gas into soluble nitrogen compounds
   N   Decay bacteria release nitrogen compounds/ammonia from dead bodies, faeces and urine.

5. Bacteria/fungi/decomposers; ammonium ions; Nitrosomonas; nitrites; Nitrobacter; Rhizobium; Azotobacter.

BY4: Homeostasis and kidney function

1. (a) Nephron.
   (b) (i) A: glomerulus; B: Bowman's capsule; C: proximal convoluted tubule; D: loop of Henle; E: distal convoluted tubule; F: collecting duct.
   (ii) Create a concentration gradient/low water potential in medulla.
   (iii) Longer.
   (c) (i) ADH/antidiuretic hormone.
   (ii) Pituitary gland.
   (iii) I: Hypothalamus; II: wall of collecting duct.
   (iv) G: Makes more permeable; H: makes less permeable; I: increase/hypertonic; J: decrease/hypotonic; K: decrease; L: increase.

2. (a) (i) Glomerulus.
   (ii) Urea or amino acids/fatty acids/glycerol/salts/small proteins.
   (iii) Ultra-filtration.
   (iv) Hydrostatic or blood pressure is decreased; less filtrate formed/lower rate of filtration.
   (b) (i) Loop of Henle.
   (ii) Microvilli provide a large surface area for absorption; many mitochondria for active transport.
   (c) (i) Fish; ammonia bird; uric acid; mammal; urea.
   (ii) Uric acid.
   (iii) Light for flight/little mass for storage.

3. Endocrine; homeostasis; negative feedback; hypothalamus; water potential; posterior pituitary; blood; collecting duct/distal convoluted tubule; receptors/glycoproteins; osmosis; tissue fluid; urine.

BY4: Coordination

1. (a) X: myelin sheath; Y: node of Ranvier.
   (b) Lipid/phospholipid.
   (c) Insulation.
   (d) Speeds rate of transmission of impulses; since impulses jump from node to node/saltatory conduction/local currents.

2. (a) Transmit impulses between neurones; impulses travel in one direction only; filter out low level stimuli; act as junctions.
   (b) Nerve net – shorter, branched neurones, can transmit in both directions, slow.
   Vertebrate neurones – longer, unbranched, transmit in one direction, rapid.
   (c) (i) As fibre diameter increases, speed of conduction increases; much more rapid response in myelinated; below a diameter of 1.0µm non-myelinated is faster, above 1.0µm myelinated is faster; myelinated is linear, non-myelinated is rapid at start and then plateau.
   (ii) They conduct more slowly than non-myelinated.
   (iii) Increase diameter; myelination; higher body temperature; longer distance between nodes.

3. (a) An involuntary/brain not involved; response to a stimulus.
   (b) A: motor; B: relay/intermediate/connector; C: sensory.
   (c) X: myelin sheath/Schwan cell; Y: node of Ranvier; Z: cell body.
   (d) (i) Sodium channels/gates open; sodium ions diffuse in; ATP is used to re-establish the sodium/potassium pump.
   (ii) More active neurones generate more action potentials so more ATP is needed to provide energy for the pumps. ATP also needed for the resynthesis of acetylcholine.
   (iii) Slope of action potential would be less steep; so would take longer to generate an impulse OR the diffusion gradient is less steep so it takes longer for sodium to diffuse in.

4. (a) (i) Proteins.
   (ii) Phospholipids.
   (b) (i) Sodium ions are actively pumped out faster than potassium ions are pumped in/three sodium ions pumped out for every two potassium ions pumped in; potassium ions diffuse out more rapidly than sodium ions diffuse in/membrane has a higher permeability to potassium ions than sodium ions.
   (ii) There is a change in the permeability of the membrane to sodium ions/sodium channels open; sodium ions diffuse in.

5. (a) (i) Stimulation causes sodium ions to diffuse in; inside becomes less negative/some depolarisation; threshold not reached/reference to all or nothing law; sodium voltage gated channels remain closed/no action potential.
   (ii) Sodium ions diffuse in; threshold reached; sodium channels open; depolarisation; inside becomes + 40mV; action potential generated; sodium channels close and potassium channels open; potassium ions diffuse out; repolarisation takes place; refractory period; sodium potassium pump restores resting potential.
   (b) (i) Excitory – normal transmitter mimicked; inhibit breakdown of transmitter/cholinesterase; blocks uptake back into pre-synaptic knob; increases number of receptors on post-synaptic membrane.
   (ii) Inhibitory – prevents release of transmitter substance; bind with receptors on post-synaptic membrane and block it; prevents entry of calcium ions into pre-synaptic knob.

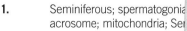

BY5: The genetic code and cell function

1. (a) (i) X: transcription; Y: translation

(ii)
Structure	Letter
Messenger RNA	M
Nuclear pore	N
RNA polymerase	O
Codon	P
Ribosome	Q
Transfer RNA	R
Template/ sense strand of DNA	S
Anticodon	T

(b) CCT ACA GCA CGT

2. (a) AAUAGAAAGCCCUAC

(b) Tyrosine, arginine, alanine, serine, leucine.

(c) Degenerate code, there is a start code which does not code for a specific amino acid.

(d) Gene mutation.

(e) There would be a different sequence of amino acids (as it is a triplet code) and a different polypeptide would be produced.

3. (a) (i) K: chromatid; L: centromere; M: chiasma/chiasmata.

(ii) Meiosis.

(b) Crossing over; independent assortment/random assortment.

(c) (i) A change in the base sequence of a gene; resulting in the alteration of protein/non-functional protein.

(ii) Radiation/carcinogens/named chemical/non-disjunction.

(iii) A mutation increases the amount of variation in the gene pool for natural selection/reference to selective advantage/an explained example.

4. (a) (i) Whole chromosome moving to poles/crossing over has taken place.

(ii) Anaphase 1 because whole chromosomes separate.

(iii) One of each chromatid per cell.

(b) Genetic variation/recombination in gametes/allows evolution by natural selection.

5. (a) (i) Transcription; Translation; Enzyme synthesis.

(ii) At temperatures greater than 33°C white fur is produced/at temperatures below 33°C black fur is produced; at 33°C and above enzyme activity is suppressed/at temperatures below 33°C enzyme activity is activated/shaving and keeping cool means white fur is replaced with black fur.

(b) (i) The new-born rabbits have been inside the mother and have developed at a body temperature of 33°C.

(ii) The extremities listed, ears, nose, paws and tail, are cooler than the rest of the body.

BY5: Human repro

1. Seminiferous; spermatogonia acrosome; mitochondria; Se

2. (a) (i) A: spermatogonia; B: primar C: secondary spermatocyte;

(ii) Sertoli cell.

(iii) Nutrition of sperm/supplies products.

(b) (i) Mitosis.

(ii) In meiosis four cells are produced from each primary spermatocyte.

3. (a) A: Graafian follicle ; B: corpus luteum; C: primary follicle.

(b) Egg has not been fertilised.

(c) (i) Diploid.

(ii) Spermatogonia/primary spermatocyte.

4. (a) Fallopian tube/oviduct.

(b) (i)
	Name	Structure	Function
R	Middle piece	Mitochondrion	ATP/energy for movement of tail
S	Nucleus	Chromosomes	Carry genes

(ii) Acrosome/T contains enzymes; which digest the zona pellucida/jellycoat.

A: petals; B: stigma; C: anther; D: sepals; E: ovary.

(ii) Large petals; stamens/anther/stigma inside flower; carpel inside flower; nectar.

(b) (i) Growth is controlled by the tube nucleus; enzymes are released; these digest a path through the tissue; products are absorbed and used for growth.

(ii) Micropyle.

(iii) Embryo sac.

(iv)

Fruit	Ovary
Testa	Integuments
Endosperm	Triploid endosperm nucleus
Embryo plant	Zygote

2. (a) 1: Exine; 2: pollen tube; 3: male nuclei; 4: tube nucleus.

(b) One of the male nuclei fuses with the female egg nucleus; the other male nucleus fuses with both polar nuclei.

(c) Double fertilisation.

(d) Useful: food for insects; disadvantageous: a cause of hay fever/allergy.

3. (a)

Nucleus	Fuses with	Function of fusion product	Number of chromosomes in fusion product
S	Q	Zygote which develops into embryo plant	12
T	NO	Triploid endosperm nucleus	18

(b) (i) Fruit.

(ii) Dispersal; by animals to avoid competition with parent plant and reduces overcrowding.

4. (a) Hydrolysis of food reserves/endosperm by enzymes; starch converted to sugars/glucose/maltose; sugars pass to embryo; when first leaves are produced photosynthesis occurs; resulting in increase in biomass of the seedling.

(b) (i) Amylase/enzyme/carbohydrase from the seed; converts starch to maltose; by the process of hydrolysis.

(ii) Less amylase/enzyme produced in the absence of the embryo.

(c) Cotyledon.

BY5: Inheritance

1. (a) The alternative form of a gene.

(b) (i) Parental genotypes   Rr   ×   Rr

Possible gametes   R r   R r

Genotype of bird with no cheek patches = rr

(ii)

Parental genotypes	SG	×	GG
Possible gametes	S G		G
F1 genotypes	SG		GG
F1 phenotypes	silvery-grey		grey

(iii) SSrr

(c) (i) X^eO/X^eY

(ii) X^eX^e

(iii) X^EX^E; X^EX^e

(d) Different base sequence in the gene/allele; different triplet code/sequence of codons; different sequence of amino acids; different protein/enzyme/polypeptide.

2. (a) Carried on the sex/X chromosome; only expressed if both chromosomes carry the allele; always expressed in the male; allele is a different form of the same gene.

(b) (i) X^NX^n; (ii) X^nY; (iii) X^NY.

3. (a) Dominant: smooth, coloured.

Recessive: wrinkled, colourless.

(b) Linked/on same chromosome/genes are inherited together.

(c) (i) Smooth, colourless wrinkled, coloured.

(ii) Crossing over.

(d) (i) F1 ScCc.

(ii) F2 Sscc or ssCc or SScc or ssCC.

BY5: Variation and evolution

1. (a) (i) The zebra has stripes but the donkey does not have stripes;
The zebra has short ears but the donkey has long ears.
   (ii) Male.
   (iii) 52.
   (b) Contribution of a different number of chromosomes by the male and female; chromosomes unable to pair up; unable to produce gametes.
   (c) Hybrid vigour.

2. (a) Polyploidy/triploid.
   (b) A normal gamete from the blackberry with a haploid number = 28; fertilised/fused with an unreduced gamete of the raspberry (28 + 14 = 42) .
   (c) The chromosome number doubles by a mutation.

3. (a) Unable to interbreed to produce fertile offspring.
   (b) Populations physically/geographically separated; populations cannot interbreed; different mutations in each population; environmental conditions differ; different selection pressures; leads to different gene pools/demes; leads to difference in physical characteristics/behaviour/appearance.

4. (a) Loss or decline in food supply; reduced cover or protection from predators/introduction of new predators; loss of nesting sites.
   (b) (i) The gene pool is reduced/population now has a very small gene pool/variants destroyed/reduced number of genes.
      (ii) The number of alleles reflect the degree of variation; present day forms have fewer alleles/show less variation; resulting in inbreeding.
Less able to survive environmental changes/unable to adapt to change, e.g. a disease could wipe out a whole population.
      (iii) Small sample size/15 specimens not representative of the population/samples compared have different sizes.

5. (a) Only the organisms best adapted to the environment will live long enough; to reproduce/produce offspring/transmit their genes.
   (b) (i) Brown.
      (ii) 1. Green shells are better camouflaged/less conspicuous in green pasture than against a mixture of green and brown stems.
2. Pink shells are visible and readily selected in both habitats.
      (iii) Banded pattern breaks up the shell shape and the rough herbage presents a mottled background to which the banded shells are well camouflaged; dark bands form a contrast against uniform green of green pasture; lighter bands show up against uniform brown of woodland floor.
      (iv) Thrushes cannot see colour of shell and dig out snails randomly by chance.
      (v) 1. Temperature; 2. Reflects heat.

1. (a) (i) Size/milk yield/proportions
   (ii) Sex.
   (iii) Absence of horns.
   (b) Breed/cross from bulls and cows known to produce high milk yield; use artificial insemination – more rapid results.
   (c) (i) To ensure that important alleles, such as for disease resistance, are not lost from the gene pool.
      (ii) Inbreeding causes a loss in variability; increase in degree of homozygosity and chance of recessive alleles coming together; genetic drift with loss of alleles.
   (d) Could influence parents in avoiding having a child/increase in rate of abortions; changes in human gene pool.

2. (a) (i) I: blastocyst; II: surrogate.
      (ii) Implantation.
   (b) (i) DNA was not removed from the egg of S.
      (ii) Implantation of the manipulated embryo did not take place.
   (c) (i) Because udder cells are mature/differentiated and it was thought that only early embryonic/undifferentiated cells could be used.
      (ii) Cytoplasm and DNA are derived from different individuals.
   (d) Loss of genetic diversity/limiting the gene pool/inability to adapt to changing environmental conditions.

3. (a) Genetically identical; from small groups of cells; artificial/agar nutrient medium.
   (b) These cells have no nucleus so mitosis cannot take place/cells are mature, differentiated, no longer totipotent.
   (c) (i) Genetically identical; grow at the same rate; same appearance; same size; same flavour; consistently high quality; all uniform.
      (ii) Genetically identical, no variation, and are all susceptible to disease; reduction in gene pool.
   (d) (i) Chromosome
      (ii) Breakdown of spindle fibres during mitosis/non-disjunction/chromatids do not separate.
      (iii) Bivalents cannot form/pairing of homologous chromosomes cannot take place; no meiosis; no gametes produced.
   (e) Reversion of virus to disease-causing form; bacteria/virus could be toxic to humans or insects; virus/bacterium could transfer to another species; ethical reason – why change the colour of leaves when there is no nutritional value.

CTTAAG

The enzyme breaks strands where G is next to A.

(c) (i)

A	A	T	T	C			G

G					C	T	T	A	A

   (ii) The bases of one are in the reverse order to those in the other / palindrome.

(d) Sticky ends.

(e) Restriction enzyme.

(f) (i) Plasmid.

   (ii) DNA ligase.

(g) (i) Reverse transcriptase.

   (ii) DNA polymerase.

   (iii) Does not carry 'junk' DNA/introns/process does not produce a variety of other fragments which first have to be screened out/much mRNA present but only two copies of the gene.

(h) Human Genome Project; records the complete base sequence of human DNA and identification and location of genes.

5. (a) (i) DNA.

   (ii) R: restriction endonuclease; S: ligase.

   (iii) K: TTA; L: CGA.

(b) (i) Less herbicide required to kill weeds between crops/greater crop yield because of less competition.

   (ii) Gene for herbicide resistance may spread by cross pollination to other closely related plants.

6. (a) Autolysis/breakdown of cell walls allowing micro-organisms to enter.

(b) (i) UGCA; TGCA.

   (ii) Transcription.

   (iii) 'Antisense' gene produces mRNA which binds to the mRNA produced by the polygalacturonase gene; preventing tRNA from attaching; so that translation is prevented; and no enzyme is produced; during protein synthesis.

(c) Check that genetic manipulation does not increase levels of toxins/reduce vitamin content/toxic side effects.

BY5: Energy and ecosystems

1. (a) Reflection of solar energy at sea surface; light of 'wrong' wavelength for photosynthesis; light energy transmitted, i.e. does not 'hit' phytoplankton.

(b) (i) $6300 - 1260 = 5040$ KJ m^{-2} year^{-1}

   (ii) $(1008 + 93 + 403 + 71) = 1575$ KJ m^{-2} year^{-1}.

2. (a) (i) 15576

   (ii) C2 = C3 + R3 + E3 / C3 = C2 − (R3 + E3)

(b) (i) $972 + 3732 + 110 + 20 = 4834$

Total energy expelled for area of wood = 4834 Kj $\times 25,000$ = $120,850,000/1.2085 \times 10^{-8}$.

   (ii) Passes to decomposers/detritivores; respired by decomposers; lost as heat.

3. (a) (i) Reflected off leaves/pass between leaves/used to evaporate water from leaf surface.

   (ii) Gross production = $1,970,000 − 1,946,820 = 23,180$ Kj
Net production = $23,180 − 3,668 = 19,512$ Kj

(b) (i) $1,603 − (192 + 88) = 1,323$ Kj

   (ii) Faeces/urine/dead bodies.

(c) (i) Rabbits.

   (ii) It takes only 30 days to produce the same weight of meat compared with 120 days for the cow/greater gain per day.

   (iii) Rabbits have a larger surface area/they are more active/they have a higher metabolic rate.

   (iv) Keep rabbits in heated sheds/reduce their movement; this would increase meat production.

4. (a) The change in structure and composition of species in a community over time.

(b) Less distance for seeds to travel to Krakatoa; greater diversity on neighbouring tropical islands; reference to warmer climate.

(c) Death of plants provides humus/developing soil; decomposition of plant materials leads to increased nutrients in soil; humus retains water.

(d) Increase in number of niches; increase in variety and availability of food.

BY5: Effects of human activities

1. (a) (i) Mutation.
   (ii) Warfarin acts as a selective pressure and resistant rats survive because they have a selective advantage; they are able to reproduce; to pass on the beneficial allele to their offspring; which in turn become resistant; increasing the proportion of resistant alleles in the gene pool.
   (iii) Migration; sexual reproduction/interbreeding.
   (b) If warfarin is not used there is no selective advantage; disadvantaged rats possessing the allele need large amounts of vitamin K; so they are selected against.

2. (a) (i) With heavy fishing the greatest biomass is in the four-year-old group, with moderate fishing it is in the five-year-old group/the average age is less in heavily fished areas.
   (ii) The biomass peak in the heavily fished population is exceeded after only one breeding season rather than two; so the moderately fished population would be expected to produce more offspring.
   (b) The peak would be higher/the peak would be with the older fish/the biomass would be greater.
   (c) Limit fishing to avoid breeding season/impose quotas/exclusion zones/increase mesh sizes to avoid catching younger fish.

3. (a) Gases form an insulating layer around the Earth which allows light to enter but prevents heat from escaping. This leads to an increase in temperature on the Earth's surface.
   (b) (i) The trees regrow a covering of leafy branches; this canopy effect reduces the impact of heavy rain on the soil. Also roots remain and bind the soil, resisting erosion.
   (ii) Slash and burn destroys habitats, and forests are replaced by monocultures; coppicing provides a variety of habitats because the trees are at various stages of development.

4. (a) Housing/somewhere to live; logging/wood products; industry/roads/development; fuel.
   (b) Provides fertile soil/acts as a fertiliser; good crop/yield; no need to buy fertiliser; removes pests.
   (c) Less fertile soil; less material to burn; less plant growth during fallow period; less ash to provide fertility; less time for soil to regain fertility.
   (d) Two crops can be grown, food crop and rubber crop; cash crop provides an income; sustainability.
   (e) (i) Far fewer species/very little diversity; only two plant types/trees and herbaceous plants; no climbers, epiphytes or shrubs; 360 species compared with 10 species.
   (ii) All types represented in both; fewer tree species; fewer epiphyte or shrub species; more herbaceous species; approximately same number of species of climbers; less diversity; 360 species compared with 260 species.
   (f) Depends on agriculture; plantations seem to be destructive; monoculture/does not permit species diversity; agroforestry allows forest to regenerate; maintains fairly high level of diversity.

Knowledge check answers

Knowledge checks BY4

1. universal; ATPase; phosphorylation; mitochondria; muscle/secretory/nerve.
2. glycolysis; cytoplasm; two; pyruvic; mitochondrion; Krebs; electron transport system.
3. 1: B; 2: A; 3: B; 4: A; 5: A & B.
4. thylakoid membrane; energy; antenna complex; chlorophyll a; acceptors.
5. ribulose bisphosphate; NADP; light-dependent; glucose.
6. 1: B; 2: A; 3: C.
7. 1: C; 2: B; 3: A.
8. 2; 3; 4; 5.
9. 1: B; 2: C; 3: A; 4: D.
10. 1: D; 2: A; 3: C; 4: B.
11. insecticide; resistance; Biological; prey; hedgerows; integrated pest control.
12. 1: E; 2: D; 3: B; 4: C; 5: A.
13. 1: B; 2: C; 3: D; 4: A.
14. hypothalamus; pituitary; ADH; collecting duct; medulla; smaller; concentrated.
15. 1: B; 2: C; 3: A.
16. brain; spinal cord; sensory; motor; involuntary.
17. sensory; effector; motor; cell body; axon; myelin sheath; insulator.
18. 4–3–1–7–6–2–5.
19. day length; photoperiodism; phytochrome; leaves.

Knowledge checks BY5

1. 1: C; 2: B; 3: D; 4: A.
2. 1. GGU CCU CUC UUA AGU AAA. 2. CCA GGA GAG AAU UCA UUU. 3. Six.
3. 1: C; 2: B ; 3: A ; 4: D.
4. 1: B; 2: A; 3: C; 4: D.
5. 1: both; 2: meiosis; 3: both; 4: both; 5: meiosis.
6. 1: E; 2: D; 3: B; 4: C; 5: A.
7. seminiferous tubules; spermatogenesis; primary spermatocytes; secondary spermatocytes; spermatids; Sertoli.
8. oogenesis; mitosis; meiosis; follicle; meiotic; ovulation.
9. 1: B; 2: A; 3: D; 4: C.
10. 1: B; 2: C; 3: D; 4: A.
11. 1; C; 2: A; 3: B; 4: E; 5: D.
12. oxygen; enzymes; radicle; endosperm; plumule; photosynthesis.
13. 1: C; 2: B; 3: A; 4: D.
14. homozygous; heterozygous; recessive; co-dominant.
15. 1: B; 2: A; 3: D; 4: C.
16. 1: D; 2: A; 3: C; 4: B.
17. 1: E; 2: D; 3: C; 4: B; 5: A.
18. in vitro; mitosis; surrogate; embryo.
19. nuclear transfer; udder; fused; donor.
20. chloride; water; osmosis; amino acid; somatic; liposomes; inhaler/aerosol.
21. 1: B; 2: D; 3: C; 4: A; 5: E.
22. 1: B; 2: C; 3: A.
23. 1: C; 2: B; 3: D; 4: A.
24. 1: D; 2: A; 3: E; 4: C; 5: B.
25. 1: D; 2: C; 3: B; 4: A.
26. Algal bloom; light; photosynthesis; saprobiont/saprophyte; oxygen; nitrite.

Glossary

abiotic A factor which makes up the non-biological environment.

absorption spectrum The range of a pigment's ability to absorb various wavelengths of light.

acetylcholine A neurotransmitter which diffuses across a synapse.

acetyl CoA The entry compound for the Krebs cycle in cellular respiration.

action potential A rapid change in the membrane potential of a nerve cell, caused by stimulus-triggered, selective opening and closing of sodium and potassium ion channels.

active transport Process by which substances are moved across a cell membrane against a concentration gradient, with the help of energy input and specific transport proteins.

adaptation A feature that increases the chance of survival of an organism in its environment.

allele An alternative form of a gene.

allele frequency The number of times an allele occurs in the gene pool.

anaerobic Occurs in the absence of oxygen.

antibiotic A chemical that kills bacteria or inhibits their growth.

antibiotic resistance Mechanism in micro-organisms that prevent the effect of antibiotics.

antibody An antigen-binding immunoglobin, produced by B lymphocytes, that attacks non-self proteins in the body.

anticodon A specialised base triplet on one end of a tRNA molecule that recognises a particular complementary codon on a mRNA molecule.

antigen A non-self protein that is recognised by the immune system and elicits an immune response.

artificial selection The selective breeding of domesticated plants and animals to encourage the occurrence of desirable traits.

asexual reproduction A type of reproduction involving only one parent that produces genetically identical offspring.

ATP (adenosine triphosphate) Nucleotide produced during respiration; important in the transfer of energy.

autosome A chromosome that is not directly involved in determining sex, as opposed to the sex chromosomes.

autotroph An organism that obtains organic food molecules without eating other organisms. Autotrophs use energy from the sun or from the oxidation of inorganic substances to make organic molecules from inorganic ones.

axon A process extending from a neurone which conducts an action potential away from the cell body.

backcross A genetic cross that reveals whether an individual with a 'dominant' phenotype is heterozygous or homozygous dominant.

biodiversity An expression of the number of different species living in a given ecosystem.

biomass The dry mass of organic matter comprising a group of organisms in a particular habitat.

biological control The control of a pest by using a control agent, e.g. a predator that feeds on the pest (its prey).

biotechnology The industrial use of living organisms or their components to improve human health and food production.

biotic An ecological factor that makes up part of the living environment.

Calvin cycle A biochemical pathway that forms part of the light-independent reaction of photosynthesis.

carbon cycle The movement of carbon between living organisms and the non-living environment, and involving the processes of photosynthesis, respiration and decomposition.

carcinogen A chemical, a form of radiation, or other agent that causes cancer.

carnivore An animal that eats other animals.

carotenoids Accessory pigments in the chloroplasts that absorb wavelengths of light that chlorophyll cannot.

carrier An individual who is heterozygous at a given genetic locus, with one normal allele and one potentially harmful recessive allele. The heterozygote is phenotypically normal for the character determined by the gene but can pass on the harmful allele to the offspring.

carrying capacity The maximum population size that can be supported by the available resources.

central nervous system Part of the nervous system (brain and spinal cord) that connects sensory and motor neurones.

centrifugation Process of separating particles of different sizes and densities by spinning at high speed.

chemiosmosis The production of ATP using the energy of hydrogen ion gradients across membranes to phosphorylate ADP.

chlorophyll The green pigment located within the chloroplasts of plants.

chromatid One of the two copies of a chromosome that are joined together by a centromere.

chromosome A thread-like, gene-carrying structure found in the nucleus.

clone A population of genetically identical individuals or cells.

climax community The organisms that make up the final, stable stage of an ecological succession.

codon The basic unit of the genetic code; a three-nucleotide sequence of DNA or mRNA that specifies a specific amino acid.

co-dominance Where both alleles for one gene contribute equally to the phenotype.

colony (of bacteria) A cluster of bacterial cells (clone) which arose from a single bacterium.

community All the organisms that inhabit a particular area; populations of different species that interact.

competition The struggle between organisms to obtain resources. Competition can be interspecific (between species) or intraspecific (within species).

conservation The management of habitats to maintain or restore species diversity and ecosystem function.

continuous variation Variation in which organisms do not fall into distinct categories but show gradations from one extreme to the other.

crossing over The reciprocal exchange of genetic material between non-sister chromatids during synapsis of meiosis I.

cytochrome An iron-containing protein, a component of electron transport chains in chloroplasts and mitochondria.

decomposer Organisms, fungi and bacteria that break down dead organic matter to obtain nutrients.

deforestation The removal of trees from a forest, for timber and/or to obtain land for cultivation.

denitrifying bacteria Bacteria that convert nitrates to nitrogen.

depolarisation When a nerve impulse is transmitted a temporary reversal of charge occurs on the membrane of a neurone, whereby the inside of the cell is made less negative relative to the outside.

detritus Dead organic matter.

diploid (cell) A cell containing two sets of chromosomes ($2n$), one set inherited from each parent.

differentiation Process by which cells become specialised for different functions.

discontinuous variation Variation shown when the characters of organisms fall into distinct categories.

dominant allele In a heterozygote, the allele that is fully expressed in the phenotype.

double fertilisation A mechanism of fertilisation in flowering plants (Angiosperms) in which two male nuclei unite with two nuclei in the embryo sac to form the zygote and the endosperm

ecological efficiency The ratio of net productivity at one trophic level to net productivity at the next lower level.

ecological niche How an organism fits into its environment; described by its behaviour, etc.

ecosystem A level of ecological study that includes all the organisms in a given area as well as the abiotic factors with which they interact.

electron transport chain A sequence of electron-carrier molecules that shuttle electrons during the redox reactions that release energy used to make ATP.

endangered species A species that is in danger of extinction throughout all or a significant portion of its range.

effector An organ, muscle or gland, that reacts to a nerve impulse, resulting in a response.

eutrophication The artificial 'enrichment' of aquatic habitats (streams, rivers, ponds, lakes) by excess nutrients (e.g. due to run-off of fertilisers from farms), resulting in a fall in the oxygen level of the water.

evolution All the changes that have transformed life on Earth from its earliest beginnings to the diversity that exists today.

extinction The process by which a species ceases to exist on Earth, e.g. due to a failure to adapt successfully to a changing environment.

facultative anaerobe An organism that makes ATP by aerobic respiration if oxygen is present but can switch to fermentation under anaerobic conditions.

feedback inhibition A method of metabolic control in which the end product of a metabolic pathway acts as an inhibitor of an enzyme within that pathway.

fermentation A process that makes a limited amount of ATP from glucose without an electron transport chain and produces alcohol or lactic acid as an end product.

fertilisation The fusion of male and female gametes to produce a diploid zygote.

food chain The relationship of organisms in each successive trophic (feeding) level in a community.

food web Interconnecting food chains in a community.

founder effect A cause of genetic drift attributable to colonisation by a limited number of individuals from a parent population.

gamete A sex cell containing half the number of chromosomes as body cells. It is haploid in diploid organisms.

gene A section of DNA on a chromosome coding for a polypeptide.

gene pool The total of all the alleles in a population at any one time.

gene probe A short sequence of DNA used as a 'genetic marker'.

genetic drift Changes in a gene pool of a small population due to chance.

genetic engineering The modification of an organism's DNA, usually by the insertion of additional DNA. The changed organism will then have desirable traits (e.g. resistance to disease) which are inherited by its offspring.

genetically modified organism An organism (e.g. a crop plant) which has had its DNA changed by genetic engineering.

gene therapy The treatment of a genetic disease by the replacement or masking of a defective gene with a functional gene.

genome The complete complement of an organism's alleles.

genotype The genetic make-up of an organism.

global warming The increase in the Earth's temperature due to the build-up of heat trapping 'greenhouse gases' (e.g. carbon dioxide) in the atmosphere.

greenhouse gases Gases such as carbon dioxide and methane present in the atmosphere causing the trapping of heat energy, and so raising the temperature of the Earth's surface.

gross primary productivity The total primary productivity of an ecosystem.

haploid Cells that contain only a single copy of each chromosome; found in sex cells.

herbivore A heterotrophic animal that eats plants.

heterozygous Having one dominant and one recessive allele for a given characteristic.

homeostasis The maintenance by organisms of a constant internal environment.

homologous chromosomes Chromosome pairs of the same length that possess genes for the same characters at corresponding loci. One homologous chromosome is inherited from the father, the other from the mother.

homozygous Having two identical alleles for a given characteristic.

Human Genome Project An international collaborative effort to map and sequence the DNA of the entire human genome.

incomplete dominance A type of inheritance in which the F1 hybrids have an appearance that is intermediate between the phenotypes of the parents.

introns Portions of DNA within a gene that do not code for a polypeptide.

in vitro **fertilisation** Fertilisation of the ova in laboratory containers followed by artificial implantation of the early embryo into the mother's uterus.

Krebs cycle A chemical cycle that completes the metabolic breakdown of glucose molecules to carbon dioxide with the release of energy.

linked genes Genes that are located on the same chromosomes.

locus A particular place along the length of a certain chromosome where a given gene is located.

meiosis A two-stage type of cell division in sexually reproducing organisms that results in gametes with half the chromosome number of the original cell.

micropropagation A technique by which individual plants are grown from a cluster of rapidly dividing cells on a nutrient medium, i.e. in tissue culture.

mitosis A type of cell division that conserves the chromosome number (diploid) by equally allocating replicated chromosomes to each of the daughter nuclei.

monoculture The cultivation over a large area of a single crop plant.

motor neurone Neurone that transmits an action potential from the CNS to an effector.

mutagen A chemical or physical agent that interacts with DNA and increases the rate of mutation.

mutation A permanent change in the DNA structure or the chromosome number of the cell.

natural selection The differential success in the reproduction of different phenotypes resulting from the interaction of organisms with their environment. It is a process that encourages the transmission of favourable alleles and hinders the transmission of unfavourable ones so contributing to evolution.

negative feedback A primary mechanism of homeostasis. When there is a change in a monitored physiological variable a response is triggered to counteract the initial fluctuation, restoring it to its normal level.

net primary productivity The gross primary productivity minus the energy lost through respiration. It represents the energy in an ecosystem available to consumers.

neuromuscular junction A synapse between a neurone and a muscle.

neurotransmitter A chemical messenger released from the synaptic terminal of a neuron at a chemical synapse that diffuses across the synaptic cleft and binds to and stimulates the pre-synaptic cell.

nitrifying bacteria Bacteria that convert ammonium compounds to nitrites then nitrates.

nitrogen fixation The conversion of atmospheric nitrogen into nitrates, Can take place by means of symbiotic and free-living bacteria, as well as by physical means such as industrial processes and by lightning.

niche An organism's role in an ecosystem.

omnivore A heterotrophic animal that consumes both meat and plant material.

oncogene A gene that causes increased cell division leading to the growth of a tumour.

osmoregulation The control of water balance in organisms.

osmosis The diffusion of water molecules across a selectively permeable membrane from a dilute solution to a concentrated solution; water diffuses from a region of high water potential to a region of lower water potential.

oxidative phosphorylation The production of ATP using energy derived from the redox reactions of an electron transport chain.

oxygen debt The amount of additional oxygen required to break down lactic acid, which builds up during anaerobic respiration.

pathogen A disease-causing microbe.

pesticide A manufactured chemical used to kill pests in managed environments.

phage A virus that infects bacteria.

phenotype The expression of an organism's genotype; the physical and physiological characteristics of an organism.

photolysis The splitting of a water molecule by light.

photophosphorylation The process of generating ATP from ADP and phosphate by means of a proton-motive force generated by the thylakoid membrane of the chloroplast during the light reactions of photosynthesis.

photosynthesis The conversion of light energy to chemical energy stored in glucose; the process in green plants by which carbon dioxide and water combine, using light energy, to form glucose and water.

pioneer species A plant species that can colonise bare rock.

plankton Microscopic organisms that occur near the surface of oceans, ponds and lakes.

plasmid A small circular piece of DNA found in bacterial cells.

pollination The transfer of pollen onto the stigma of a carpel by wind or animal carriers.

polymerase chain reaction A technique for increasing the quantity of DNA *in vitro*.

population A group of individuals of one species occupying a given unit of space at a given time.

predator Animals specialised in feeding on another species (prey).

primary productivity The rate at which light energy is converted to chemical energy of organic compounds by autotrophs in an ecosystem.

primary succession The colonisation of bare rock through a series of stages to reach a climax community.

protein synthesis The assembly of proteins from amino acid 'building blocks' in the cytoplasm of cells, under the direction of DNA in the nucleus.

proton pump The active transport mechanism in cell membranes that uses ATP to force hydrogen ions out of a cell and, in the process, generates a membrane potential.

pyramid of biomass A diagram used to represent the decrease in biomass of organisms at each trophic level in a food chain.

pyramid of energy A diagram which represents the total energy requirement of each successive trophic level in a food chain.

pyramid of numbers A diagram used to represent the relative numbers of individuals at each trophic level in a food chain.

receptor A cell or group of cells that detects changes in the environment.

recessive allele The form of a gene which, when inherited, is only expressed in an organism's genotype if no dominant allele is present.

recombinant DNA An organism's DNA to which a section of DNA from another species has been added in genetic engineering.

reflex arc A nerve pathway leading to a rapid, involuntary response to a stimulus.

refractory period The short time immediately after an action potential during which the membrane cannot be depolarised.

resting potential The membrane potential characteristic of a non-conducting, excitable cell, with the inside of the cell more negative than the outside.

repolarisation A return to the resting potential after the completion of an action potential.

rubisco Ribulose biphosphate carboxylase, the enzyme that catalyses the first step of the Calvin cycle.

saltatory conduction Conduction of a nerve impulse along a myelinated nerve where the action potential jumps from node to node.

secondary succession The recolonisation of an area replacing a destroyed earlier community.

selection Organisms best-adapted in a population survive and reproduce.

selection pressure An environmental force that alters the frequency of alleles in a population.

sensory neurone A neurone that transmits an action potential from a sensory receptor to the CNS.

sickle-cell anaemia Genetic disorder where red blood cells become sickle-shaped and less able to transport oxygen.

sex chromosomes The pair of chromosomes responsible for determining the sex of an individual.

sex-linked gene A gene located on a sex chromosome.

sexual reproduction Reproduction involving two parents, each of which provides a gamete which fuse during fertilisation, resulting in offspring that have unique combinations of alleles.

sister chromatids Replicated forms of a chromosome joined together by the centromere and eventually separated during cell division.

sodium—potassium pump A special transport protein in the plasma membrane of animal cells that transports sodium out of and potassium into the cell against their concentration gradients.

speciation The origin of a new species from existing species.

species A group of populations of organisms capable of interbreeding with one another to form fertile offspring.

species diversity The number and relative abundance of species in a community.

stem cells Undifferentiated cells capable of dividing and differentiating into various cell types. Found in embryos and bone marrow.

stimulus A detectable change in the environment of an organism.

substrate-level phosphorylation The formation of ATP by directly transferring a phosphate group to ADP from an intermediate substrate in catabolism.

succession A progressive sequence of changes in the flora and fauna of a region, from pioneer to climax communities.

synapse A junction between neurons.

taxonomy The branch of biology concerned with naming and classifying the various forms of life.

testcross The breeding of an organism of unknown genotype with a homozygous recessive individual to determine the unknown genotype.

trophic level A feeding level in a food chain or food web.

tumour Swelling in an organism; made up of cells that continue to divide in an abnormal way. A plant tumour is called a gall.

ultrafiltration Filtration assisted by hydrostatic or blood pressure.

variation The differences in characteristics of members of the same species.

vector A carrier, for example a plasmid carries DNA into a cell.

water potential The physical property predicting the direction in which water will flow; the tendency for water to leave a system.

zygote The diploid product of the fusion of haploid gametes in sexual reproduction.

Index

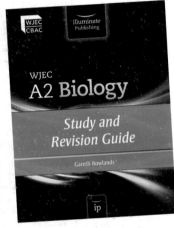
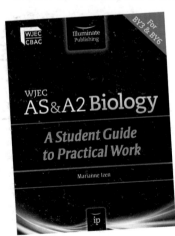